# SCIENCE AND HUMAN TRANSFORMATION:
## SUBTLE ENERGIES,
## INTENTIONALITY AND CONSCIOUSNESS

by

William A. Tiller, Ph.D.

**Publisher's Cataloging-in-Publication**

(*Provided by Quality Books, Inc.*)

Tiller, William A.
    Science and Human Transformation: Subtle Energies,
Intentionality and Consciousness / William A. Tiller
    p. cm.
    Includes bibliographical references and index.
    ISBN: 0-9642637-4-2


    1. Parapsychology and science.  2. Occultism and science.
3. Consciousness.   I. Title.

BF1045.S33T55 1997                    133.01'5
                                      QBI97-40469

LC - Library of Congress Catalogue Card Number:
97-066498

PAVIOR
TRANSFORMATIONAL CONCEPTS BROUGHT TO LIFE

Printed in the United States of America

To

My Loving Wife

JEAN

A True and Indispensable Companion

On The Path

*Overall, this book is a paradigm-breaking book for science in that it reveals in some detail a viable larger perspective and framework for a scientific description of nature and human evolvement in that framework. It is also a consciousness-raising book and a hope-raising book for humanity in that it shows people how to use their own intentionality to bring about . . .beneficial . . .changes . . . in their own bodies. Such changes naturally lead to a significant growth in the individual's consciousness.*

*Prof. Wm. A. Tiller*

# ● CONTENTS ●

# ● PREFACE ●

The exponentially increasing event density of our lives compounds the intractable stresses penetrating from without and expanding from within. Our world seems pretty "screwed up" at the moment with so many seeming dilemmas that we long for a simpler time. We tend to feel somewhat lost at the scale of events pushing our lives and if this is what "reality" is all about, is it really worth it? Things appear to be very much out of balance and proper balance can only be restored if we can gain a new perspective on the overall scene.

The old perspective is perhaps best exemplified by the accepted scientific framework wherein everything in the world obeys purely objective laws with no influence arising from human consciousness or human intentionality. This level of science has shown us that the light we sense with our eyes is but a very small portion of the total electromagnetic spectrum expressed by Nature. It has also shown us that the sound we hear with our ears is but a very small portion of the acoustical spectrum expressed by Nature. And it has assumed that Nature expresses itself only in the band accessible by our physical sensory system.

It has often been stated that physics has always concerned itself with the nature of things, that is, of real objects. By real objects is meant those objects perceived by the physical sensory system since this is the only sensory system that is fully operational in the general mass of present-day humanity. However, those objects perceived by other sensory systems in a much smaller segment of present-day humanity, are no less real. Rather, they are objects for which statistical concensus does not presently exist. Almost a century ago, Steiner wrote about these supersensible domains of Nature[1] and how one might proceed to develop self towards cognition of the vast information territories of these supersensible domains.

This book deals with these supersensible domains of Nature and how we might expand our present-day scientific thinking to meaningfully map out these new territories. The break with the past will come, in part, by accepting that, like light and sound, our present band of cognition gives us a window on only a very small portion of Nature's total modes of expression. Likewise, space and time, although key variables the brain uses for cognition of the information impinging on our physical sensor arrays, are not necessarily the only variables or the best variables for cognition of the broader domains of Nature.

Becoming aware of these larger aspects of general nature and of ourselves is a major step towards full self empowerment, where we have grown in consciousness enough to meaningfully influence the properties of matter around us. By then, we will know what true balance means and can set about restoring it in the world. Overall, this book is a paradigm-breaking book for science in that it reveals, in some detail, a viable larger perspective and framework for science's description of Nature and human evolvement in that framework. For the general person, it deals largely with concepts and models for understanding how humans can be transformed to higher states of function and how they can then manifest phenomena that seem inexplicable based upon the conventional scientific paradigm. It is also a consciousness-raising and a hope-raising book for humanity in that it shows people how to use their own intentionality to bring about inner self-management at emotional and mental levels so that beneficial electrophysiological, hormonal, energy and structural changes develop in their own bodies. Such changes quite naturally lead to a significant growth in the individual's consciousness and these have significant implications for human health and societal functioning.

Chapter 1 defines subtle energies as all those beyond the familiar ones associated with the four fundamental forces accepted by the conventional physics model. It lays out an appreciable body of experimental data, much of it from the author's experimental studies over the last 30 years, demonstrating correlates of these subtle energies acting on physical phenomena. It unfolds a working hypothesis for human science to follow in its future exploration of this new territory. Chapter 2 very briefly recounts where conventional physics stands today on the building blocks for physical matter, the vacuum, hyperspace and force unification. The inner experience models of yoga, Qigong and HeartMath are then briefly recounted to illustrate an entirely different perspective on the important dimensions of nature. Then the author's "simulator" model of higher dimensional spaces, substances and radiations is qualitatively expressed with the differences between this model and the conventional physics paradigm clearly delineated. Finally, many of the consequences of the author's model are laid out to show how a natural bridge can be fashioned between the conventional view of physical nature and psychoenergetic-type phenomena which spring from domains beyond the purely physical frame.

In Chapter 3, the relationship between electromagnetic energy emissions from different physical substances and the state of that substance is laid out to illustrate the spectral distributions of radiation to be expected from the human body. Antenna theory is then explored for physical and biological systems to show how organization and aspects of coherence enter these radiation fields and how the human "aura" is a natural consequence of any multidimensional antenna. Chapter 4 recounts our current understanding of neural circuit development and functioning in humans so that we might begin to understand what makes our physical sensory systems function as they do and how both conscious and unconscious information trains are registered and acted upon in our brains. Here, we see the importance of "mindset" on the individual's perception arising from these signals and also learn how to bring about intentional changes in both the physical and subtle level structures of our bodies.

With Chapter 5, the laser concept is utilized as a metaphor to understand the nature and potential of coherence development in individuals, groups, corporations and societies. Via this path, one comes to learn that we are the product of the overall process designed into the simulator system and, choosing the path of inner self-management at physical, emotional and mental levels, leads to both great self empowerment and significantly higher levels of functioning. Chapter 6 takes us back to devices for enhancing our latent subtle energy capacities. Many of us need these devices as crutches until we have built the necessary subtle level circuitry inside. Then, we can dispense with any external aids to manifest our new-found abilities. These crutches have been labelled "training wheels" and many of them are expected to lead to vast new technologies as well as meaningfully enhancing the efficiencies and capabilities of existing technologies in the future.

The closing chapter (Chapter 7) wraps things up and teaches us a viable path for both harmonizing the earth at consciousness levels and becoming true stewards for this evolving planet.

This book is meant for everyone, although many may consider it appears too technical for them. However, if they are able to persevere in the reading, to just try and get the overall sense of what is presented without trying to understand everything in detail on the first trip through, they will find great benefit from exposure to the material.

I owe a considerable debt to several individuals who helped in the materialization of the book. First, to my long-time secretary, Miriam Peckler, for typing assistance with many precursor papers that found their way into the book and, more recently, to Vickie Thompson who converted my handprinted pages to beautifully typed pages and a computer diskette. Next, to my student, Nicolas Cuendet, for converting many drawings and tables to computerized form and especially for constructing many of the direct space/inverse space companion figures via the Fourier Transform procedure using Mathematica. I also wish to thank Rollin McCraty, Mike Atkinson and Glen Rein for allowing me to present some of their published material. Next, I want to thank my friends Ernie Pecci, Ed Sheppie and Joanne Walsh for bringing the manuscript to the printed book stage with its appealing format. And, most of all, I want to thank my dear wife, Jean, who walked the path of inner self-development with me as we, together, cognitively explored the Subtle Domains. She has been indispensable to my unfoldment process, keeping me balanced, grounded, stable and cheerful as I tried to walk the fine line between the conventional 4-space perspective and the Subtle Domains perspective. Although I am the visible ingredient in the unfolding drama, Jean has been my unseen cooperating partner without whom this work would not have reached fruition.

January 19,1997
William A. Tiller

References

1.R. Steiner, "Occult Science: An Outline" (Rudolph Steiner Press, London, 1979 edition).

# ● FORWARD ●

D r. Tiller, in this groundbreaking book, has taken on the difficult task of bridging the gap between conventional scientific thinking and esotericism, a metaphysical or vertical leap into a whole new paradigm of reality unattainable by the limited methods of inquiry of conventional science. Modern scientific research operates under the premise that by expanding infinitely new bits of linear information, i.e., the discovery of ever new relationships and correlations between 3-dimensional phenomena, the divine plan of the universe will be revealed. What is actually needed is a vertical leap to an entirely new paradigm which gives a higher order of importance to the unseen than to the seen.

This is far more than a book on an innovative scientific theory. It is a compilation of research findings and mathematical connections which largely adheres to the principles of the "scientific mind", using the biological capacity of the human body as an instrument of technological study. Although new ideas generally tend to trigger skepticism and defensiveness, Dr. Tiller does not threaten any of the currently held ideas of the scientific community, but instead expands upon them in a way that challenges the limits of its imagination.

Dr. Tiller painstakingly points out each stepping stone to travel from point A across the great abyss to point B. But, even after arriving at point B, one can go no further until one surrenders all of their old paradigms of reality, because there is no scientifically-oriented continuum that takes us from the horizon of physical reality to other dimensional realms. The breach might never be spanned were it not for the fact that our own physical bodies are liquid crystal-like receptors of sensitive subtle energies and our right brains, freed from the limitations of the left brain, are capable of quantifying the reception of subtle energies from other dimensions.

The motivated reader must be willing not only to follow Dr. Tiller along his path of mathematically logical steps to increasingly broader perceptions of the world as we know it, but to be willing to take the leaps leading unerringly to a new paradigm which must be entertained for some time with faith until the active flow patterns stimulated in the right brain can come into a resonance that makes it all "feel right".

My acquaintance with Dr. William Tiller dating back some thirty years has offered me the unique experience of observing the gradual development of his thinking processes through the stages of higher and higher levels of intuitive "modelling", in search of the implicate order behind observed reality.

As an instructor in the department of Material Sciences and Engineering at Stanford University, Dr. Tiller's interests appeared to be at the opposite pole of my own specialty in the field of psychiatry which deals primarily with everyday consciousness and emotion. His two books: the Microscopic and the Macroscopic Science of Crystallization (Cambridge Press 1991) certainly qualify him as one of the world's most knowledgeable research scientists in the basic structure of material substances. Through his increasingly more abstract levels of mathematical modelling, based upon both intuition and experimental studies on anomalous and little understood phenomena such as ESP, dowsing, Kirlian photography, and even the enigma of "pyramid power", he has arrived at a unified theory of matter, energy and consciousness that appears to satisfy Einstein's attempt to quantify a paradigm of an energetic-field-like universe. At higher dimensions, according to Tiller, seemingly disparate equations covering common as well as anomalous phenomena appear to merge.

About twenty years ago, Dr. Tiller began to formulate his ideas in a series of papers describing his modelling of a lattice framework of the universe. Within this model he further envisions subliminal energies creating wave-patterns throughout this lattice-like grid travelling at speeds exceeding the velocity of light.

The primary functions of subliminal energies, according to Dr. Tiller, are as carriers of messages which unlock or modify the already existing high energy potential within every cubic centimeter of space. Thought energy is one important category of subliminal energy capable of triggering the cosmic computer system, which, when properly focused is quite capable of altering the vibration of water into that of wine or triggering even more impressive phenomena that currently fit into the category of miracles. Evolutionary energy is also a specific subliminal energy messenger that triggers the encoded information within a seed such as an acorn to unfold into an oak tree.

Thus, through the study of the structure and the flow of energy bands through crystals which allow them to function as energy amplifiers, transformers, capacitors, modifers and focusers of energy, Dr. Tiller has developed a paradigm for subliminal energies flowing through the structure of the universe. He expands upon Newton's 3rd law, "Every action has an equal and opposite reaction", by hypothesizing that every spatial pattern has a correlate which is a frequency pattern. In the case of the crystal, its correlate in reciprocal space is a set of lines in a grid pattern existing in a negative space/time framework.

He intuits that the nodal points of this reciprocal lattice have a hexagonal pattern. This is consistent with Plato's comments in his *Timeus* that the universe consists of tightly packed microscopic tetrahedrons. And while he also states, as did Plato, that the physical is but a shadow of higher dimensions, he insists that we have receptors within the mental and sensory systems of our physical body which are receptive to and can be trained to bring to conscious awareness the energies of the negative space/time lattice.

Energies not available to everyday consciousness form the field in which all observed activity takes place. It is a multidimensional field, described by Dr. Tiller as a perfectly ordered lattice framework, a microscopic pattern of complex, geometrically harmonic grids filling in all of space free from the limitations of time-space, where cause and effect is only an illusion, and where "accidents" or randomness cannot exist.

God might be described by Tiller as "consciousness pulsating through creation", a Source echoing a rapidly pulsating energy of pure thought emitting vibratory sound or photons of light forming perfectly harmonic geometric grids in space, creating the matrix which determines the evolutionary growth and shape of all living forms as well as the placement of the stars. Consciousness radiating in the form of information at an infinite speed could simultaneously be present in an infinite number of places in an infinite expanse of space. Thus "God" resides within the core of every atom.

There is an unseen matrix which gives form to the seen. It is in constant flow and harmony through an instantaneous exchange of information in every direction. From a higher dimensional perspective the multiplicity of seemingly disparate laws that govern our observational experiences appear to come from a common simple origin. According to Tiller, "---the entire human species seems to be part of one vast organism". Thus, each individual influences the dynamic equilibrium of this multidimensional model. In Tiller's negative space/time model, the subtle energies which make up our etheric body vibrate at speeds faster than light. The flow is not only outward, but echoes back to the source in a panholographic pattern that reflects the state of each individual element, the part reflecting the whole and the whole influenced by every part. Each person may be defined in terms of a vibrational tone, merging with others into chords creating greater or lesser harmony, all part of a grand symphony with harmonic and subharmonic scales and overtones all merging into the one note of Creation, the vibration of love.

Dr. Tiller insists that there is an inherent capacity of every organism, gland, or living cell to resonate to the frequency of love, which would occur automatically in a system without free-will which presents resistance. For a person as a transmitter the channel that limits the communication is generally the human being himself. We are our own impedance, and fear creates the major interference pattern.

As a psychiatrist, I am naturally interested in the way in which the mind of a man such as Dr. Tiller gradually evolves the complex conceptualizations that results in his envisioning the hidden framework of the universe. Several years ago, after hearing a lecture by Dr. Tiller on his lattice model of space, I thought, "He has come to this point, but there is no way he can go any further". However, after a period of time working on one particular plateau of thought, his mind would make a quantum leap to a higher conceptualization and he did go further.

There is currently confusion between thinking and consciousness. Thinking is an autonomous activity of the brain which, in most people, proceeds outside of conscious awareness and has little or no power to affect the environment except as part of the general energy state of the individual. When analyzed, it can reveal the history of that person's prior experiences, replayed as fragments of a redundant tape.

Conscious thinking toward the creation of a new thought pattern in order to shed new light upon the solution of a perplexing problem, is a much different matter. Here, in a creative individual, the energy of will is exercised directly upon the mind which becomes progressively more freed from the limitations of prior programmed constructs, opening up momentarily, through the act of persistent willing, to the thought energy of higher dimensions, to receive what is called intuitive insight. In a highly creative individual the brain must be trained to create new thinking channels in order to access in logical terms what the philosopher-scientist is experiencing on an intuitive level. Ideally, these two processes, i.e., the acquisition of higher mental states and the training of the brain to access them, proceeds in harmonious tandem.

Walter Freeman, a neuroscientist at U.C. Berkeley, and J. Scott Kelso, director of the Center Complex Systems at Florida-Atlantic University have concluded independently that the brain is fundamentally a pattern-forming, self-organizing system. As such, it fits in with chaos theory in that, according to Freeman, "only systems in chaos can give rise to new patterns." Whirlpools and tornadoes are examples of self-organizing systems. Such phenomena, also called "dissipative structures" by Nobel Laureate Iflya Prigogine, maintain their own shape while in a state of open exchange with their surroundings.

Kelso also envisions the process of brain functions more like the flow of a river in which patterns emerge and disappear, than a static landscape. Perception, cognition, intention and action cannot be separated out. They seem to be facets of cohesive, self-organizing complexes within the larger system of the self.

Biophysicist Beverly Rubik, director of Temple University's Center for Frontier Sciences, theorizes, much like Tiller, that information carried along subtle energy fields is a unifying concept linking homeopathy and psychic healing. To explain electromagnetic healing, she invoked the theory that the living human organism contains many highly sensitive natural oscillators that join to form a collective "biofield." This field is a collective property of the organism and cannot be reduced to biomolecular events. In this case information is transmitted by external fields of similar frequency, with healing occurring through a "tuning" effect.

Bohm coins the term, "active information" to describe data that, in Rubik's words, "are potentially active everywhere, but become active only where meaning is drawn". The idea of active information implies that matter has a mindlike quality. It also implies that information may be causal.

Our language was created by, and limits us to, the reality created by our finite perceptions and the consensus precepts of our society. A new language is needed to describe a new paradigm of reality. Mathematics has the potential for providing this language. But even then, it must be preceeded by the conceptualizations of a highly developed and attuned right brain, which then directs the left brain toward the formulas which lead to the already arrived upon right brain understanding. Einstein, for example, is said to have felt within his body the truth of the relationship $E=mc^2$, and then had to work backwards to formulate his intuition into mathematical terminology. Herein lies the genius of Dr. Tiller, himself. Through years of training, coupled by focused questioning, like Einstein or Tesla before him, he dares to *challenge the idioms* of scientific knowledge.

I find particularly intriguing the wedding of Dr. Tiller's formulations with my own special interest in Sacred Geometry. According to the tenets of Sacred Geometry all of creation exists as energetic patterns of waveforms which can be described in terms of frequency (vibration) and form (geometry). As the vibrational energy, like a step-down transformer, flows down to the 4th dimension, interference patterns result in the crystallization of matter in the shape of the Platonic solids.

Our eyes can visualize only 3-dimensional configurations, while remaining oblivious to the panoply of subliminal energies from other dimensionalities interwoven into a flowing pattern. Our left brain attempts to analyze the isolated fragments it can perceive, and constructs beliefs to make sense of and to add predictability to these observations.

Sacred geometry unites the harmony of music with the symmetry in crystals, and even the placement of the stars. Each molecule of matter reveals the structure of the universe. The law of correspondence between all things small and large is attributed to Hermes Trismegistus, the architect of the Great Pyramid: *"That which is below reflects that which is above"*. This applies not only to geometric proportions and form, but to the harmonic relationships between one fixed point and another. The relatively few repetitive symmetries seen in the structure of all living things, and man no less, reveals the imprint of a divine plan, consistent in form, shape and harmonic relationships from the atom to the farthest galaxy.

Dr. Tiller's work has enormous implications to the field of psychology regarding the meaning and purpose of life. The final goal of meaningful psychotherapy is not merely crisis intervention or problem-solving per se, but encouraging the pushing through discomfort toward a transformation of identity, . . . "it is necessary to proceed past the state of mere intellectual awareness to the state of consistent, if not automatic, organismic response to this transcendental image of man." Conventional psychology misses the mark if it focuses only upon daily activity and past experiences lacking the grander vision of the total development and evolution of the soul and its task of reharmonizing to the Whole, and rather than support the ego in a way that fixates the individual into a limiting identity, to break free from the constraint of family and social influences into a remembrance of our Source. Dr. Tiller's description of the "band broadening" effect, when two people work together on a problem, helps explain the benefits derived from active listening in psychotherapy. More healing may occur in the space between words than by the words themselves.

Impulses of information and energy bombard our bodies every moment; their effects are dependent upon our receptivity and our interpretations based upon past perceptions or beliefs. We can only comprehend truth to the extent to which it resonates with some portion of already perceived reality. However, we are capable of raising our level of awareness, enlarging our consciousness through a repeated desire to hear the sound of Truth until we can hear even the voice of the Divine.

By consciously altering our attitudes through affirmation and intentionality, humans can be transformed to higher states of functioning. If we believe with sincere conviction in our connection to a higher Source, we not only become more receptive to healing energies (experienced as love), but we can mirror back the information in a way that influences the subtle energy system to make manifest our innermost desires.

Dr. Tiller also offers a model for inner management, not dissimilar from the goals of the practices of the various forms of yoga, but one more suitable to the lifestyle and the stresses of today's world. His model can be simplified to one major principle, i.e., the breaking of old habit patterns of depression and fear by consciously focusing upon the heart with thoughts of appreciation, thus utilizing the heart's capacity to entrain the physical body to the vibration of love. Moreover, even a small group of properly entrained individuals can have an exponential effect upon the general level of consciousness on the population of the planet.

To fully appreciate the message of Dr. Tiller is to be willing to see ourselves and the world we know in a new context, one which challenges our old paradigms, ultimately for an enhancement of our own complexity and value as a life form with untapped potential.

All energy in its various manifestations on different dimensions is essentially an ongoing information transfer process. Furthermore, there is an instantaneous space-time interconnection among points, each with an influence upon every other depending upon position, angle and number. There is an antenna system within our brain and, yes, our hearts, that is constantly feeding us the information of Truth. To find Truth we must look, not only outside of ourselves, but within. In this book, Dr. Tiller offers a convincing unified theory of matter-energy and consciousness with vast implications regarding the way individuals and groups create their environment through their preconceived belief system and thought patterns.

Adding tremendous support for Dr. Tiller's beliefs regarding healing and intentionality, a Menninger Clinic team has found that significant bursts of electromagnetic energy correlated with the directed "intentional" efforts of certain healers.

What does this mean personally? It is imperative that humans begin consciously to resonate to the vibrations of love and appreciation and resist the self-addicting emotions of fear, anger and hate. The sense of helplessness, depression, and fear which now pervades the surface of planet earth can only be dispelled by an awakening of our true superhuman potential and the power of the mind, or more exactly, the belief systems held within our minds, to influence massively our environment.

What is God? What is consciousness? What is the basic nature of the universe? For centuries, philosophers have attempted to apply the faculty of critical thinking to the understanding of the nature of reality. Through the mental exercises of empirical, rational, and inductive reasoning, they have largely succeeded primarily in questioning the validity of any basic assumptions from which to make a beginning. Emmanual Kant concluded that we, as humans, do not possess the capacity to fully comprehend reality. Descarte stated, *I think, therefore I am.*" He would have come closer to the truth if he stated, "I feel therefore I am" in as much as perception must be experienced to be fully known.

Critical thinking has succeeded in creating a consensus reality of a very finite segment of our world based upon physical perceptions. But it is the subliminal sensations created by the antenna system within our brain and, yes, our hearts, that is constantly feeding us the information of Truth. To find Truth we must look, not just outside of ourselves, but more concentratedly within.

Dr. Tiller has examined the nature of physical matter from the macroscopic structure down to the illusive atom as thoroughly as any scientist upon this planet, and has found in the repetitive geometric, crystalline patterns not the truth, but a clue to the truth, much as a dream, having no substantive reality of itself, gives clues as to the nature of the dreamer. Thus, from the seen, he has made a creative leap to the unseen. Tiller is asking us not to comprehend the incomprehensible, but to acknowledge its existence.

However large the initial readership of this first edition, the power of its content most assuredly will send a ripple through the unified panholographic consciousness-internet, planting new seeds of thought that will sprout in their time.

— Ernest F. Pecci, M.D.

*Is there a student of science, theology, metaphysics who does not desire to have more evidence of the existence of a powerful force which is omnipresent — that can be called upon for assistance, nourishment, knowledge and direction? The theologian might call this force "God," the scientist might use the term "energy," and the general student might use the term "spirit."*

*Dr. William Tiller, in this magnificent study which explains carefully and fully this force, has proven, I believe to even the most exacting scientist, the existence of such an omnipresent force which he identifies as "subtle energies."*

*Tiller has written a very special story about becoming! I know that anyone who is exposed to this book in any depth will come away with a different mindset, one that will provide tremendous enthusiasm for life and just how to use this new understanding to develop a more effective set of values and attitudes.*

Jack H. Holland, Ph.D., D.S.D.

# CHAPTER
# 1

## RESETTING OUR PHYSICS PERSPECTIVE

*The soaring edifice of personal mind,*
*So capable of touching all the glories of the universe*
*Sees not glory when too rigidly constrained*
*By old concepts and dogmas --*
*Then an unseen prison does the personal mind become.*

As we ride the "River of Life", the great consciousness adventure, we perceive events occurring around us but, more often than not, we do not perceive the true reality in those events. This is so because what we take as the reality of the observation is actually a convolution between (1) what is actually there and (2) our mindset or belief structure. We are thus always making observations through the distorting lens of our mindset and we have no way at present to perform the deconvolution and perceive the pure information. It is not only important to be aware of this fact, but it is valuable for one to periodically check his/her mindset or system of beliefs to see if it is still operationally valid.

A century ago, science was self-congratulatory because it had made such great strides in understanding the physical universe and believed that almost everything was understood about physics. It also believed that, for the future, it was largely a matter of just filling in a few details and refining the accuracy of key constants involved in the physical descriptions. And then a new door opened, and we awoke to the concepts of quantum and relativity perspectives with which we must view a broader universe. It wasn't that Newton was wrong when Einstein described the realities of Relativity Theory; rather, Einstein showed that there was a valid larger perspective or new mindset needed to properly describe physical phenomena in the limit of very large velocities. Thus, it was just that the Newtonian picture was incomplete.

For much of this century, science has worked hard to quantify, test and apply our understanding of Quantum Mechanics and Relativity Theory. This process continues. However, science has again entered a self-congratulatory phase because it has discovered and verified the existence of four fundamental forces operating in the universe and the assertion is that, with these, all the observable phenomena of the universe can be explained. These are the electromagnetic force, the weak nuclear force, the strong nuclear force and the gravitational force. Theoretical unification of the first three forces has already been achieved, and establishment scientists feel that it is only a matter of time before a grand unification theory will be developed that will unify all four of these forces and then we will have a "Theory of Everything".

Unfortunately, establishment science has failed to make a reality check on its mindset because, for many decades, a growing body of experimental data has appeared that seems completely inexplicable based upon consideration of only these four forces. A new door has opened, and we once again seem like babes "crawling on the floor of the universe". A new adventure is afoot for science, and the purpose of this chapter is to give a partial listing of some of the data fragments that require an expanded perspective, beyond the accepted four physical forces, if one is to understand them and integrate that understanding with these four physical forces. Ultimately, we must find a valid, larger perspective or new mindset which is needed to quantitatively describe this class of seemingly strange phenomena on an equal footing with our conventional scientific phenomena.

## The Dynamic Equation of Nature

For much of this century, science and medicine have seen living organisms as operating largely by means of the following sequence of reactions:

$$\text{Function} \Leftarrow \Rightarrow \text{Structure} \Leftarrow \Rightarrow \text{Chemistry} \tag{1.1}$$

In the past, whenever an organism wasn't functioning properly, we tended to blame structural defects in the system arising out of chemical imbalances originating within or as the result of outside invasion. To cure the problem, we usually tried to adjust this balance by making inputs to the right hand term in equation 1.1. This was thought to drive the reaction to the left, to restore the proper structure and thus also proper function. With the passage of time, we used ever more sophisticated chemical complexes and larger dosages to trigger the organism's defense and repair mechanisms. Unfortunately, both the organism and the threatening invaders gradually adapt to any new chemical complex, becoming less and less sensitive to it, and so an escalation of potency must continue. Worse still, the unnatural chemical content begins to influence other levels of body functioning besides the one being treated. The effect is particularly serious in agriculture, where the chemicals are applied to the soil. A chemical equilibrium begins to develop between the plants and the soil, percolation spreads the chemicals over a large area and the whole ecosystem begins to suffer from gradual chemical pollution. The immune systems of all the biological organisms involved begin to weaken. By mid-century, it became clearer and clearer that humankind must find a better way of understanding and dealing with functional flaws in living organisms. However, so long as we continued to see living organisms only within the limits of Equation 1.1, we were stuck with the old methods. We tend to characterize medicine based on the Equation 1.1 philosophy as "allopathic medicine".

The most obvious weakness in Equation 1.1 is that it ignores applied electromagnetic fields. Everyone is familiar with the use of x-rays for tumor treatment and of diathermy (electrically-induced heat) for muscle relaxation. In addition, for the past several decades, neuropsychiatry has shown us that small electric currents between specific points in the brain give rise to the same behavioral changes that are observed with certain specific brain-stimulating chemicals[1]. During the same decades, it has been shown that small D.C. electric currents (1 trillionth to 1 billionth of an ampere per square millimeter) can stimulate certain cellular regeneration, tissue repair and fracture healing[2] while larger current densities produce cellular degeneration. In fact, such techniques are presently being strongly pursued to accelerate the healing of all types of human fractures. Finally, in the past decade, we have seen the use of light therapy for the treatment of human depression and a host of other disorders. Thus, as we approach the end of this century, it seems clear that Equation 1.1 must be replaced by

$$\text{Function} \Leftarrow \Rightarrow \text{Structure} \Leftarrow \Rightarrow \text{Chemistry} \Leftarrow \Rightarrow \overset{\text{Electromagnetic}}{\text{Energy Fields}} \qquad (1.2)$$

In fact, as one digs deeper into the nature of living systems, one finds that they are very complex photoelectrochemical devices[2] that emit a wide spectrum of photons, and that homeostasis at the chemical level requires a network of fields and currents flowing within the fabric of the body's cells and tissues.

Unfortunately, although we have seen some aspects of the healing benefits of electromagnetic (EM) energy fields, and sense that much more is to come, today we are also becoming uncomfortably aware of the fact that there can be harmful and unpleasant side effects associated with the increased use of electromagnetic energy fields in our ecosystem. Electromagnetic pollution is growing and the mindset associated with Equation 1.2 is no salvation! As we dig deeper to try and understand more about the biological susceptibility of humans to EM fields, we find that, just as certain individuals can be incredibly sensitive to specific chemicals with debilitating allergic reactions[3], other individuals can have debilitating allergic reactions to specific frequencies of electromagnetic fields[4]. Such sensitive individuals find it almost impossible to live in our societal ecosystem and need a very unique environment, free of both chemical and EM pollutants, in order to sustain any quality of life. To be able to help them, we must dig deeper.

One obvious defect of Equation 1.2, is that it takes no account of mental effects. Under hypnosis, the human body has been known to exhibit truly remarkable feats of strength and endurance attesting to a mind/structure link. In Aikido, Zen or Yoga disciplines, one finds a conscious link between mind and both structure and function. On another front, modern psychotherapy shows us that certain chemical treatments influence mental states and certain mental treatments influence chemical states[5].

Human body acupuncture points, known since ancient times in Asia as special points for the treating of bodily dysfunction, are found to have different electrical characteristics than the surrounding skin even though no striking histological difference has been detected[2]. Variations in mental alertness is known to cause significant changes in the electrical characteristics of these skin points[6]. Some Soviet investigators have found that mental concentration techniques can be used to increase the "effective" voltage difference between similar points on the left and right sides of the body. By connecting an electrical meter between such points on the hands (see Fig. 1.1), the voltage difference can be changed from 50mV to 500mV by such mental concentration. More general biofeedback techniques[7,8] show us that directed mind can not only control various autonomic body functions like skin temperature, pain, etc., but can also repair the body. Certainly the experiments in which Jack Schwarz[8] thrust needles through his body and mentally allowed bleeding or not bleeding to occur clearly confirms this human ability. There is no doubt, then, that mind must be included as another factor on the right of Equation 1.2 so our newly modified equation becomes

$$\text{Function} \Leftarrow \Rightarrow \text{Structure} \Leftarrow \Rightarrow \text{Chemistry} \Leftarrow \Rightarrow \overset{\text{Electromagnetic}}{\text{Energy Fields}} \Leftarrow \Rightarrow \text{Mind} \qquad (1.3)$$

It is one thing to utilize self-directed mind to influence various aspects of one's own body; it is something else again to utilize self-directed mind to influence some device or object remote to that body. We have all heard of such psychokinesis claims, but few of us have directly experienced such phenomena. In order to clarify this issue, I designed and built in the mid-1970's (with the help of two of my Stanford students) a detector to register such mind-directed energy from the body[9] and it is useful to discuss those experiments at this point.

4

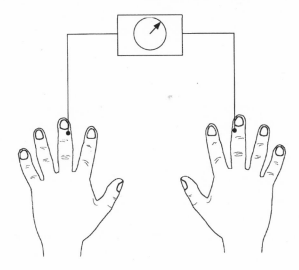

**Fig. 1.1** Illustration of intention-driven current flow technique be-tween symmetrical acupuncture points as a training vehicle to increase psychokinetic ability.

**A Biological Radiation Detector:** The actual detector, illustrated sche-matically in Fig. 1.2, has a sandwich-like shape with the gas isolated between two parallel planar dielectric surfaces (the bread in the sandwich). The gas (the meat in the sandwich) has a thickness of ~2 millimeters and an edge to edge distance of ~10 centimeters. Thin gold electrodes of ~4 centimeters diameter were deposited on the outside of the dielectric surfaces. An external voltage, generated by a high voltage power supply schematically illustrated in Fig. 1.2a, powers the device to a level <u>below</u> the electrical breakdown voltage of the gas (the closest analogy here is to lightning formation during a thunderstorm when the voltage difference between a cloud and the earth is large enough). The electrical operating regime for this device is called the Townsend Regime[10] so that, although there is no sustained discharge across the gas, small microavalanches of electrical charge (micro lightning bolts) form in the gas. These clusters of charge are illustrated in Fig. 1.3a.

The current output from this device passes through a sensing resistor (see Fig. 1.2a) and can be detected by either an oscilloscope or a pulse counter. With such a pulse counter, any current pulse larger than a preset value is re-corded as a single count. The electrical current versus time characteristics of a single pulse was revealed by the oscilloscope and gave a typical result like that shown in Fig 1.3b. A single pulse recorded on the counter involves a time-correlated burst or volley of microavalanches. By adjusting the sensitivity of the pulse counter, one can arrange to just <u>not count</u> the largest microavalanches in Fig. 1.3a. Thus, during background or baseline runs, a counting rate of <u>zero</u> was generally selected; the counter sensitivity setting sometimes allowed a few counts to be recorded in a five-minute test period. With such a baseline, the human's intentionality effect on the device functioning could be determined via an increased number of counts in a five minute test period.

After showing that the important human interaction with the device was via a dynamic effect rather than via a static capacitive effect[9], a variety of experiments were carried out to reveal key features of the dynamic effect utilizing the following protocol:

(1) The voltage and frequency were set and the pulse height sensitivity adjusted periodically to bring the background counting rate into the desired range; then the system was allowed to run at this base level for ~1 hour.

(2) Next, the subject stood or sat ~1 meter in front of the detector, located horizontally at a height of ~1 meter above the floor, for a period of 5 minutes without paying any particular attention to the detector. The total counts for this 5-minute period were recorded and tabulated as the "without hands" (WOH) result.

(3) For the next 5-minute period, the subject stood or sat closer to the detector with their hands placed around but not touching the detector (within 3 centimeters) and mentally focussed their intention on increasing the counting rate. The total counts for this 5-minute period were then recorded and tabulated as the "with both hands" (WBH) result.

(4) Next, the subject stepped back to the original position for a period of 5-15 minutes (or sometimes longer) to allow the counting rate to return to the original base-line rate. The additional counts during this "run-on" period were also recorded.

(5) The system was then available for a second test following steps 2, 3 and 4.

Over the three year period from 1977 to 1979, several thousand different tests with several dozen different subjects under a wide variety of different experimental conditions were conducted with some extremely encouraging results[9]. Fig. 1.4 illustrates schematically both the change in counting rate and the total accumulated counts during the WBH period and its associated run-on period. Typically, if the counting rate was zero during the WOH segment, this persisted for approximately 1-2 minutes into the WBH segment and then sporadic bursts of counts could be both heard and seen as pulses of illumination through the gold electrode (with a semi-dark room). Table 1.1 provides typical data-gathering sequences with subject A on two different days using a leaded glass dielectric and a gas composition of 30% xenon and 70% carbon dioxide. These were the best device operation parameters of the many tested.

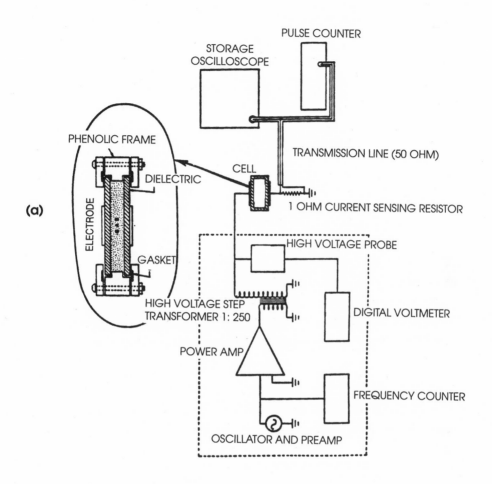

(a)

PULSE COUNTER

STORAGE OSCILLOSCOPE

PHENOLIC FRAME

DIELECTRIC

CELL

ELECTRODE

TRANSMISSION LINE (50 OHM)

1 OHM CURRENT SENSING RESISTOR

GASKET

HIGH VOLTAGE PROBE

HIGH VOLTAGE STEP TRANSFORMER 1: 250

DIGITAL VOLTMETER

POWER AMP

FREQUENCY COUNTER

OSCILLATOR AND PREAMP

(b)

**Fig. 1.2** (a) Schematic diagram for the gas discharge system showing the detector (cell), high fidelity power supply (lower) and monitoring system (top) and (b) a photograph of the operational detector from the high voltage side.

7

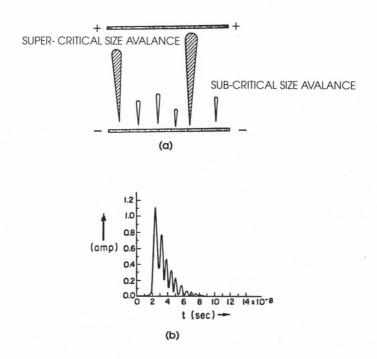

**Fig. 1.3** (a) Relative size illustration for subcritical and supercritical electron avalanches involved in event counting and (b) a typical oscilloscope trace of total electron avalanche current versus time.

On the days when the device was working well, anyone could produce a positive result -- young people, old people, students, nonstudents, healers, nonhealers, etc. Generally, from a purely subjective viewpoint, anyone with a high ability to focus their attention (their mind) produced a high ratio while those with only a small ability to concentrate produced a low ratio. Subjects with considerable previous experience using the device generally produced a higher counting rate than new subjects[9]. On some occasions, for periods of one to several days, no one was able to produce an enhanced counting rate and we were not able to determine why. No correlation was found with rain storms, phases of the moon, etc., however, no consideration was given to geomagnetic field activity. On still other occasions, it required great personal effort to produce an enhanced counting rate and, at these times, some subjects could not achieve an enhanced counting rate.

Extensive studies were carried out to see if this human energy could be shielded from the device or if an alternate inanimate energy source could also trigger the device. The answer was essentially "no" to both questions.

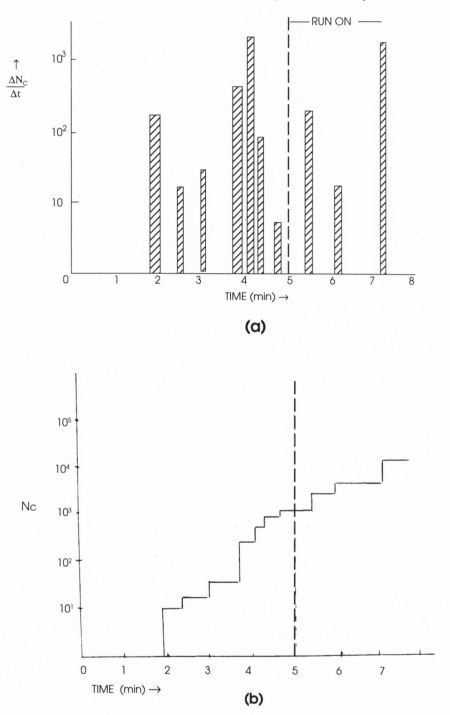

**Fig. 1.4** (a) Schematic illustration of counting rate, $\Delta Nc/\Delta t$, as a function of time during a five-minute WBH period plus run-on period and (b) total accumulated counts, $Nc$, during (a).

Table 1.1 **TYPICAL COUNTING BEHAVIOR FOR THE DETECTOR**

| $V_a$ (Volts) | Frequency (Hz) | Time Increment (min) | Hand Condition | Total Counts | Date |
|---|---|---|---|---|---|
| 4350 | 475 | 5 | WOH | 0 | (1/20/79) |
| | | 5 | WBH | 18,248 | |
| | | 8 | run-on | 27,043 | |
| | | 17 | run-on | 32,049 | |
| | | 25 | run-on | 41,071 | |
| | | 20 | run-on | 46,134 | |
| | | 110 | run-on | 46,134 | |
| 4325 | 475 | 5 | WOH | 0 | (2/13/79) |
| | | 5 | WOH | 0 | |
| | | 5 | WBH | 53,972 | |
| | | 30 | run-on | 60,672 | |
| | | 60 | run-on | 60,672 | |
| | | 30 | run-on | 68,293 | |
| | | 60 | run-on | 68,293 | |
| | | 30 | run-on | 68,293 | |
| | | 30 | run-on | 68,293 | |

In particular, an electrically grounded fine-mesh copper screen box was constructed to fit completely around the detector (a small Faraday cage). In all cases, the detector was first completely enclosed in a thin plastic bag before the shield was fitted in place (to prevent electric arcing). The presence of the plastic and the Faraday cage had <u>no apparent effect </u>on the response of the detector[9]. Thus, whatever energy was being emitted by the human to cause the enhanced counting effect, it was <u>not </u>a classical <u>electromagnetic energy</u> with wavelength larger than the mesh size of the cage. Planar sheets of magnetic shielding material and metal sheets were interposed between the subject's hands and the detector <u>without effect</u>; however, a complete enclosure in a box of magnetic shielding material was not tried. D.C. and A.C. electric and magnetic fields plus EM radiation from infra red through ultraviolet to gamma-rays were used as possible perturbing sources with essentially no effect[9]. Although both nitrogen and air worked satisfactorily as the gas in the detector while pure xenon or pure carbon dioxide did not, the mixture of 30% Xe + 70% $CO_2$ worked best.

Three experiments were carried out to test the influence of self-directed mind (intentionality) on the enhanced counting rate[9]. In the first, after step

2 of the standard protocol, and for the next 5-minute period, the subject stood or sat in the same location and focussed their intention on increasing the counting rate of the detector without putting their hands around the device. The total counts for this 5-minute period were recorded and tabulated as the "with mind" (WM) result. A compilation of this data is presented in Table 1.2 where we see that, in all cases, the WM result is larger than the WOH result.

In the second experiment, steps 1, 2 and 4 of the standard protocol were the same, but step 3 involved placing the hands around the detector and focussing the intention on an enhanced count. Step 5 was a repeat of step 2 while step 6 was similar to step 3 except that, with the hands around the detector, **during the entire WBH counting period, the subject withdraws his/her mental focus from the detector and places it on a simple mental addition excercise such as 2+2=4, 3+3=6, 4+4=8,. . . 52+52=104,. . . etc.** During this period, the mind is <u>never for a moment</u> allowed to rest on the detector. After step 6, there is another run-on period.

Table 1.2  **Enhanced Counting Rate without the Use of Hands** [†]

| Time Increment (min) | WOH Counts | WM Counts |
|:---:|:---:|:---:|
| 5 | 0 | 6043 |
| 5 | 920 | 1814 |
| 5 | 0 | 241 |
| 5 | 415 | 3864 |
| 5 | 2795 | 7016 |
| 5 | 0 | 7937 |
| 5 | 3231 | 12,997 |
| 5 | 0 | 11335 |

[†] **(Subject A, high lead glass cell with air, 475 hz)**

Table 1.3 presents some results for this second experiment where we can clearly see that, even though the hands are around the detector, if the intention/attention is focussed elsewhere, <u>no enhanced counting rate is observed.</u> It was noticed during this experiment that, if a subject was coming down with a cold and couldn't focus his/her attention too well, it was not possible to maintain a zero counting rate during the "mental addition" segment.

To make an initial test of the nonlocal nature of this phenomenon, experiment three involved placing a subject in a large Faraday cage about 10 feet

Table 1.3 **With Both Hands but Intention Focussed on Addition †**

| Frequency (Hz) | Time Increment (min) | Hand Condition | Total Counts | Intention Condition |
|---|---|---|---|---|
| 475 | 5 | WOH | 0 | Subject C |
| 475 | 5 | WOH | 0 | |
| 475 | 5 | WBH | 53,725 | Focus on Detector |
| 475 | 5 | WOH | 0 | |
| 475 | 5 | WOH | 0 | |
| 475 | 5 | WBH | 0 | Focus on Addition |
| 475 | 5 | WOH | 0 | |
| 475 | 5 | WOH | 0 | |
| 475 | 5 | WBH | 16,931 | Focus on Detector |
| 475 | 5 | WOH | 14 | Subject A |
| 475 | 5 | WBH | 11,335 | Focus on Detector |
| 475 | 5 | WOH | 55 | |
| 475 | 5 | WBH | 42 | Focus on Addition |
| 475 | 5 | WOH | 51 | |
| 475 | 5 | WBH | 12,965 | Focus on Addition |
| 475 | 5 | WOH | 0 | Subject D |
| 475 | 5 | WBH | 23,333 | Focus on Detector |
| 475 | 5 | WOH | 0 | |
| 475 | 5 | WBH | 0 | Focus on Addition |
| 475 | 5 | WOH | 0 | |
| 475 | 5 | WBH | 18,201 | Focus on Detector |

**† (High lead glass cell with air, 4325 volts)**

from the detector which was surrounded by its own Faraday cage. The protocol was essentially the same as the first experiment except that steps (2) and (3) required the subject's location to be inside the 7-foot cubic Faraday cage. When the subject focussed his attention on enhanced counting of the detector for a 5-minute period, widely scattered large bursts of counts occured to change from a zero count condition during stage 2 to about 23,000 counts during stage 3. There were no run-on counts. Only two trials of this type of experiment were run and both were successful.

It would seem reasonable to conclude from this directed-intention study, with our microavalanche detector, that mind should definitely be a term in Equation 1.3 but also that there is perhaps another unique energy form emitted by the body that should be located between mind and electromagnetic energy fields!

**A Few Other Psychokinesis Studies:** At least five other valuable psychokinesis (PK) experiments should be mentioned before moving on. A relatively early experimental program by Forwald [11] studied about 15,000 PK events involving small wooden cubes over a 15 to 20 year period. He showed a mathematical relationshiop between his ability to influence these cubes, as they slid down a specially designed ramp, and both the thickness and chemical (nucleus) nature of the films that coated these cubes. Much more recently, Jahn and Dunne[12] have reported on a variety of very carefully conducted studies on micro-PK with great statistical analysis to positively underscore the reality of human/machine linkages via directed mind action.

Swann also performed two significant experiments in the PK area[13]. In the first, he mentally altered the temperature of a small piece of silicon (a thermister) located 12 inches from his body. In the second, he seemingly influenced the decay rate of a very sensitive magnetic field detector (squid) located behind vast metallic and concrete shielding at Stanford University. Hasted[14] conducted an extensive study of "metal-bending" by children. As part of this study, he used latch keys with attached strain gauges suspended from the ceiling ~3-10 feet from the subjects so that there could be no physical contact between the key and the child. The electrical output from the strain gauge was registered on a strip chart recorder. Abrupt voltage pulses ( one second or more duration) of ~millivolts to 10 volts (limit of recorder) were observed. Sometimes the key was also observed to swing or to fracture. When multiple latch keys with their associated strain gauges and recorders were used, with the keys being separated by various distances, simultaneous strain signal events were often recorded. As a final PK example for mention here, Motoyama[15] placed a person, with marked psychic ability, and a second person, with ordinary abilities, in separate rooms shielded by concrete walls lined with lead. The gifted person concentrated his mind on the other person (subject) while Motoyama monitored some of the subject's bodily functions. Remarkable changes were noted in the subject's pulse, blood flow, skin resistance and respiration rate during the concentration period of the psychic subject (see Fig. 1.5). Since the two rooms were well shielded against information transfer via physical energies, such PK effects on the human subject appear to require some non-physical energy involvement.

An analogous but more therapeutic remote influence falls under the category of healing and healers[16-18] with the process involving not only the mental domain but the emotional and spiritual domains as well. References to other healers, from Jesus to Arigo[19] continue to appear in a variety of publications. Thus, these categories of unique energies also need to be added to the far right of Equation 1.3. Our difficulty is that, although we use the words mental, emotional and spiritual to mean different things, we have great difficulty in drawing fine lines of discrimination between them. Even the lovely quote from

Starcke[20], "When the spirit in which you live is more important to you than the results of your living, you are spiritual. When the results are more important than how you go about getting them, you are material.", doesn't help one to discriminate this special class of energies one from another as needed for the extension of Equation 1.3.

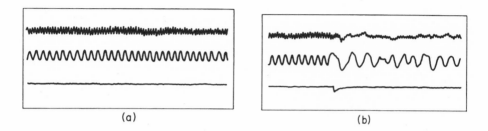

(a)                                         (b)

**Fig. 1.5** (a) From top to bottom, plethysmogram, respiration and galvanic skin resistance recordings in an ordinary person occupying a shielded room before the period of mental concentration by an accomplished psychic person occupying a separate shielded room and (b) the recordings after the onset of mental concentration by the accomplished individual.

Thus, at this point in time, I propose that we just call them all "subtle" energies until we have enough discriminated experience to truly understand the differentiations. Subtle energies are therefore all those beyond those formed from the four well known and accepted classes of forces that are needed to explain the natural phenomena discussed in this chapter. Equation 1.3 is thus transformed into

$$\text{Function} \Leftleftarrows \Rightrightarrows \text{Structure} \Leftleftarrows \Rightrightarrows \text{Chemistry} \Leftleftarrows \Rightrightarrows \overset{\text{Electromagnetic}}{\text{Energy Fields}} \Leftleftarrows \Rightrightarrows \overset{\text{Subtle}}{\text{Energy Fields}} \quad (1.4)$$

**Monitoring Subtle Energy Events From A Healer:** In a recent study of "sensitive" individuals in a specially designed copper wall environment, such as illustrated in Fig. 1.6[21], it was found that energy projectors (healers and Qigong masters) sometimes generated anomalously large voltage pulses as measured by an electrode attached to the ear lobe.

For information receivers (clairvoyants, etc.) and for ordinary subjects, no such pulses were observed. Instead of the usual 10-15 millivolt baseline with ~1 millivolt ripple, the ear lobe voltage often plunged -30 to -300 volts and then recovered to baseline in ~0.5 to ~10 seconds. This is an astoundingly large voltage pulse, ~$10^5$ times normal! In a single 30 minute healing session that took place inside this special environment, one particular healer manifested 15 of these anomalously large voltage bursts (each greater than 30 volts) with each main burst (see Fig. 1.7 for a pair of such bursts) being composed of 5-6 sub-pulses convolved in one envelope (see Fig. 1.8).

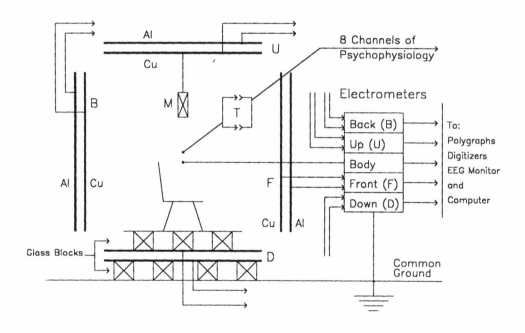

**Fig. 1.6** Schematic diagram of copper-wall meditation room. Four pairs of insulated copper (Cu) and aluminum (Al) panels float in electrical space around a research chair which also floats electrically, insulated from the bottom wall (down) by glass construction blocks. All panels reach a common electrical ground through their electrometers.

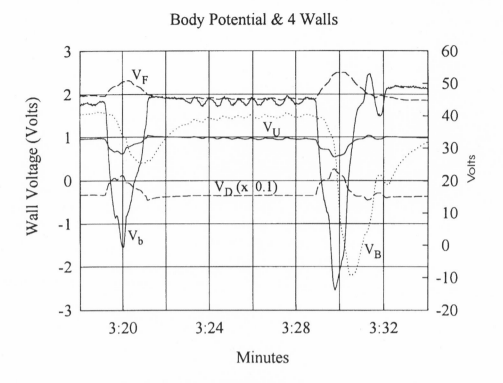

**Fig. 1.7** Simultaneous body (right hand scale) and wall (left hand scale) potentials for the anomalous voltage bursts at 3:20 and 3:30 from the healer.

In Fig. 1.7, we see the voltage trace for the body electrode ($V_b$) plus the voltage traces for each of the four separately monitored walls ($V_F$, $V_B$, $V_U$, $V_D$). The present working hypothesis for explaining these voltages is that (1) from some location of the body a subtle energy pulse is emitted, (2) the subtle body structure responsible for this pulse is coupled somehow to the physical body structure so that a transduced effect materializes at this level. It is proposed that a pulse of magnetic vector potential, A, is generated from this transduction, (3) from standard electrodynamics[22], a pulse of magnetic vector potential, like that shown in Fig. 1.9b, generates a pulse of electric field, E, like that illustrated in Fig. 1.9c, (4) such an electric field would cause the ions of the local body electrolyte to separate and produce an electric charge dipole that first expands to a maximum extent and then collapses to zero again after a short time. (5) It is this charge dipole that creates the large voltage swing at the ear electrode and on the walls.

In setting up a mathematical description of the voltage generated from some unique body location in the experimental environment, one finds that it is a five variable problem (two for the origin location in the body, one for the angle of the dipole relative to the horizontal, one for the total amount of charge moved and one for the distance over which it is moved). Fortunately, there are five independent pieces of information also available (the ear voltage plus the four wall voltages) so the mathematical description can be fitted to the experimental data. When this was done for the fifteen pulses in the 30-minute healing session, thirteen of the pulses had the same origin -- lower abdomen, frontal area of the body (~location of the "Dan Tien" point or "Hara" point or "Second Chakra" point). This electric dipole length was predicted to be very large -- it extended from the ear (negative charge end) to the feet (positive charge end) but it required only quite small electric current flows to achieve this result[23]. For the other two pulses, although the ear was at a negative voltage and the bottom wall was at a positive voltage, the upper wall was also at a positive voltage. Such a condition requires the presence of a second electric dipole located in the head with the negative end towards the ear and the positive end towards the upper wall. In this study, one sees the large electrical voltage pulses as physical level correlates of the subtle level energy manifestations associated with the healer's intentionality to create a healing event[23]!

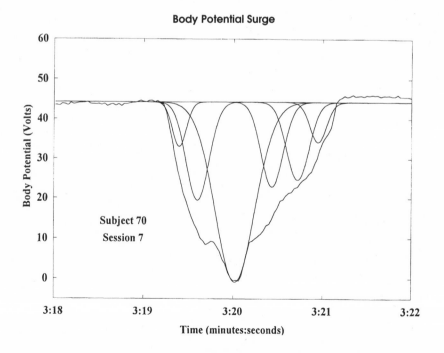

**Body Potential Surge**

Subject 70
Session 7

**Fig. 1.8** Illustration of the Gaussian-type subpulse deconvolutions for the body-potential, $V_b$, surge at time 3:20 in Fig. 1.7.

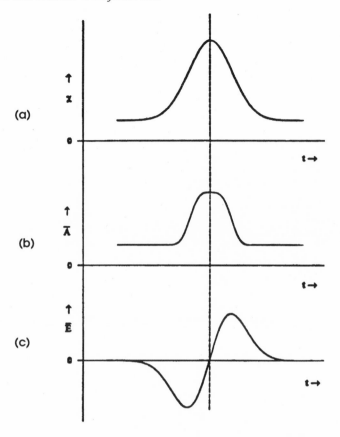

**Fig. 1.9** (a) Schematic illustration of a subtle energy pulse $\chi$, which generates the magnetic vector potential pulse, A, shown in (b) which, in turn, generates the electric field, E, shown in (c) at some specific origin in the healer's physical body.

**Some Photographic Evidence of Subtle Energies:** Over twenty years ago, a very spiritually evolved gentleman named Stan came to see me to see what I thought of some photographs he had taken. Stan had grown up thinking that he was something of a "clutze" with cameras because, when people would hand him their camera to take their picture, something a little strange would usually happen to the picture. Eventually, he observed a correlation between a feeling in his 7th cervical plus 4th thoracic vertabrae and the appearance of strange phenomena appearing on the developed film. He showed me 10-20 of his photographs to illustrate his point; the film was Kodak Kodacolor, the processing was standard Kodak processing and the camera he was using at that time was a simple Kodak camera with a plastic lens. Fig. 1.10 is a composite of four of these photographs. In all cases, the camera was placed stably on a tripod and tripped via a two foot long shutter release mechanism.

In the photographs of Fig. 1.10 and in the others shown to me, there appeared to be an inhomogeneous deformation to the film, parts of it were in sharp focus and parts of it were somewhat out of focus, but with no apparent relationship between these regions. The camera had been sent to Kodak and certified to be in good working order. The photographs had been sent to Kodak specialists to determine what kind of picture-taking error had transpired but these results did not fall into the standard error-mode categories.

**Fig. 1.10** Anomalous photographs taken with a human energy field-sensitized camera using standard film and standard commercial processing.

Stan could obtain such photographs with other people's cameras but he needed to carry such a camera next to his body for several days before he tried to take pictures. In this way, he seemed to be able to sensitize the camera so that such anomalous pictures as Fig. 1.10 could be readily obtained. If he had passed a sensitized camera to someone else to take pictures then, initially, some anomalous effects would be present on the film. However, after 1-10 hours, no anomalous pictures could be taken by others. It seemed that his energy field was necessary to keep the process "pumped up" so that such anomalous photographic results became commonplace.

Stan was of the Bahai faith and practiced prayerfulness throughout the day, every day, and his intentionality with respect to this type of picture-taking was just to "reveal God's universe". He found that the "anomalies" recording process intensified at three locations, (1) spiritual rock concerts, (2) spiritual shrines and (3) high energy lectures on metaphysics.

On learning all of this, I was very intrigued and designed a dual-camera experiment to do with Stan. A tripod platform was constructed to hold the two cameras at a 12-inch separation and a special shutter release mechanism was created to open the two shutters simultaneously. Because we could no longer purchase a duplicate of his favorite Kodak camera, we used a Minolta camera as the unsensitized camera on the tripod. The film in both cameras was standard Kodacolor, the processing was the standard Kodak processing and Stan was never allowed to touch the film roll. Someone else always loaded and unloaded the cameras and sent the film away for processing.

The results of our dual-camera experiments were quite astonishing. Three examples are provided in Figs. 1.11-1.13. In Fig. 1.11a, the Minolta records the physical scene while, in Fig. 1.11b, the Kodak records semitransparent portions of one individual's body through which we can see the branch figure hanging on the wall. In Fig. 1.12a, the Minolta records the presence of one man and two ladies standing on stage in front of a blackboard. In Fig. 1.12b, the Kodak shows us a semitransparent man through which we can see the blackboard. In addition, some type of "stuff" seems to be transferring between or connecting at least one of the women with the man. In Fig. 1.13a, the Minolta shows us an audience and some lightwells in a large auditorium. In Fig. 1.13b, the Kodak shows us this audience but with some amazing banners of "something", perhaps light, coming from these lightwells.

An additional set of four hand-held single camera shots were taken inside the Stanford church. The first picture was with the lens-cap off the camera while the following three had the lens-cap on the camera. The results were: (1) picture one was relatively dark, (2) picture two was significantly brighter and is given in Fig. 1.13(c), (3) picture three is somewhat darker (but still brighter than (1) and is given in Fig 1.13(d) and (4) picture four was totally dark without any distinguishable features.

From this study, I deduce that subtle energies exist for which the camera lens cap and the human body are at least semitransparent. Further, it seems that photographic film has a layer or layers of subtle substance capable of registering an imprint from a pattern of subtle energy entering the lens. The presence of Stan's energy field appears to allow interaction between this subtle substance imprint and the silver halide grains of the physical film so that an imprint transfer takes place that is ultimately recorded by the photographic development process. Indeed, this expression of God's universe shows us that there are many more levels of manifestation in nature than our science has thus far uncovered.

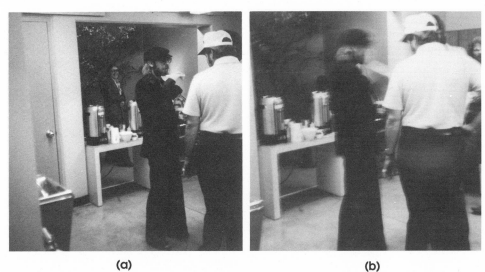

(a)                                      (b)

**Fig. 1.11** Example from the dual camera study, (a) unsensitized camera result and (b) sensitized camera result (especially note the tree branch on the wall and the leg locations of the man standing in front of it).

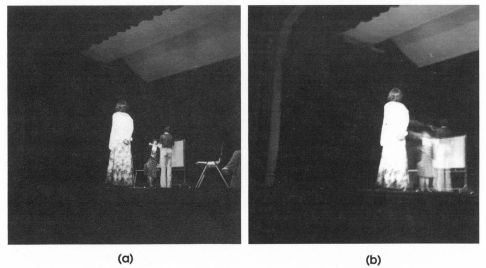

(a)                                      (b)

**Fig. 1.12** Example from the dual camera study, (a) unsensitized camera result and (b) sensitized camera result (especially note the blackboard and the degree of opacity of the man standing in front of it).

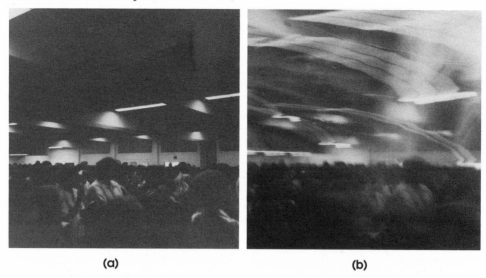

**Fig. 1.13** Example from the dual camera study, (a) unsensitized camera result and (b) sensitized camera result (especially note the character of the light emanating from the light-wells in the ceiling).

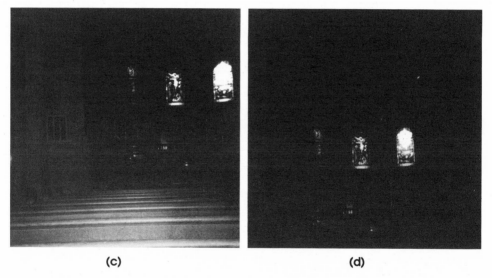

**Fig. 1.13** Examples from a single hand-held camera taken indoors but with the lens-cap on the camera, (c) the first shot through the lens-cap and (d) the second shot through the lens-cap

**A Partial Catalogue of Subtle Energy Phenomena:** A partial list of subtle energy phenomena is presented in Table 1.4. The list is separated into two categories, one dealing primarily with sensing while the other involves, in addition, action. As I view this list, I feel that a subgroup may provide us with insights concerning another level of discrimination in Equation 1.4, so let us now look at that subgroup.

Experiments on remote viewing[13,24a,24b] have shown that individuals can (a) perceive and accurately describe objects placed several miles away from them without using their own physical sight, (b) be given the longitude and latitude coordinates of a location on the earth and accurately describe the terrain of that location even when it is thousands of miles away and (c) tune-in to a specific individual and view a remote locality through that individual's eyes. In the latter case, the remote viewer may even perceive the scene before the target individual gets there. Thus, in general, the future time coordinate as well as the remote distance coordinate can be accessed by using a well-defined set of techniques[24a], possibilities not allowed via the presently accepted paradigm. It is important to note that extensive, independent replication of remote viewing results has been documented[24b]. Here, we see applied mental activity producing results that seriously bring into question our understanding of space-time and which must certainly involve some subtle energy linkage. It is almost as if there is another level of structure in our brains wherein the internal points of the structure are in interactive communication with external distant space coordinates at the physical level of reality. Dual coordinate systems that were inverses of each other would exhibit such a relationship (see Chapter 2).

Table 1.4  **A Partial List of Subtle Energy Phenomena**

| |
|---|
| Remote Viewing |
| Precognition |
| Telepathy/Mind Reading |
| Auric Sight/Clairvoyance |
| Clairaudience |
| Psychometry |
| Dowsing |
| Healing/Qigong |
| Psychokinesis/Telekinesis |
| Dematerialization/Materialization |
| Levitation |
| Homeopathy |

A very different type of inverse relationship appears when we consider homeopathic medicine relative to allopathic medicine. Hahneman was the first to come upon the idea that a substance which can produce symptoms in a healthy person can cure them in a sick person. This has since been called "The Law of Similars". He developed a systematic procedure for testing substances (called "proving") on healthy humans in order to elucidate the symptoms characterizing the actions of that particular substance. During a proving, a substance is introduced into a healthy organism at a sufficiently high concentration to disturb the organism and mobilize its defense mechanisms. The body's defense mechanism then produces a spectrum of symptoms on the physical, emotional and mental levels of the organism and this spectrum of symptoms characterizes the peculiar and unique nature of the substance. Fortunately for the therapeutic end of homeopathic practice, it is found that the symptom pictures of the remedies match, quite accurately, the symptom pictures of virtually all illnesses in existence, in all their variety[25].

Hahneman also discovered in the late 1700's that, when the remedy is diluted with water and, at the same time, succussed (shaken vigorously in a particular way) between dilutions, the effect of the remedy is greatly increased. This dilution enhancement effect can occur well past the point when, theoretically, no molecules of the original physical substance are still present in the solution (for potencies above 12x), yet the solution is still observed to exert a significant action on a living organism (see Chapters 2 and 6). This particular method of dilution with succussion, called "potentizing", quite fortuitously exposed a natural phenomenon of profound biological significance. It is really an incredible result when viewed from the entrenched allopathic viewpoint and, of course, brings into serious question the sufficiency of that viewpoint.

Perhaps as important as the many studies of homeopathic remedies on humans are the few studies that have been made on other living organisms. Boyd[26] found statistically significant effects from potentized mercuric chloride in his research on the activity of the enzyme diastase, which is importantly involved in the hydrolysis of starch. In addition it has been claimed that, in the last British epidemic of Hoof and Mouth Disease, homeopathic Borax, administered by vets and by farmers, gave total or excellent protection while animals on nearby farms, not using the homeopathic Borax, were dying with the disease.

**Children As Subtle Energy Detectors:** A third unique type of experiment rounds out the proposed perspective on a type of "inverse" or "mirror" relationship functioning in nature. These experiments, conducted over a four year period in the 1970's by Jim Carlton and myself used children as sensors for subtle energies[27]. Jim initiated this research which utilized a "Punch and Judy" type of open box ( ~2 feet wide by ~3 feet high by ~2 feet deep) containing two large flat vertical electrodes ( ~10 inches square) separated by about 10 inches (see Fig. 1.14). The box is painted white on the inside walls and a soft diffuse light shines down into the air gap. The children, one at a time, sit about 6 to 10 feet in front of the box and observe the space between the electrodes. Jim applies an increasing voltage to the plates and soon reaches a voltage where the child suddenly begins to see a colored pattern in the air gap (adults generally see nothing). As the voltage is increased, a level is reached where suddenly a different pattern is seen by the child and, at a still higher voltage, another pattern shift occurs; etc., as the voltage is increased from 0 to 15,000 volts, these patterns are perceived by the children as being colored and of straight line geometrical shapes such as stripes, triangles, squares, etc. (see Fig. 1.15).

**Fig. 1.14** Interior air space of the "Punch and Judy" type viewing box containing large electrodes between which the subject sees auric manifestations depending on the type of filtered light coming from the ceiling fixture in the box.

On any one day, the same patterns are drawn by a particular child at the same voltage, whether going up the voltage scale or down, in the morning, afternoon and evening. However, on a different day at the same voltage, the same child may draw a different pattern. Likewise, on the same day, a different child generally draws a different pattern at the same voltage. Further, on any day, if we change the frequency of light shining down into the air gap through the visible range (by the use of filters), for any particular child at a <u>fixed voltage, there are bands of frequencies where the patterns could be seen</u>

and bands of frequencies where they could not be seen. The band edges between pattern/no pattern perception was found to be different for different children.

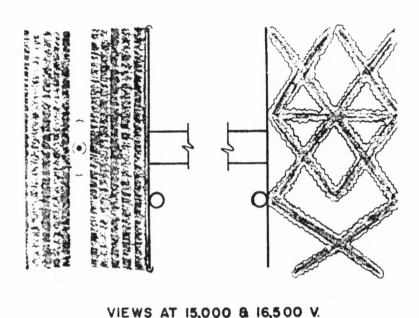

**VIEWS AT 15,000 & 16,500 V.**

**Fig. 1.15** Black and white examples of coloured patterns drawn by a single subject on a single day at two different voltage differences between the electrode plates (with no filter used in the ceiling fixture).

When one uses magnetic pole pieces instead of the electric plates, the perceived patterns were different in that they now consisted primarily of curved lines instead of straight lines. All the young children (ages 7 to 15) were able to perceive these patterns with less than an hour's training by another child. For these children, we noted that the more creative was a child in normal play, the more discrete patterns would that child perceive within a given voltage excursion. Thus, we see in this phenomenon something clearly objective and something clearly subjective; i.e., something which comes from the outside of the individual and something which comes from the mental state of the individual.

At this point, I entered Jim's experimental program with two new experiments based upon my theoretical modeling (to be discussed in Chapter 2). Using the concept of a special "mirror" relationship existing between the physical realm and the next more subtle realm, I proposed that, whereas physical light slows down in going through condensed matter like a glass lens or a prism, the light associated with this next more subtle realm should speed up on going through such a lens or prism. Thus, if the children are not seeing these patterns via physical light (since adults don't see the patterns) but via the light of this next more subtle realm, then some clear predictions could be made and tested in the laboratory. This led to the design of (1) a telescope magnification experiment and (2) an index of refraction experiment:

## (1) The Telescope Experiment

If we look with our physical eyesight, using the unaided eye, at a distant object, we perceive it to have a certain size. If we then look at the same object with a simple telescope, we perceive it to be magnified in size and to be inverted in orientation. If the children measured the size of a feature in one of the patterns (call it $l_F$) with the unaided eye and then used the same subtle realm eyesight to measure the same feature using the simple telescope (call it $l'_F$), the theoretical prediction is that the child should see a demagnified image and an erect image -- just the opposite of what is observed with the physical eyesight. Such an experiment was carried out by Jim Carlton who tabulated the magnification ratio, $M_r = l_F/l'_F$. His results for twelve different subjects are given in Table 1.5 where we see that, in all cases, $M_r$ is greater than 1, as predicted if the mirror principle holds and the children are using subtle realm eyesight. In all these cases, the images through the telescope were observed to be erect. To illustrate the variability of $M_r$ with time, forty observations of $M_r$ were obtained from one subject periodically over a 6-month period (mostly in the evenings or on weekends). These results are shown in Table 1.6 where we see that, in most cases, $M_r$ is greater than unity. For this individual, the statistical mean of $M_r$ is between 1 and 2, just as it is in Table 1.5 for the twelve different subjects.

## (2) The Prism Experiment

When physical light impinges on the smooth surface of a transparent substance like water or glass, part of it is reflected and the rest is refracted (bent) into the medium. This bending is due to the reduction in the velocity of light upon entering the glass or water. A measure of this velocity reduction is given by the index of refraction of the medium, N, where $N = V_1/V_2$. Here, $V_1$ is the velocity of the light in air while $V_2$ is the velocity in the condensed medium. Since $V_2$ is smaller than $V_1$, N is always greater than 1 (typical values are ~1.4 to 1.7 for different glasses and different light frequencies). Such a slowing down of the light in a glass prism leads to the color spectrum first observed by Newton who then explained the phenomenon of rainbow formation and the order of the colors in the rainbow.

Table 1.5 **Experimental Magnification Ratio ($M_r$) Data Obtained From 12 Subjects for the Telescope Phenomena**

| SUBJECT | $M_r$ | SUBJECT | $M_r$ |
|---------|-------|---------|-------|
| 1. Bobby S. | 3.00:1 | 7. Heather H. | 3.18:1 |
| 2. Len C. | 3.43:1 | 8. Betty P. | 8.06:1 |
| 3. David P. | 1.73:1 | 9. David F. | 3.96:1 |
| 4. Jenny P. | 3.07:1 | 10. Keith M. | 1.02:1 |
| 5. Jay C. | 1.82:1 | 11. Douglas W. | 1.83:1 |
| 6. Cathy P. | 2.70:1 | 12. Al W. | 1.49:1 |

Table 1.6 **Experimental Magnification Ratio ($M_r$) Data Showing the Variability of the Telescope Effect for Len.**

| | | | |
|---|---|---|---|
| 1. 0.66:1 | 11. 1.12:1 | 21. 1.51:1 | 31. 2.05:1 |
| 2. 0.79:1 | 12. 1.15:1 | 22. 1.53:1 | 32. 2.14:1 |
| 3. 0.81:1 | 13. 1.18:1 | 23. 1.53:1 | 33. 2.19:1 |
| 4. 0.85:1 | 14. 1.19:1 | 24. 1.70:1 | 34. 2.20:1 |
| 5. 0.94:1 | 15. 1.21:1 | 25. 1.71:1 | 35. 2.42:1 |
| 6. 0.94:1 | 16. 1.26:1 | 26. 1.72:1 | 36. 2.90:1 |
| 7. 0.98:1 | 17. 1.26:1 | 27. 1.86:1 | 37. 4.00:1 |
| 8. 1.05:1 | 18. 1.28:1 | 28. 1.91:1 | 38. 5.58:1 |
| 9. 1.07:1 | 19. 1.31:1 | 29. 1.92:1 | 39. 7.92:1 |
| 10. 1.11:1 | 20. 1.34:1 | 30. 2.00:1 | 40. 14.03:1 |

Because of the "Mirror Principle", if subtle realm light impinges on a prism, it is expected to speed up in the prism and give rise to a reverse order spectrum to the Newton spectrum. Thus, if normal light contains at least these two components, one should expect to see via refraction both a bent down spectrum from the physical component and a bent up spectrum from the next subtle realm (etheric) component as illustrated in Fig 1.16a.

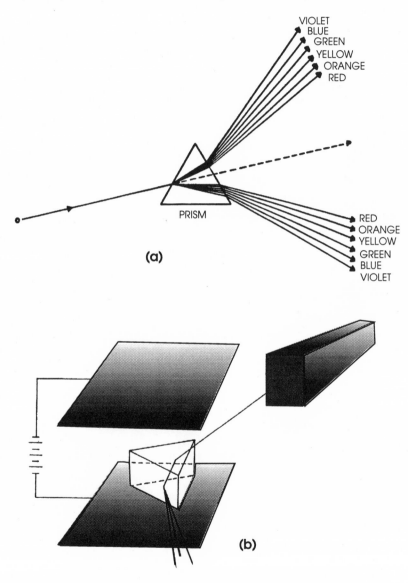

**Fig. 1.16** Illustrations from the prism experiment, (a) expected refracted colour spectra for EM and ME radiations based upon the "Mirror Principle" and (b) schematic of the light source/prism arrangement.

A special device was constructed for this test with a large voltage difference being applied across the prism and with the children looking along a rotatable "gun" sight through the prism to find the angle or angles at which light spectra are observed[27]. It was found that the children do, indeed, see the Newton spectrum with their physical eyesight and they also see a bent-up spectrum with their auric eyesight. Different children saw the bent-up spectrum at somewhat different angles indicating different indices of refraction, $N^*$, for this light component. In all cases, $N^*$ values less than unity were found. However, the order of the spectral colors in the subtle energy spectrum was often not as expected according to Fig. 1.16a. When our most sensitive subject (Bobby) looked carefully through the angular variation, he observed the data recorded in Fig. 1.17. Instead of a single refracted spectrum, he observed three distinct spectra or octaves of radiation. This is what one might expect if we are dealing here with a diffraction phenomenon rather than a refraction phenomenon. The radiation detected in the slightly bent down orientations is thought to be due to the inclusion of a "deltron" effect (to be discussed in Chapter 2).

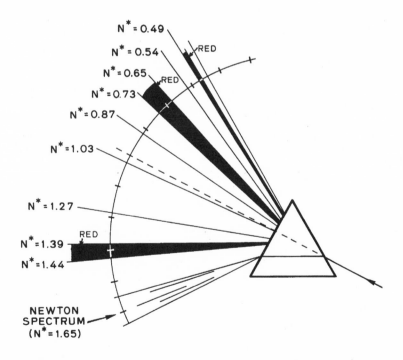

**Fig. 1.17** The spectral order and dispersion of deltron-mediated superluminal radiation seen by one subject. In each spectral order, reading clockwise the observed colours are red, yellow, green, blue and violet.

With physical light diffraction, one sees several orders of light interference spectra, 0th, 1st, 2nd; etc., as a function of angle relative to the extended incident light direction. The 0th order is narrower and brighter than the first order which is, in turn, brighter and narrower than the second order; etc. However, Bobby's result showed that the spectral width decreased and the spectral intensity increased in going from the 0th to the 1st to the 2nd order spectra -- just what one would expect from the "mirror principle" for the subtle energy component!

From this study, we can conclude that children, apparently using their peripheral vision, can detect a subtle energy hidden from the optical sensory system of most adults (not all adults). This subtle energy appears to be a component of a normal light beam and it speeds up in glass relative to air to yield an index of refraction for this light component that is less than unity. Finally, this light component is diffracted rather than refracted either by some unexpected periodic order in the glass material or by the structure of space within the prism volume. These are rather remarkable results even though the experiments were not carried out in a "double blind" fashion. They do tend to confirm the concept of a type of "mirror" relationship functioning between the physical level and the next, more subtle level (etheric level) of reality.

**Magnetism As A Factor In The Subtle Energy Arena:** Since the substance of the etheric domain is thought to be composed of magnetic particles (see Chapter 2), we should look at some of the seemingly strange magnetic effects found by various investigators before writing down our concluding equation of this chapter.

In terms of a historical perspective, it is probably important to begin considering magnetic energies as distinct from electric energies. For this, we need to recall the days of Faraday and von Reichenback; i.e., around the 1840's-1850's. Faraday was one of the central scientific figures of his day who experimentally categorized various magnetic and electric reactions and interactions so as to place them on a very firm and objective foundation. Human intervention or influence on the family of electro-magnetic interactions elucidated by Faraday was seemingly insignificant. At the same time, the famous chemist and inventor of Creosote, Baron von Reichenback, was also looking at magnetic phenomena but he was using sensitive human subjects (clairvoyants, etc.) and sensitive circumstances to reveal and elucidate a class of phenomena that he thought was part of electromagnetism[28]. His subjects observed a blue flame-like glow from the north pole of a magnet and a red flame-like glow from the south pole. These "flames" displayed no tendency to unite, they could be diverted by blowing on them or by placing a solid object in their path and no heat could be detected from them. This magnetic light could be focussed by a glass lens and it could expose silver iodide photographic plates. He also found that a magnet would attract the arms and hands of some subjects.

These observations by Baron von Reichenback were very different from those made by Faraday and a great professional conflict developed between the two men until Faraday emerged the victor. Thus, the subtle magnetic interaction aspect tended to get pushed aside and excluded from the foundations of modern day electromagnetism which began with Maxwell's invention of his famous equations in the late 1800's. I suspect that it is time to take another serious look at Baron von Reichenback's work[28].

In terms of the psychic phenomena area of activity, professional psychics have talked repeatedly about magnetism for the last 200 years as a major source governing and determining this class of phenomena. They did not refer to electricity as such a source. However, based upon known magnetic effects, it was not possible for scientists to discover an explanation for such statements. Experimentally, on the other hand, it was observed that, if you placed a psychic subject in a Faraday cage, they work even better whereas, if you place them in a magnetically shielded room, they often lose their psychic abilities. Thus, there does appear to be some differentiation appearing in this area between the influence of electric and magnetic forces on human function.

If one looks at careful work in the dowsing area[29], one finds that dowsers are incredibly sensitive to electromagnetic energies, particularly to magnetic fields and at levels ~ one trillionth of the earth's magnetic field strength ( ~0.5 Gauss). Amazingly small perturbations in the local magnetic field appear to trigger signals in the dowser's adrenal glands. From polarized electromagnetic wave studies with dowsers, they have been shown to be especially sensitive to the magnetic wave component of the EM wave especially when the magnetic component is horizontally polarized[29].

From experiments on the enzyme Tripsin in water[30], one notes that the enzymatic activity is enhanced in strong D.C. magnetic fields and also by the action of a healer's hands. The healer effect is equivalent to that of a 20,000 Gauss magnet (see Fig. 1.18). Other experiments with water[31] revealed that magnet-treated water and healer-treated water exhibit a reduced surface tension by about 20% (see Fig. 1.19) and a reduced hydrogen bonding. Using infrared spectroscopy, the amplitude of the primary stretch mode of the $H_2O$ molecule is observed to be reduced at 3.2 microns and a new mode begins to appear at about 2.8 microns (see Fig. 1.20). The presence of this 2.8 micron mode has been utilized to test the efficacy of therapeutic touch healers[32].

If we look at the physical substance making up our bodies, we note that it is not magnetic (at least in the usual sense of a magnetic material). We may contain a very small amount of magnetotaxic substances in our bodies but this would give rise to a trivial net magnetic property. Likewise, the magnetic fields generated in the body by the circulating charge in the body's fluid circuits is also trivial compared to the magnetic field strengths needed to produce the above-mentioned water effects. And yet we find odd magnetic-type phenomena occurring around some of us generated by what appear to be, at least at the physical level, essentially non-magnetic beings.

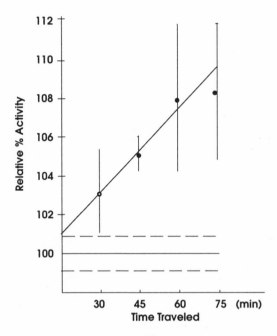

**Fig. 1.18** Data from an average of 8 sets of experiments in which native trypsin solutions were first exposed to ultraviolet radiation (decreased the activity by 20-35%) and then exposed to a healer's hands for a certain time period. The broken lines show the standard deviation of the control (horizontal line).

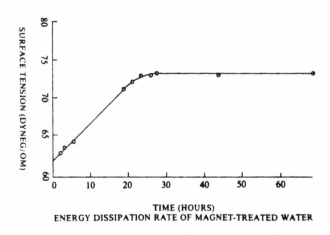

**Fig. 1.19** Relaxation of surface tension for magnet-treated water back to its normal value over a 30-60 hour period.

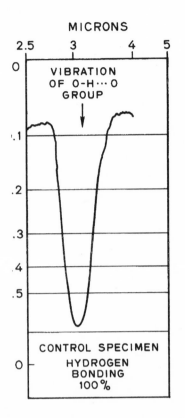
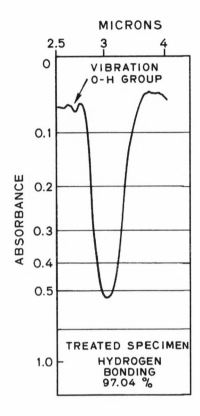

**Fig. 1.20** Infrared absorbance, via infrared internal-reflection spectroscopy, of normal distilled water (control) and of distilled water that was energized by the healer, Olga Worrall (treated).

To strenghten the point further, if one takes a DC magnet (~50-100 Gauss) and places it close to an acupuncture point on the hand or arm, local analgesia will be produced. Likewise, if one lays a subject with a kidney problem flat on a table and face up and then addresses the alarm point of the kidney meridian with a DC magnet, one leg on the subject will elongate relative to the other. Thus, we see that a magnetic effect can be transferred to the physiological response level. Table 1.7 illustrates an expanded range of biological responses ascribed to magnetic field therapy.

It is well known that the organic molecule Myosin is essential in muscle contraction. Myosin light chain phosphorylation is involved in the expression of ATPase activity which accompanies muscle contraction. It has also been shown that in-vitro cell-free Myosin phosphorylation exhibits a roughly linear increase in gamma[32]P uptake by Myosin light chains with static magnetic field strength increase[33]. Experiments with Qigong practitioners have shown that they can consistently reduce the phosphorylation due to treatment at a 2-5 foot distance from the samples. Placing the samples in an Amunel magnetic shielding box produced a significant reduction in the subjects' Qi effect in most cases -- to the border of insignificance. Thus, the Qigong practitioners appear to be projecting a type of magnetic energy but with inverse characteristics to a regular magnetic field.

Table 1.7 **Some Physiological effects of Positive (South-Pole Seeking) and Negative (North-Pole Seeking) DC Magnetic Fields**

| NEGATIVE | POSITIVE |
|---|---|
| pH Neutralizing | Acid Producing |
| Oxygenating | Oxygen Depriving |
| Resolves Cellular Edema (Pain Relief) | Evokes Cellular Edema |
| Can Relieve Addictive Withdrawal Symptoms | Can be addicting (Stress Evokes Endorphin Production) |
| Inhibits Microorganism Replication | Accelerates Microorganism Replication |
| Allows Rest, Relaxation and Sleep | Allows Wakefulness and Action |
| Evokes Anabolic Hormone Production-Melatonin and Growth Hormone | Evokes Catabolic Hormone Production |

As a final philosophical comment to this magnetism topic, let us recall that nature generally displays properties of symmetry. We have positive and negative electricity springing from electric monopoles (electric charge) and one would expect magnetism to spring primarily from the presence of magnetic monopoles but, although science has looked long and hard, no satisfactory evidence has been found to reveal its existence. The magnetism we presently understand is generated solely by the motion of electric charges. This is somewhat surprising because the presence of magnetic charges and currents along with electric charges and currents in Maxwell's equations produces a beautiful symmetry that one would expect nature to like. Very recently, Barrett[34] seems to have cleared up the dilemma by pointing out that the Maxwell equation gauge symmetry is of the U(1) form when only electric charge and electric currents are present but is of the more complex SU(2) form when magnetic charges and currents are also present. U(1) fields are known to have fewer local degrees of freedom than SU(2) fields, and SU(2) fields can be transformed into U(1) fields by a process known as symmetry breaking.

However, after symmetry breaking only <u>some</u> topological charges are conserved; electric charge is conserved but magnetic charge is not. We can conclude from this that, when one wishes to consider phenomena wherein magnetic charge is important, one must focus on a higher level of reality (SU(2)) than that of the purely physical reality (U(1)).

Including both the direct space/inverse space concept and the magnetic charge/electric charge concept, Equation 1.4 should be expanded to the form given in Equation 1.5. The upper path in Equation 1.5 is the path of allopathic medicine while the lower path is proposed as the path of homeopathic medicine. Both of these paths function in our bodies and in the fields of electromagnetism and quantum mechanics. The inverse space-time domain becomes a frequency domain and magnetic vector potential is presumed to occupy the key position on the bridge between the subtle and the physical.

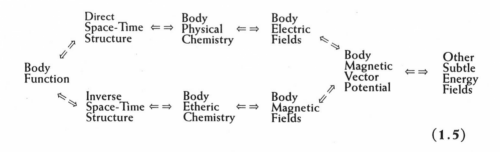

$$(1.5)$$

**A Working Hypothesis**  It is important to understand that the fragmentary data described in this chapter do not constitute satisfactory proof of the philosophical perspectives expressed by the various equations. Any individual piece of data is contestable for a variety of scientific reasons; however, taken as a whole, it is compelling circumstantial evidence that nature does, indeed, function largely as indicated by these equations. One or more centuries of study, both experimental and theoretical, will probably be needed to refine the concepts. In the meantime, Equation 1.5 seems to be a good working hypothesis via which humanity may move forward!

# References

1. Woolridge, D.E., <u>The Machinery of The Brain</u>, (McGraw-Hill Book Co., Inc., New York, 1963).

2. Becker, R.O. and Selden, G., <u>The Body Electric: Electromagnetism and the Foundation of Life</u>, (William Morrow and Co., Inc., New York, 1985).

3. Rea, W.J., <u>Chemical Sensitivity, Vol 1</u>, (Lewis Publishers, Ann Arbor, 1992).

4. Smith, C.W. and Best, S., <u>Electromagnetic Man: Health and Hazard in the Electrical Environment</u>, (St. Martin's Press, New York, 1989).

5. Hawkins, D. and Pauling, L., <u>Orthomolecular Psychiatry</u>, (W.H. Freeman and Co., San Francisco, 1973).

6. Tiller, W.A., "Some Physical Network Characteristics of Acupuncture Points and Meridians", In the Academy of Parapsychology and Medicine's Acupuncture Symposium (Stanford University, Ca., June 1972).

7. Brown, B.B., <u>New Mind, New Body-Biofeedback: New Directions for the Mind</u>, (Harper and Row, New York, 1975).

8. Green, E. and Green, A., <u>Beyond Biofeedback</u>, (Delacorte Press/Seymour Lawrence, New York, 1977).

9. Tiller, W.A., "A Gas Discharge Device for Investigating Focussed Human Attention", J. Scientific Exploration, 2 (1990) 255.

10. Nasser, E., <u>Fundamentals of Gaseous Ionization & Plasma Electronics</u>, (Wiley-Interscience, New York, 1971) p. 189.

11. Forwald, H., <u>Mind Matter and Gravitation</u>, (Parapsychology Foundation, New York, 1969).

12. Jahn, R.G. and Dunne, B.J., <u>Margins of Reality: The Role of Consciousness in the Physical World</u>, (Harcourt Brace Jovanovich, Publishers, New York, 1987).

13. Swann, I., <u>To Kiss The Earth Goodbye</u>, (Hawthorne Books, Inc., New York, 1975).

14. Hasted, J., <u>The Metal Benders</u>, (Routledge & Kegan Paul, London, 1981).

15. Motoyama, H., <u>The Correlation Between PSI Energy and Ki</u>, (Human Science Press, Tokyo, 1991).

16. Krieger, D., <u>The Therapeutic Touch</u>, (Prentice Hall, New Jersey, 1979).

17. St. Clair, D., <u>Psychic Healers</u>, (Doubleday, New York, 1974).

18. Krippner, S. and Welch, P., <u>Spiritual Dimensions of Healing</u>, (Irvington Publishers, Inc., New York, 1992).

19. Puharich, H.K., "Psychic Research and the Healing Process", In <u>Psychic</u>

<u>Exploration: A Challenge for Science</u>, Ed. J. White, E.D. Mitchell, (G.P. Putnam's Sons, New York, 1976) p. 335.

20.  Starcke, W., <u>Homesick for Heaven</u>, (Guadalupe Press, Buerne, Tx, 1988).

21.  Green, E.E., Parks, P.A., Guyer, P.M., Fahrion, S.L., and Coyne, L., "Anomalous Electrostatic Phenomena in Exceptional Subjects", Subtle Energies <u>2</u> (1993) 69.

22.  Kraus, J.D. and Carver, K.R., <u>Electromagnetics</u> (McGraw-Hill Book Co., Inc., New York, 1973).

23.  Tiller, W.A., Green, E.E., Parks, P.A. and Anderson, S., "Towards Explaining Anomalously Large Body Voltage Surges on Exceptional Subjects: Part I, The Electrostatic Approximation", J. Scientific Exploration, <u>9</u> (1995) 331.

24a. Targ, R. and Puthoff, H., <u>Mind Reach: Scientists Look at Psychic Ability</u> (Delacorte Press/Eleanor Friede, New York, 1977).

24b. Targ, R. and Harary, K., <u>The Mind Race</u> (Villard Books, New York, 1984).

25.  Vithoulkas, G., <u>The Science of Homeopathy</u> (Grove Press, New York, 1980).

26.  Boyd, W.E., "An Investigation Regarding the Action on Diastase of Microdoses of Mercuric Chloride", The British Homeopathic Journal, <u>33</u> (1943) 71.

27.  Carlton, J.B. and Tiller, W.A., "Index of Refraction Measurements for a Superluminal Radiation, Proceedings of the Tenth Annual Medical Symposium on "A Holistic Approach to the Etiology and Therapy of the Disease Process" (A.R.E. Clinic, Inc., Phoenix, 1977).

28.  Von Reichenback, C., <u>Vital Force</u> (J.S. Redfield, Clinton Hall, New York, 1851).

29.  Bird, C., <u>The Divining Hand</u> (E.P. Dutton, New York, 1979).

30.  Smith, M.J., "Paranormal Effects on Enzyme Activity", Human Dimensions <u>1</u>, (1972) 15.

31.  Miller, R.N., "Methods of Detecting and Measuring Healing Energies", In <u>Future Science</u>, Eds. J. White and S. Krippner (Anchor-Doubleday, New York, 1977).

32.  Schwartz, S.A., deMattei, R.J., Brame Jr., E.G. and Spottiswoode, S.J.P., "Infrared Spectra Alteration in Water Proximate to the Palms of Therapeutic Practitioners", Subtle Energies, <u>1</u>, (1990) 43.

33.  Meuhsam, D.J., Markov, M.S., Meuhsam, P.A., Pilla, A.A., Shen, R. and Wu, Y., "Effects of Qigong on Cell-Free Myosin Phosphorlyation: Preliminary Experiments", Subtle Energies, <u>5</u> (1995) 93.

34.     Barrett, T.W., "Comments in the Harmuth Ansatz: Use of a Magnetic Current Density in the Calculation of the Propogation Velocity of Signals by Amended Maxwell Theory", IEEE Transactions of Electromagnetic Compatibility, <u>30</u> (1988) 419.

# CHAPTER 2

## FASHIONING A MULTIDIMENSIONAL MODEL

*Craft me a bowl, large enough to hold*
*All the foundation principles of Nature,*
*And lose not the thimble of our present understanding*
*For it has been a good beginning --*
*But we have a very long way to go before we see home.*


Man is concerned with scientific enquiry because he wants to understand the milieu in which he finds himself. He/she wants to engineer and control as much of his/her environment as possible to sustain, enrich and propogate his/her life. Following this path, the goal of science is to gain a reliable description of natural phenomena which allows accurate prediction (within certain limits) of behavior as a function of an ever-changing environment. As such, science is incapable of providing us with absolute truth. Rather, it provides relative knowledge, internally self-consistent knowledge, about the relationships between different phenomena and between different things. The goal of engineering, on the other hand, is to build on this fundamental understanding in order to generate new materials, devices, attitudes, moralities, philosophies, etc., for producing tangible order, harnessing the potential in Nature's phenomena and expanding human capabilities in this ever-changing environment.

In this quest for understanding and its utilization, we generate models or "visualizations" of the phenomena as aids to our efforts or, rather, as temporary vehicles via which we gain fuller understanding. In fact, the models generally become targets against which we throw experiments in order to test the accuracy of our reasoning and our understanding. They are like the rungs of a ladder via which humankind climbs from one state of understanding to another. In any new area of enquiry, it is valuable to have a model with which to make prognostications that may be compared with the reality of experimental results. It is also important to remember that any model, no matter how seemingly successful, will eventually be proven incomplete in detail and that its primary purpose is to act as a vehicle which gives a sense of understanding that triggers the proper set of questions or experiments needed to probe deeper. Just as the classical Newtonian model had to give way to the classical Einsteinian model, the latter had to give way to the Relativistic Quantum Mechanical model--and so it goes as we ride the river of life ever onward into our future.

Some readers may find the material of this chapter technically challenging. If so, just try to grasp the main perspective and key concepts presented as you move through the chapter.

## The Conventional Physics Model

The following is a <u>very</u> brief "nuts and bolts" listing of the present categories of physical matter. It is not material that needs to be carefully remembered for what is to follow. However, it defines a location on a time-plot of human achievement that deserves recognition.

**Building Blocks**: The present physics perspective is that all physical matter is constructed from three uniquely different kinds of elementary particles called leptons, quarks and mediators[1]. There are six different types of leptons (which means "light thing") that may be grouped into three separate categories, with all being classified according to four quantum qualities; charge (Q), electron number ($L_e$), muon number ($L_\mu$) and tau number ($L_\tau$). Each of these three categories contains its associated neutrino (v) as illustrated in Table 2.1. There are also six antileptons (with all the signs in Table 2.1 reversed but with identical mass). Thus, there are actually twelve leptons in all. They are all classed as fermions because they all have spin 1/2 (any particle with an odd number of spin units ($1/2\hbar$) is a fermion, those with an even number of spin units are called bosons). In spite of their relative intangibility, neutrinos are the most common objects in the universe, outnumbering electrons and protons by about a billion to one.

In the quark family, there are six "flavors" classified according to charge (Q), strangeness (S), charm (C), bottom (B), top (T), upness (U) and downness (D). The quarks, too, fall into three categories as shown in Table 2.2. Once again, antiquarks having all the signs of Table 2.2 reversed are also found in physical nature. Further, each quark and antiquark comes in three colors (red, green and blue). Thus, there are thirty-six uniquely different quarks in all. Experimentally, it appears that quarks come in overall colorless packages to form particles called hadrons. Of these, there are particle packages of three quarks (baryons) and two quarks (mesons). From experiment, the two most stable hadrons are the proton (uud) and the neutron (dud) (see Table 2.2). Thus, the permanent physical universe is constructed from the four particles (e, $v_e$, d, u) in the top category of Tables 2.1 and 2.2. The two lower categories found in these two tables combine to form highly unstable and short-lived particles.

Every interaction between particles has its special mediators or messengers which are different depending on the level of interaction. The forces of interaction between particles of matter accepted by present-day physics are fourfold: gravitational, electromagnetic, weak and strong. Their respective mediators are the graviton, photon, intermediate vector boson and gluon, respectively. Table 2.3 provides the mediator classification (where mass is in units of the proton mass ($m_p$)). In what is called <u>the standard model</u>, there are eight gluons that carry color while the graviton has not yet been experimentally discovered.

Table 2.1    **LEPTON CLASSIFICATION**

| NAME | SYMBOL | Q | $L_e$ | $L_\mu$ | $L_\tau$ | MASS |
|---|---|---|---|---|---|---|
| Electron | e | -1 | 1 | 0 | 0 | 1 |
| Electron-Neutrino | $\nu_e$ | 0 | 1 | 0 | 0 | ~0 |
| Muon | $\mu$ | -1 | 0 | 1 | 0 | 206.7 |
| Muon-Neutrino | $\nu_\mu$ | 0 | 0 | 1 | 0 | ~0 |
| Tau | $\tau$ | -1 | 0 | 0 | 1 | 3536 |
| Tau-Neutrino | $\nu_\tau$ | 0 | 0 | 0 | 1 | ~0 |

Table 2.2    **QUARK CLASSIFICATION**

| SYMBOL | Q | D | U | S | C | B | T |
|---|---|---|---|---|---|---|---|
| d | -1/3 | -1 | 0 | 0 | 0 | 0 | 0 |
| u | 2/3 | 0 | 1 | 0 | 0 | 0 | 0 |
| s | -1/3 | 0 | 0 | -1 | 0 | 0 | 0 |
| c | 2/3 | 0 | 0 | 0 | 1 | 0 | 0 |
| b | -1/3 | 0 | 0 | 0 | 0 | -1 | 0 |
| t | 2/3 | 0 | 0 | 0 | 0 | 0 | 1 |

Table 2.3    **MEDIATOR CLASSIFICATION**

| PHYSICAL FORCE | MEDIATORS | CHARGE | MASS ($m_p$ unit) |
|---|---|---|---|
| Electromagnetism | Photon | 0 | 0 |
| Gravity | Graviton | 0 | 0 |
| Weak | $W^\pm$, Z | $\pm 1$, 0 | 85, 95 |
| Strong | Gluons | 0 | 0 |

43

In the 1850's, Maxwell synthesized the forces of electricity and magnetism. In the first half of this century, Einstein dreamed of going a step further to combine gravity and electromagnetism into a single unified field theory but he was not fully successful. In 1967, Glashow, Salam and Weinberg completed the unification of electromagnetism with the weak force and, in 1974, they and others developed <u>Grand Unified Theories</u> (GUTS) to combine the weak force, strong force and electromagnetism. At the moment, the theoretical foundations for a super unified theory which merges all the physical forces of nature into a single <u>Superforce</u>[2] are being laid. However, it is important to realise that the experimental testing of GUTS and the Superforce Theory require the availability of particle accelerators of energies vastly beyond present capabilities. This is clearly illustrated in Fig. 2.1[3].

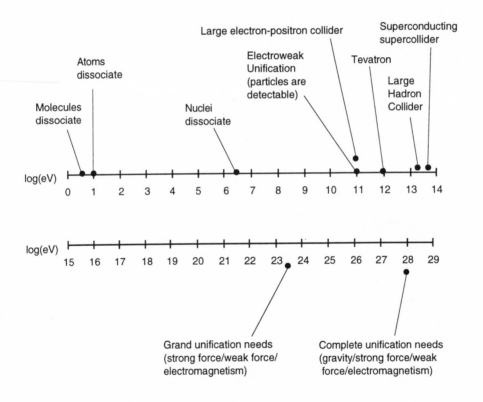

**Fig. 2.1** Illustration of the energy magnitude (electron volts) needed for various atomic and nuclear events as well as those needed to test various levels of force unification (with the accelerators available to provide such beam energies).

The foregoing picture adds up to quite a large number of supposedly "elementary" particles: 12 leptons, 36 quarks and 12+ mediators. At least one <u>Higgs</u> particle is needed as a mediator in GUTS and gravitons will be needed by any superforce unification scheme[2,4]. Thus, we have at least 61 elementary particles to contend with. Further, perhaps some of these particles are not truly elementary but are composite particles so that another, more basic, level of particles exists to be discovered.

A very appealing and summarizing comment on these elementary particles is expressed in the following quote from Davies[2], "The classification of particles into quarks, leptons and messengers completes the list of known subatomic particles. Each plays a separate yet crucial role in shaping the universe. Without the messengers there would be no forces and every particle would be oblivious of its neighbors. No structures could exist and no activity of any consequence would occur. Without quarks there would be no atomic nuclei and no sunlight. Without leptons atoms could not exist, and there would be no chemistry and no life."

**The Birthplace of Physical Matter:** At this point, one should ask the question, "Where do all these elementary physical particles come from?". In the early 1930's, Dirac proposed an answer for the electron that led to his prediction of its antiparticle, the positron[5]. His simple initial concept has since been somewhat modified by Quantum Field Theory; however, Dirac's Hole Theory provides a very useful intuitive picture for the creation of physical matter[6].

Dirac was a mathematical physicist developing a relativistic quantum mechanical equation for the formation and energy behavior of the electron. Quantum mechanics, <u>which has only an empirical foundation</u>, deals with the interaction of physical matter and everything else in the universe. At its simplest level, this means the interaction between physical matter and the vacuum state. The Dirac Equation predicted not only the existence of positive energy states but also allowed the existence of negative energy solutions. For a free Dirac electron, the available positive and negative energy levels are symmetric about $E=0$ as illustrated in Fig. 2.2. Dirac postulated that the vacuum consisted of all these negative energy states and that these states were all filled (such negative energy states are unphysical and therefore unobservable by present day instrumentation). Nevertheless, by stimulating the negative energy states via a photon with sufficient energy, a particle (electron) may be promoted into one of the positive energy states and become physically <u>real</u>. The holes left behind in the negative energy state spectrum of Fig. 2.2 are the antiparticles (positron). Thus, he proposed that we live in a sea of virtual (unobservable) particles--the Dirac sea. Since all physical observations represent finite fluctuations in energy and charge with respect to the vacuum state, this leads to an acceptable model. For example, if one negative energy particle (electron) is absent from the Dirac sea, we have a "hole" relative to the normal vacuum:

$$\text{Energy of "Hole"} = -(E_{neg}) \rightarrow \text{Positive Energy}$$
$$\text{Charge of "Hole"} = -(Q_e) \rightarrow \text{Positive Charge}$$

Thus, the absence of a negative-energy electron is equivalent to the presence of a positive-energy positron. To date, antiparticles have been found experimentally for all the particles known to physics.

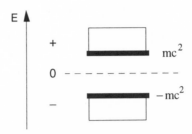

**Fig. 2.2**  Schematic energy spectrum associated with the Dirac Equation. A band gap of forbidden energies exists between $E = \pm mc^2$ for particle-antiparticle creation of total mass 2m.

Today, the vacuum is seen as a chaotic sea of boundless energy (energy density equivalent to ~$10^{94}$ grams per cubic centimeter)[7] at the quantum relativity level with incredibly large destructive interference of virtual particle wavefunctions. An interaction exists between this chaotic virtual particle sea and physical matter. It is this fundamental interaction that determines the ground state energies of all the atoms and thus all the molecules and all the condensed matter present in the universe. For example, if we could somehow alter this fundamental interaction, we should be able to change the ground state electrochemical potentials of reacting molecules in our cells and thus alter the body's state of function. In such a case, we may be able to observe the resultant physical changes but not the originating changes taking place in the Dirac sea of the vacuum because our present instrumentation is inadequate for the task.

With respect to the initial Dirac equation for the electron, it gave the correct spectrum for the hydrogen atom at the time; however, there were difficulties when it was applied to more complex problems. About two decades later, more exact measurements of the hydrogen spectrum were made by Lamb (the Lamb shift) showing that an indisputable discrepancy of 0.1% existed relative to the spectrum calculated by the Dirac equation. Somewhat later, a similar sized anomaly was detected in the magnetic moment of the electron. These anomalies arose because Dirac neglected the electron/photon interaction, which everyone did at that time because it came out to be infinite in all the existing theories. Physically, the Lamb shift is a consequence of the fact that the self-energy of an electron in the Coulomb field of the hydrogen atom is different from its self-energy in free space and depends on its specific quantum state.

The difference in these state-dependent self-energies is just the Lamb shift.

Via quantum electrodynamics (QED), self-energy is a consequence of the ceaseless emission and absorption of (virtual) photons in the vacuum as well as the ceaseless creation and annihilation of electron/positron pairs in the vacuum (with vacuum polarization consequences). The self-energy mass adds to the mechanical mass of the electron to produce the observed (renormalized) electron mass. Likewise, the observed (renormalized) electron charge includes the vacuum polarization effects.

Although this important correction to the Dirac equation set in motion a flurry of intellectual activity that ultimately led to a satisfactory QED and several Nobel Prizes, Dirac's central concept concerning the appearance of a positive energy electron out of the negative energy sea of the vacuum maintains its integrity and utility and is still quantitatively correct out to the third decimal place.

According to Einstein's General Theory of Relativity, the geometrical properties of space are related to the density of energy (and momentum) in the universe. Thus, the geometrical structure of the universe is extremely sensitive to the value of the vacuum energy density. In fact, so important is this value that a constant proportional to the vacuum energy density has been defined. It is called the <u>Cosmological Constant</u> where

$$\text{Cosmological Constant} = \frac{8\pi G}{c^4} \times \text{vacuum energy density}$$

Here, G is Newton's gravitational constant and c is the speed of light. With a calculated vacuum energy density of $\sim 10^{94}$ grams per cubic centimeter, the calculated cosmological constant would be many many orders of magnitude larger than we know it to be[8]. Most theoretical efforts concerning the Cosmological Constant now focus on finding the underlying misunderstanding, the missing piece of the standard model or some important misconception concerning the vacuum. This is one of the major present-goals of conventional physics.

For our purposes in this book, the vacuum with its negative energy states and unobservable particles is exactly the territory wherein the subtle energies discussed in Chapter 1 might exist. Further, the substructure of the vacuum would need to be such that the Cosmological Constant is smaller than $\sim 1/(10^{23}$ kilometers$)^2$ which could only occur if the vacuum energy density was reduced by at least a factor $\sim 10^{46}$. The multidimensional model to be discussed in the last section of this chapter holds the possibility of doing just that.

**Hyperspace:** All of classical physics, relativity and most of quantum physics needs only a four-dimensional description of nature in order to quantitatively express reliable relationships between most natural physical phenomena. This is called a 4-space description (three of distance and one of time). Some of the recent particle physics descriptions involved in the force unification efforts have required extensions to 10-space and to 26-space and beyond. This multidimensional coordinate framework is exceedingly complex but it allows the mathematical description of these aspects of nature to unfold in a harmonious way. Of course, unlike the simpler 4-space description, our physical brains do not cognize these additional dimensions.

The beginnings of hyperspace reasoning can be traced back to Riemann in the mid-eighteen hundreds when he extended the foundations of geometry beyond Euclid's perspective to include higher dimensional spaces[9]. Later, the 4-D expression of this geometry would form a key building block in Einstein's theory of relativity. Reimann's idea was to assign a collection of numbers to each point in space that would describe how much the local space was bent or curved. For four spatial dimensions, this collection involves ten numbers and, no matter how distorted the local space about that point, all the relevant information is encoded in this collection of ten numbers which is referred to as the Riemann <u>metric tensor</u>, written as a symmetric matrix in Fig 2.3a. In Fig. 2.3a, each g-component is a number, and orthogonal symmetry requires that $g_{12} = g_{21}$, $g_{13} = g_{31}$, etc., so that the 16 components of this matrix reduce to ten independent components.

After Einstein's use of Riemann's 4-D metric tensor to extend Newton's 3-D concepts concerning gravity, Kaluza intuited that a 4-D description was too small for the unification of both the gravitational and the electromagnetic forces and proposed a 5-D metric tensor description. Later, Klein came along and helped to complete this concept which became known as the Kaluza-Klein (K-K) theory. Here, the fifth dimension, which was not observable by experiment, was thought to have collapsed down to a circle of diameter much smaller than the size of an atom so it was too small to measure. Subsequent work by many investigators have eliminated the inconsistencies in K-K-type theories in 4+N dimensions with N dimensions curled up into a tight ball at each point of 4-space. The Riemann metric tensors in five-space and eleven-space can be expressed from a unification point of view as in Figs. 2.3b and 2.3c, respectively[9]. Fig. 2.3b illustrates a theory of gravity wherein light is explained as a vibration in five-space. Fig. 2.3c illustrates a theory of gravity and light and Yang-Mills fields wherein quarks and leptons can be explained as vibrations in this eleven dimensional space.

Even this supersymmetry picture is not complete in that certain particles are still not included. Physics has been forced to go to an even more powerful formalism called "superstring" theory which is only defined in 10 and 26 dimensions. This theory postulates that all matter consists of tiny vibrating strings in hyperspace wherein the fields of Einstein, Maxwell and Yang-Mills fit together with great precision. A 10-D universe, divided into our traditional four and an additional compacted six, forms the minimal set needed to generate this precision. These compacted six dimensions are inaccessible to both our human physical sensory systems and to our present instrumentation.

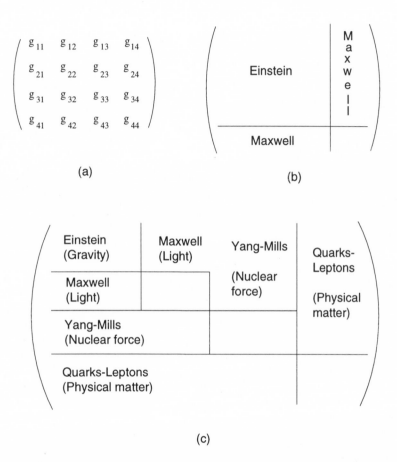

**Fig. 2.3** Visualization of the Riemann metric tensor for (a) four-space, (b) five-space and (c) eleven-space (supersymmetry).

The important thread running through all of these hyperspace considerations is that <u>the laws of nature appear simpler from a higher dimensional perspective</u>[9]! It is as if, for a very large N, there is only one law, perfectly symmetrical and perfectly beautiful, and that a cascade of sequential symmetry breakings yield the multiplicity of seemingly disparate laws that govern our physical level observational experience.

# Three Inner Self-Management
# and Direct Experience Models

Our physical sensory systems seem designed for cognizing information in our local external environment and most of our personal experience arises from looking outward. However, practices of inner self-management at mental, emotional and physical levels appear to develop additional latent sensory systems in us that allow cognizing of new information by looking inward. In the past, this has been called "the path of the mystic".

**The Yoga Model:** This is an <u>inner</u>world rather than an <u>outer</u>world model such as that of conventional physics as discussed in the previous section. The word "yoga" means unity and the techniques of yoga are methods for purifying the human nervous system so that it can reflect a greater degree of consciousness.

Our first glimpse of yoga occurs on Indian soil in the Indus Valley with objects dated around 3000 B.C. This was when nomadic pastoral tribes, called the Aryans, began to enter north-west India, bringing with them the <u>Vedas</u>, mankind's oldest records of knowledge[10a]. Because of their yoga practices, the Aryans saw no fundamental difference between the material and the spiritual worlds or between the realms of mind and matter. Therefore, to them, it was of utmost importance that thought, speech and action be life-supporting--in harmony with all other levels of the universe. The Vedas proclaimed that, if cosmic order is disrupted and harmony between the various planes of creation broken, then suffering is the inevitable result.

This was the condition when the Buddha lived. At that time, the Vedic rituals were no longer a unifying force in Indian society. They had become a religion of outer trappings, mere ritualism and empty speculation. Happily, the Buddha prescribed a cure for this condition and it was a restatement of a perennial teaching that he had verified by his own experience. He called it "the path that leads to enlightenment". To quote Shearer[10a]

"This teaching is called <u>yoga</u>. According to <u>yoga</u>, we suffer because we live in ignorance. We are ignorant of our real nature. Our true nature lies beyond the restrictions of our careworn and humdrum existence, ecstatically free and untouched by suffering. Deep within the mind, beyond the faintest flicker of thought, it is experienced as an undying and omnipresent vastness. It is absolute consciousness. Animating everything in creation, this is the source and goal of all life. <u>Yoga</u> calls it the Self.

The nature of life is to grow towards an ever more perfect and joyous expression of itself. Each living being has a nervous system, no matter how rudimentary. This acts as a localized reflector of the all-pervading consciousness, just as a mirror reflects light. The more developed the nervous system, the more it will express the qualities of pure consciousness--intelligence, creativity and bliss. <u>Yoga</u> is the transformation into the Divine and the Divine into everything. Meditation is the key."

Patanjali compiled the <u>yoga sutras</u> (sutra means thread), probably in the third century B.C. These are the most lucid and authoritative of all the texts that serve as maps for the inner journey. His message in a nutshell is that <u>yoga</u> is the setting of the mind into silence, and only when the mind is silent can we realize our true nature, the effortless Being of The Self[10a]. This practice leads to the natural development of many superphysical capabilities, one of which is to make oneself "infinitesimally small at will", which Patanjali utilized to describe something of the fundamental nature of atoms under the heading "the three Gunas". Swami Savitripriya[10b] translates the three Gunas, from the original text, to be the electron, proton and neutron, the main particle building blocks of the atom.

Out of this has come what I call here the Yoga Model which deals with a framework for describing human experience. As such, it utilizes only three dimensions for such a description: space, time and causality, or cause-effect. It is a direct experience model and, for substance experience, subtle levels up to the mind level were included.

As an extension of this approach, between 1895 and the 1930's, two well-known and accomplished theosophists, Annie Besant and W.C. Leadbeater, utilized their superphysical capabilities (the siddi-knowledge of the very small) to directly perceive the fundamental particle nature of the atoms of different chemical elements[11]. They called these units of matter "Ultimate Physical Atoms" (U.P.A.). They found that these particles were only of two types and that one was the mirror image of the other. In particular, for the hydrogen atom, they "saw" 18 U.P.A.'s grouped into 6 spheres of 3 apiece with the spheres appearing to be arranged at the corners of interlacing triangles (see Fig. 2.4a). Today, it is known that the hydrogen nucleus is a proton which, from the previous section, is comprised of three quarks (uud) so that at least some of the small spheres in Fig. 2.4a could be quarks. The two chiral forms (mirror images) of these U.P.A. were perceived as shown in Fig. 2.4b. Phillips[12] has proposed that the three dots in each of the small spheres in Fig. 2.4a represent a more fundamental particle than the quark which he calls the Omegon and these seem to have much in common with the color aspect of the quarks. If so then, as stated in the previous section, a colorless package requires the use of red, green and blue quarks and this would account for the three dots seen in each sphere. Only the mirror image triangle of three spheres remains to be accounted for. The multidimensional model of the next section provides a ready explanation for such a mirror image relationship.

Although this direct perception yoga model is largely an inner-directed model, the internal self-management at the mental and emotional levels needed to achieve these superphysical qualities is clearly capable of providing useful, if not extremely important, inputs to the conventional physics model of the previous section. In the yoga method, one tries to still the mind by working directly with the mind. The body is given small consideration in this quest to conquer the mind.

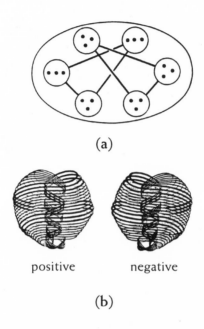

(a)

positive    negative

(b)

**Fig. 2.4** Illustration of inner sight detection for the number and geometry of ultimate physical atoms (U.P.A.) in hydrogen, (a) 18 U.P.A. detected in the hydrogen nucleus and (b) two chiral forms of the U.P.A. in this nucleus.

**The Qigong Model:** This is an ancient Chinese philosophical system of harmonious integration of the human body with the universe. It integrates the bioenergies of the body with the mind and spirit via systematic discipline. In ancient times (as much as 7000 years ago) it was assumed that all things in the world had spirit and intelligence. People were to keep in harmony with nature and absorb vital energy from outside the body to supplement their needs. This viewpoint gradually led to the formulation of the ying/yang theory of traditional Chinese medicine. Overall, it is a system of physical, mental and philosophical training for cultivating moral and body strength, prolonging life and developing human potential. Qi (or chi) stands for subtle energy while gong stands for power and, during the various exercises, the focus of attention is on the "Dan Tien" or "Hara" point in the abdomen about two or three finger widths below the "belly button" (this also appears to be the second chakra point to be discussed in Chapter 3). Here, one stills the mind by working with the Dan Tien point. The functioning of the physical body is given major consideration in this technique. As with the yoga method, qigong adepts develop superphysical abilities.

An essential aspect concerning the notion of Qi involves the human interaction with one's environment. The body is thought to contain a supply of Qi that flows throughout the acupuncture channels of the body and is exchanged with the Qi in one's surroundings. Thus, good health relates to a balance and unobstructed flow of Qi both inter-body and intra-body. In China, Qigong is a committed daily practice by millions of people who, over the course of many years have developed the skills and disciplines associated with healing and the martial arts. The Chinese terminology draws the distinction between <u>internal Qigong</u>, which refers to practitioner-manipulated Qi for the benefit of the body, and <u>external Qigong</u>, which refers to the production of effects outside the body via practitioner-manipulated Qi. Anticipating the results of the last main section of this chapter, Qi is most readily equated with etheric energy (although deltrons would also be a necessary component in order to produce effective utilization of the etheric energy).

Since 1980, the "body science" group of Shanghai's Jiao Fong University have been conducting thermal imaging experiments on Qigong masters. This work, under the direction of Professor Shen Han Chang, found that Qigong masters emit infrared (IR) radiation in the ~1 to 4.5 micron range, that their palm temperatures elevate ~4°-5° centigrade over the background ambient temperature and that this electromagnetic (EM) energy is one detectable correlate of their manifested healing abilities. Even the strictly EM component was found to have strong therapeutic benefits for 100 patients with chronic active hepatitis via their construction and use of an IR transmitting device in this frequency range.

**The HeartMath Model:** A more recently developed set of techniques for inner self-management involves placing the focus of attention on the physical heart and using one's intentionality to express love, care, appreciation, etc., through the heart. Here, the computer mainframe of the body and its higher dimensional constructs is thought to be the heart while the brain and other biological oscillators of the body are thought to be work stations that function best under central direction from the heart. In this method one stills the mind by focussing on the heart and, just as in the other methods of inner self-management, adepts very naturally develop superphysical abilities as a consequence of continual use of the techniques in their daily lives.

Since this model, its experimental techniques and its results will be discussed rather extensively in Chapter 5, only a broad brush perspective need be given here. Practitioners of these techniques[14,15], with as little training as six months, attain unique inner states having electrophysiological correlates, revealed by electrocardiogram (ECG) and electroencephalogram (EEG) studies, that are remarkably therapeutic to the body. Chemical correlates in both the immune and hormonal systems also show beneficial changes associated with attainment of these unique inner states. In addition, directed intention while the individual is in one of these states (as revealed by ECG data) allows the individual to influence the properties of water and DNA held <u>outside</u> the body. The HeartMath model is essentially a consciousness model, unlike the conventional physics model which is an energy model. Practicing the heart-focus techniques allows the individual to make transitions to higher bands of consciousness wherein properties of surrounding matter can become a function of the state of consciousness of the individual.

# The Tiller Model:  Level One

The model to follow was primarily shaped by my intuition and unfolded as a part of the avocational inner work that I carried out over a large span of years. In the mid-1960's, I decided to invest a portion of my time to seriously look at the area called by many psychoenergetics, the paranormal, psychic phenomena, etc., and to do this in parallel with my professional work in the area of materials science as a Stanford University professor. This avocational time committment was partitioned into roughly equal thirds. The first third was involved with experiential development of self so that I might have a truer feeling for this class of phenomena (it involved daily meditation, being with and observing individuals with developed or developing psychic capabilities, attempting to reproduce some of the phenomena myself, etc.). The second third was devoted to understanding how the universe might be constructed in order to allow this class of seemingly "crazy" phenomena to comfortably coexist with our more accepted and understood conventional physical phenomena. The third third was devoted to designing and conducting experiments to keep the theory "honest". Many of the results discussed in Chapter 1 resulted from this latter intention.

My overall goal was to build a bridge between the conventional territory of science and this new, strange territory, and to make it strong enough that my colleagues might be willing to walk across the bridge and join in the exploration. In all of this, I trusted my intuitive intelligence more than my logical intelligence but used both to sculpt the clay of my understanding. Thus, I often felt something was so before I was logically able to rationalize why it might be so. This process is still unfolding within me and I feel ready to move from the qualitative modeling perspective to the challenging quantitative modeling perspective. However, before that next step is seriously taken, it seems important to lay out the qualitative picture to follow and then to point out the key differences between this model and the present conventional physics model.

**The Simulator:** This is primarily an energy, as compared to a consciousness, dimensional model. My working hypothesis is that we are primarily elements of spirit, indestructible and eternal and "multiplexed" in the Divine. As such, we have a mechanism of perception which is a ten-dimensional mind domain. In turn, this mind mechanism creates a vehicle for our experience -- our cosmos, our local universe, our solar system, our planet, our physical bodies, etc. This is all a "simulator" for our experience which we view from the spiritual level of self which is outside the simulator[16]. Thus, we are spirits having a physical experience. As such, the simulator is analogous to a huge 10-D interactive television set wherein signals enter the set from the next higher dimension to set the grand panorama in motion and we, the dancing figures on the screen, interact with the flow of the drama and thus modify the input signals to the set via our thoughts, attitudes and actions and these, in turn, alter the details of the play. Our concerns about physics deal with the various laws governing the interactions of the objects in the set with each other and with the basic machinery of the set. Our concerns about personal health and about medicine relate to the maintenance of the simulator at various different levels of substance. Our concerns about human spirituality relate to the "why" of the simulator. The Simulator is a teaching machine of absolutely wonderful capabilities – created by God's love for us so that we might experience and grow and be!

One visualization of the simulator is given in Fig. 2.5. Its substructure involves two interpenetrating and conjugate 4-spaces (the physical and the etheric substance domains that together form an 8-space) imbedded in a 9-space (emotional domain) which is, in turn, imbedded in a 10-space (mental domain). Each of these domains contains its own spatial substructure, substances and radiations and our average evolved capacity to sense the radiations and substance of these various domains is presently limited to the simplest level, the physical. With the passage of time, our inner self-management will grow sufficiently for us to sense the rich expression of the more subtle levels of the simulator with its organismic, biological-like (adaptive) ability to transform itself.

These conjugate 4-spaces are thought to bear a special "mirror"-type relationship to each other, one being of the distance-time variety and the other being of its inverse (a frequency domain). The former is the home of electric matter of positive mass travelling at velocities slower than the speed of light, c, while the latter is the home of magnetic matter of negative mass travelling at velocities faster than the speed of light, c. Images of the magnetic charges in the "mirror" form magnetic dipoles in the distance-time domain so that the interaction of the electric charges with these magnetic dipole images constitute our conventional electromagnetism. Images of the electric charges in the "mirror" form electric dipoles in the frequency domain so that the interaction of the magnetic charges with the electric dipole images constitute another field of the magnetoelectric variety in that domain that is not observable by our conventional senses. To a close approximation, the configuration of magnetic substance in the frequency domain bears a "Fourier Transform" type of relationship with the configuration of electric substance in the distance-time domain. It is the interaction between these "matters", as viewed from the distance-time side of the "mirror", that constitutes what we presently call quantum mechanics. Further, it is precisely the direct space/inverse space pair of coordinate frames that lead to the wave/particle duality manifestations of nature on a microscopic level. Other possible 4-space pairs would not yield such behavior.

This is the main conceptual structure that appeared to my intuitive mind in the early 1970's as a possible structure of the universe which would allow new classes of phenomena to exist in the universe and be as valid as those perceived by our five physical senses but not be directly perceivable by that limited set of senses. My intellectual mind sought possible violations of fundamental laws, as distinct from accepted "mind-sets", created by this conceptual structure and, over the years, became able to intellectually articulate the concepts in clearer and clearer fashion without violating any such laws. For those not familiar with the Fourier transform relationship between information patterns in the direct space domain and the frequency (wave number) domain, the reader is directed to appendix 2.1.

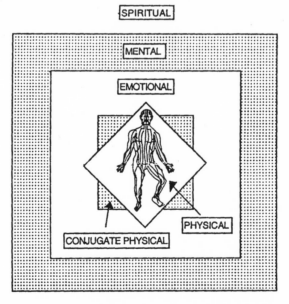

**Fig. 2.5** A visualization of dual four-space frames (physical and conjugate physical (etheric)) imbedded in a nine-space (emotion frame) imbedded in a ten-space (mind frame) and this embedded in an eleven-space (spirit frame).

So how is this wonderful piece of adaptive machinery thought to come about?

The Level One model sees it as a holographic construct. We now know that, if you shine a coherent beam of light off an object and you (1) reflect that beam onto a film plus (2) also directly illuminate the film with the original reference beam, the film stores the information about the object in the phase differences between the two beams imprinted on the film (see Fig. 2.6)[17,18]. Later, one can take this developed plate of film, set it up as in Fig. 2.6 and shine a suitable laser beam through it, then the original pattern of the object will be restored. One can look at the film and actually see the object pattern projected into space in the location where the object was originally located relative to the film.

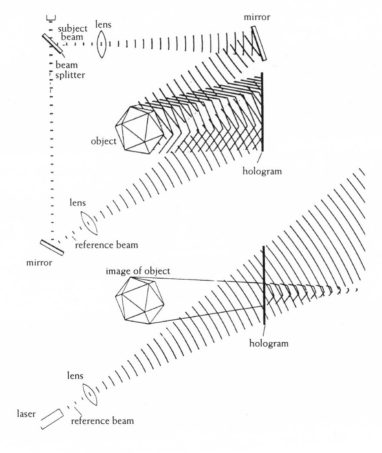

**Fig. 2.6** Illustrating the procedure for making a hologram (top) via the interference from a laser reference beam and the derived beam that illuminates the object as well as the reconstruction of the holographic image when the hologram is illuminated by the reference beam alone.

In the simulator construction case, the primary beam comes from the spiritual or Divine level of self. It impinges upon the frequency patterns that we have built at the mind level and it projects them onto a screen--really two screens. These are the nodal network grids of the two conjugate 4-spaces represented in figure 2.5 (the meaning of these nodal networks will be explained shortly). Substance at these two levels interacts with the potentials stored on these two grids. Thus, the events that come to us in life arise from the various potentials stored on these grids. We respond to these events with thoughts, attitudes and actions and the essence of these responses are fed back to the nodal network points of the mind grid. Thus, the alterations of the potentials stored at the mind nodal network sites causes a change in the holographic pattern projected onto the two 4-space grids. This, in turn, modifies the collective potentials stored there which, by interaction with substance, alter the next sequence of events generated in time, etc. This is how the simulator device is thought to work at this level of modeling.

If we wish to use a "big bang" analogy then, at the inception of our universe, a burst of higher dimensional energy propogated outwards in 11-space and organized itself into a 10-D grid of active nodal points at the mind level. Thus, this space is not a continuum but has an ordered and granular structure. The 3-D analogue of this 10-D structure is thought to form a hexagonal close-packed array of nodal points with a lattice spacing, $\lambda_m \sim 10^{-27}$ meters; i.e., the nodal points form an extremely fine grid.

This primary lattice of mind nodal points contains within itself two sub-lattices which are both reciprocals of each other. The first sublattice is also a reciprocal of the primary mind lattice. This first sublattice has uniquely identifiable nodal points at a spacing of $\lambda_- \sim 10^{-17}$ meters and, at a 3-space level, is also of the close-packed hexagonal type but rotated by $90°$ with respect to the primary lattice. This is called the negative space-time frame (-VE S-T) or inverse space-time frame and is the domain wherein etheric substance functions. The second sublattice is also formed from uniquely identifiable nodal points at a spacing of $\lambda_+ \sim 10^{-7}$ meters and, at a 3-space level, is also of the hexagonal close-packed type but rotated a further $90°$ with respect to the -VE S-T sublattice. This coarsest grid is called the positive space-time frame (+VE S-T) and is the domain wherein physical substance functions. Fig. 2.7a presents a picture of these nodal structures of space in a perfect lattice form. Fig. 2.7b illustrates how the situation might look when defects and disorder of the nodal points are present in the space. Thus, overall, we have three distinguishable types of nodal points forming networks with spacings that differ from each other by factors of $\sim 10^{10}$. Order-disorder transformations are involved in the two coarsest networks so they can exhibit amorphous, polycrystalline or single crystalline type of character. Here, one grain is thought to differ from another largely by the orientation of a special spin vector, tensor, torsion or other quality of the particular nodal network under consideration. The boundaries constitute relatively abrupt transitions from one vector, tensor, etc., direction to another. The nodal points themselves are not displaced in a particular polycrystalline array and the mind lattice is largely single crystalline. These grids of nodal networks are unique in that the waves travelling through the networks exhibit qualities of consciousness as distinct from energies. The conversion from consciousness to energies occurs at the nodal points themselves. The nodal points act as transponders converting consciousness to energies in the form of various subtle level and physical level mediators needed to interact with the various types of matter in the environment.

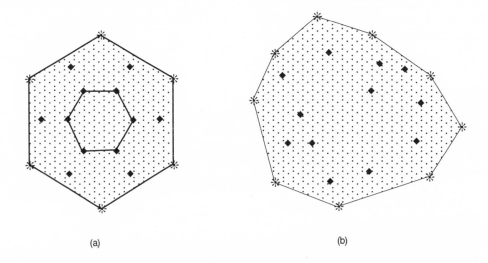

(a)                                        (b)

**Fig. 2.7** Two-dimensional visualization of the three hexagonal nodal networks from the smallest (mind) with a 90° rotation to the next larger (inverse S-T) plus an additional 90° rotation to the largest (+VE S-T) for two cases, (a) single crystalline for all three networks and (b) single crystal for the mind network but polycrystalline for the other two.

The origin of substance in these different networks occurs much like that in the physical domain -- because of the drive for physical nature to create entropy. Uniquely identifiable positive energy states contribute configurational entropy to the system and thus lower the free energy of the system. This is the thermodynamic quantity that governs all exchanges and reactions in the physical universe so it seems reasonable to assume that, in all of nature, the driving force for change is still the efficient modification of free energy, G, given by

$$G = H - TS$$

Here, G is the Gibb's free energy, H is the enthalpy (slightly different than energy), T is temperature and S, entropy.

The easiest way for the system to gain entropy is to dissociate part or all of a nodal point into the interstitial territory of the network. These can be considered as point defects in the network and, although it costs energy to break these particles away from the nodal points, the entropy gained more than compensates in the free energy equation (especially at large T). Fig. 2.8 illustrates how the physical level free energy, G, is reduced by increase in the concentration, $C_j$, of the jth distinguishably different defect up to its equilibrium concentration, $C_j^*$. A similar lowering of G occurs for each of the j-species. Initially, at very high physical temperatures, close to the origination point of the Big Bang, these j-species will be in the plasma state. Later, at lower T, they will transition to the gaseous state and, later still, at a further lowering of T, they will transition to the condensed states of liquid and solid. This will be the process for the formation of both mental and emotional atoms. The appropriate type holes left in the nodal points of the mind lattice will be the antimatter for these two types of substance.

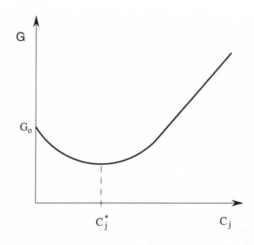

**Fig. 2.8** Schematic illustration of free energy, G, change of a crystal from the state of perfect order, $G_o$, as point defects are formed at concentration, $C_j$.

A similar mode of description could be utilized for the formation of both etheric and physical substance. However, the following imagery has more appeal as it reveals some of the inherent symmetries in the process.

Think of a fluctuation occurring in empty 9-space, that produces two polar opposites that are each 4-space types of substances. One half of the fluctuation is electrical in nature, has positive mass and energy, travels at velocities slower than the light velocity, c, and curves 4-space in such a direction as to produce gravitational forces. The other half of the fluctuation is magnetic in nature, has negative mass and energy, travels at velocities faster than c and curves 4-space in such a direction as to produce levitational forces. From this fluctuation, represented schematically in Fig. 2.9, the opposite sign masses cause the particles to be repelled from each other. In time, the electric-type particles combine with each other to form atoms, molecules, rocks, membranes, cells, organs, organic bodies, planets and worlds. Likewise, the magnetic-type particles combine with each other to form atoms, molecules, rocks, membranes, cells, organs, organic bodies, planets and worlds. One half of such fluctuations unite to produce a well-defined thermodynamic system of positive free energy. The other half of such fluctuations unite to also produce a well-defined thermodynamic system, but of negative free energy. Because of the light barrier at v=c, the two systems are designed to stay isolated from each other. If the initial particles formed in the fluctuations, were formed as an equilibrium fluctuation, then the free energy of formation was zero. Later, when the worlds have formed, the sum of the free energies for the two systems is still zero.

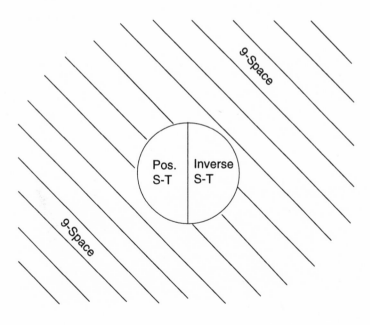

**Fig. 2.9** Representation of fluctuation-type formation of positive mass (electric) and negative mass (magnetic) substances from a higher dimensional embedding frame (e.g. 9-space).

The electric particle world is our physical matter world while the magnetic particle world is called the etheric matter world. Fig. 2.10 shows how each of these particles increases its energy as its velocity increases.

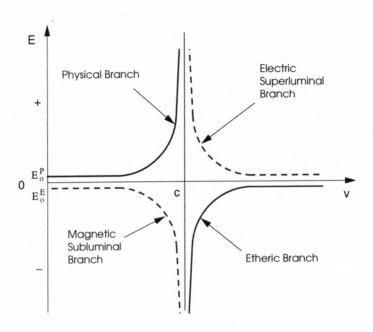

**Fig. 2.10** Energy-velocity diagram for a particle illustrating the singularity at v=c and the four different characters associated with each quadrant.

In the upper left hand quadrant ($E>E_o^P$ and $v<c$), we see the physical reality where, at $v=0$, the rest mass energy is $E_o^P$. In the lower right hand quadrant ($E<E_o^E$ and $v>c$), we see the etheric reality where, at $v \gg c$, the magnetic particle energy is $E_o^E$. The physical branch can be obtained from Einstein's Equation but not the etheric branch. This is because we do not yet have the necessary mathematical description. However, we expect it to involve a key term of the form

$$E \quad \alpha \quad \beta \big/ [\, 1 - (v/c)^n\,]$$

where $\beta$ and $n$ are some positive coefficients. When $v/c<1$, E is positive, going to infinity when $v=c$. However, when v exceeds c very slightly, E becomes minus infinity and then increases to less negative values as v increases further. Even without such a higher dimensional description, the Klein-Gordon or the Dirac Equation[5], written in the form,

$$E \quad = \quad \pm [p^2 + m^2]^{\frac{1}{2}}$$

allows both positive mass, m, with positive momentum p=mv, and negative mass, m', with negative momentum, p'=m'v.

The upper right hand quadrant in Fig. 2.10 is the electric superluminal (tachion) branch first discussed by Sudarshan[19]. For this branch, mass is imaginary; i.e., m'=im (i=(-1)$^{1/2}$). By symmetry, the lower left hand quadrant must be the magnetic subluminal branch, m"=-im. Terletskii[20] showed that, within the framework of relativistic kinematics and dynamics, there are no grounds for excluding any of these particles. The present framework of the theory of relativity admits three types of essentially different systems: (1) systems with positive proper mass, m$^2$>0, E>0, (2) systems with negative proper mass, m$^2$>0, E<0 and (3) systems with imaginary proper mass, m$^2$<0. Systems of the second and third kinds appear to be forbidden by our present understanding of macroscopic causality and the propositions of macroscopic physical thermodynamics. However, systems of the second kind obviously include the Dirac antielectrons of negative mass (as contrasted with the hole in the vacuum having a positive effective mass) while systems of the third kind include the virtual particles of the quantum theory of fields.

Returning to our physical and etheric materials, a type of "mirror relationship" is thought to occur between their properties, just as an inversion mirror type of relationship through the v=c point occurs in Fig. 2.10. Table 2.4 illustrates some of these mirror relationship properties.

Interaction between physical and etheric particles is not possible unless something additional is added to the picture, because the light barrier at v=c in Fig. 2.10 keeps bare particles of these two types insulated from each other. To overcome this difficulty, I have postulated the existence of a 9-D substance, called the "deltron", which does not suffer the singularity at a velocity equal to c. The deltron particles can interact with etheric particles traveling at v>c and also interact with physical particles traveling at v<c and can thus bring about energy exchange between them. Increasing the focus of human intention from the 10-D level increases the deltron content at the 9-D level and thus the coupling between physical and etheric substances at the 8-D level. In the physical atom, a shell of etheric particles is thought to exist in a narrow zone just inside and just outside the nucleus.

In 1924, De Broglie proposed a novel idea.[21] He postulated that the motion of a physical particle is governed by the propagation of certain "pilotwaves" which are intimately associated with the particle. A plot of the net pilot wave profile must be qualitatively like the curve shown in fig. 2.11a with the physical particle being located somewhere within this ellipsoid-like envelope. From straight-forward mathematical analysis[22], one finds that the velocity of the individual oscillations of the pilotwaves, v', is always greater than the velocity of light, c, and its relationship to the velocity of the particle, v, is given by

$$v' = c^2/v$$

Thus, the slower is the physical particle velocity, the faster is the pilot wave velocity with $v'$ having a lower limit of $v'=v=c$ and having a $v= 1$ cm/s value of $v' = c^2$.

Table 2.4 **ASPECTS OF THE MIRROR PRINCIPLE**

| PHYSICAL | | CONJUGATE PHYSICAL ≡ ETHERIC |
|---|---|---|
| Direct space & Direct time ⟺ left hemisphere sensing | | Inverse space & Frequency ⟺ right hemisphere sensing |
| Nodal network grid spacing ~$10^{-5}$ cm | M | Nodal network grid spacing ~$10^{-15}$ cm |
| Polycrystalline HCP | I | Disordered HCP |
| Electric monopoles | R | Magnetic monopoles |
| Forms atoms, molecules, etc. | R | Forms atoms, molecules, etc. |
| Allopathic medicine | O | Homeopathic medicine |
| Positive mass | R | Negative mass |
| $v<c$ | | $v>c$ |
| Positive energy states | | Negative energy states |
| $E_p$ increases as v increases | | $E_E$ increases as v increases |
| Positive entropy, $S_p$ | | Negative entropy, $S_E$ |
| Positive free energy, $G_p=H_p-T_pS_p$ | | Negative free energy, $G_E=H_E-T_ES_E$ |
| Positive temperature | M | Negative temperature |
| Gravitation | I | Levitation |
| Body sensory systems delineated | R | Body sensory systems not delineated |
| Photons at velocity c | R | Photons at velocity c'>>c (~$10^{10}$ c) |
| Fastest in vacuum | O | Slowest in vacuum |
| Slows down in dense material | R | Speeds up in dense physical matter |
| Faraday cage screening | | Screening by magnetic cage |

If we choose the electron as our physical particle, then its pilotwave will be defined as the magnetic monopole or "magnon". Because the magnon is travelling so fast, it weaves a pilotwave shape around the electron and, since it is non-observable by our present instruments, it is located in the vacuum reality and can thus have negative energy and negative mass. The detailed shape of the pilotwave envelope (magnon) will be the Fourier Transform of the detailed electron shape. From appendix 2.1, when one develops the Fourier Transform, one defines the wave number, $k = 2\pi n/\lambda = 2\pi v/c$ where $\lambda$ is the physical space wavelength. This leads to the conventional view of the Fourier Transform. For our utility in treating magnetic particles travelling at $v' > c$, we use $v'/v' = v/c$ so that the same topographic map which is the Fourier Transform profile just shifts to a higher frequency band to express the etheric nature of the magnon ($v'/v = v'/c$). Of course, the basic nature of the magnon wave is not electromagnetic.

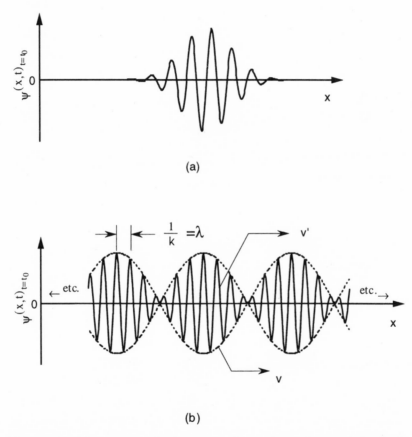

(a)

(b)

**Fig. 2.11** (a) A group of pilot waves for a physical particle located somewhere in the group and (b) The sum of two sinusoidal waves of slightly different frequencies and wavenumbers, k. The waves propogate at velocity v' while the group propagates at velocity v.

Although the foregoing description focussed on the interstitial particles of physical and etheric substance, we must not forget the holes left in 9-space when these substance fluctuations form. The holes are thought to find their way into the corresponding nodal networks of the inverse S-T and the +VE S-T sublattices. Thus, they become the antimatter for the physical and the etheric levels of substance.

To round out the picture, we need to mention here that, at each level of substance, special radiations (mediators) are present to allow the various substances to undergo their spectrum of energy transitions (more details are given in Chapter 3) and allow communication between the various particles of their intrinsic domain. At the physical and etheric levels, electric and magnetic radiations are generated. These couple together to produce electromagnetic (EM) radiations. Since we know that EM waves travel through vacuum, we see that this can occur via the two nodal networks much as sound waves (phonons) travel through a crystal lattice. We can also deduce that the two sublattices must be polycrystalline at this point in time, and on a relatively fine scale for the +VE S-T nodal network, because the vacuum appears to be spatially isotropic on a fairly large scale. We can also anticipate the presence of a much higher velocity ($v >> c$), largely magnetic-type, wave traveling along the inverse S-T nodal network (referred to as magnetoelectric (ME) radiation). At the 9-D, emotional or astral (theosophical term) level, the radiations are of the deltron type (at this point, we are using the word deltron to represent both the 9-D particle as well as its mediator). What we call light, then, is a composite quantity consisting of at least EM, ME and deltron radiations. Most of us presently perceive only the EM radiation portion.

**Key Differences With the Conventional Physics Model:** Although both models are extended to include a hyperspace description as a unification scheme, the Level One Model introduces some new types of symmetries associated with observational frames, particle mass and particle velocity. In the conventional physics model, the inaccessible dimensions are tightly balled up at each point of normal space while, in the Level One Model, the higher dimensions are inaccessible to the physical sensory system, or to present-day instrumentation, by virtue of the requirement that passage through the inversion mirror at the light barrier ($v=c$) is a prerequisite for observation in these dimensions. For example, accessing information in this conjugate four-space requires the sensory capacity to discriminate and interpret wave number-type of information. It seems as if nature is imprinting more information into a four-space medium via a process akin to multiplexing wherein one sensory system reads the direct 4-D signals while another (not yet fully developed in most of us) reads the inverse 4-D signals. Still another aspect of human sensory system capability is thought to allow access to information imprinted at the still higher dimensional levels.

With the conventional physics model, empty space is implicitly the vacuum and space is a continuum while the vacuum is considered by many to be a negative energy sea of virtual (mathematically imaginary) particles. The Level One Model sees space as a granular ordered network with the vacuum having a variety of substructures and negative energy bands filled with both negative mass (mathematically real) particles as well as virtual particles.

The conventional physical level physics model sees magnetic effects as only coming from the rotational aspects of electric charge while the Level One Model also utilizes real monopole magnetic charges but operating in a normally inaccessible domain (v>c) for our standard physical sensory system. The SU(2) versus the U(1) gauge differences between magnetic and electric charge in the conventional picture appear to be relevant here and may soften differences between the two approaches on this issue.

In the conventional physics model, wave-particle duality was a surprising observation that became a cornerstone of quantum mechanics. In the dual four-space construct of the Level One Model, it springs naturally from the inversion relationship between the two spaces. Other individuals have proposed and studied conjugate four-space systems, but the Level One Model arrangement of an 8-space comprised of two conjugate 4-spaces (inverses of each other) seems not to have been considered to date.

Finally, in the conventional physics model, although consciousness is tacitly allowed as a factor involved in the collapse of a wave function, there appears to be little room for <u>robust</u> mind action or applied human intention. However, in the Level One Model, this factor is central to the flow of events in human experience and is easily accomodated. In fact, the whole purpose for the <u>simulator</u> is the human learning of applied intentionality and applied love in the evolution of self towards higher states of structural organization and consciousness (see later chapters).

It is information waves, the "stuff" of consciousness, that propagate along the nodal networks placing potential maps on the vast array of nodal points of three different size scales and types. These nodal points translate the information waves into transmitted energy patterns of communicator/mediator particles for interacting with the various particles of substance, physical and subtle.

## Some Consequences of This Level One Model

**1. Key Distances and Energy Scales**: In conventional physics, a particle of wavelength $\lambda_p$ has an energy, $E_\lambda = hc/\lambda_p$ where h is Planck's Constant ($h = 6.6 \times 10^{-27}$ erg seconds). In the Level One model, the nodal network grid sizes for the three sublattices are

67

$$\lambda_+ \sim 10^{-7}\text{m} \quad, \quad \lambda_- \sim 10^{-17}\text{m} \quad, \quad \lambda_m \sim 10^{-27}\text{m}$$

and, just as the grid sizes go down by ten orders of magnitude ($10^{10}$) with changes between domains, the basic quantal unit of energy goes up by $10^{10}$ at each change. At the physical level, this unit is h, Planck's Constant. To compare with conventional physics, corresponding distance and energy scales are illustrated in Table 2.5. We thus see that an interesting correspondence exists between these key numbers in the two models.

Table 2.5     **KEY DISTANCES AND ENERGIES**

| LEVEL | $\lambda$ (m) | $E_\lambda$ (eV) |
|---|---|---|
| Photon from H atom | $\sim 5 \cdot 10^{-7}$ | 10 |
| Vector boson | $\sim 5 \cdot 10^{-17}$ | $\sim 10^{11}$ |
| Grand unification | $\sim 5 \cdot 10^{-28}$ | $\sim 10^{24}$ |
| Planck | $\sim 10^{-31}$ | |

    **2. Cosmological Constant:** Because the Level One model involves both positive and negative masses at the 4-space level, the value of the cosmological constant would be expected to be much closer to zero than present predictions based upon only positive mass and positive energies. This would help to resolve an important, long-standing problem for conventional physics. Of course, additional changes occur in going from the conventional continuum model of space to a nodal network model of space.

    **3. Magnetic Particles:** The presence of magnetic particles functioning in a domain having a mirror-type relationship with physical (electric) particle behavior accounts for both the chiral relationship of the two basic types of fundamental ultimate particles (see Fig. 2.4b), seen by the two theosophists following the yoga inner model, and the second triangle of spheres seen in the hydrogen nucleus (see Fig. 2.4a). The presence of magnetic particles in the Level One model restores a sense of symmetry to electromagnetism and helps one to understand why it has been so difficult to detect magnetic monopoles using conventional instrumentation. Since they are postulated to travel at v>c and have negative mass, they fall into the category of "nonphysical" and nonobservable. However, their effect is felt in electromagnetism via the electric/deltron/magnetic interaction. In the Level Two model, one must be able to show how the quantitative details of this interaction lead to our present equations of electromagnetism--and perhaps also some interesting additional magnetic effects that will help us understand more of the phenomena of Chapter 1

**4. Lattice Networks of Space Nodal Points:** This concept of a periodic arrangement of nodal points has much in common with a 3-D crystal lattice such as the one shown in Fig. 2.12a where phy   al atoms are located at each intersection. In a crystal, the spacing betv   n two adjacent atoms is about 1-ten billionth of a meter ($10^{-10}$m). The nodal points of the space grids are not atoms--at least not in the conventional science sense. One of the most significant characteristics of a nodal network or a physical crystal is that they diffract waves of appropriate types and wavelengths.

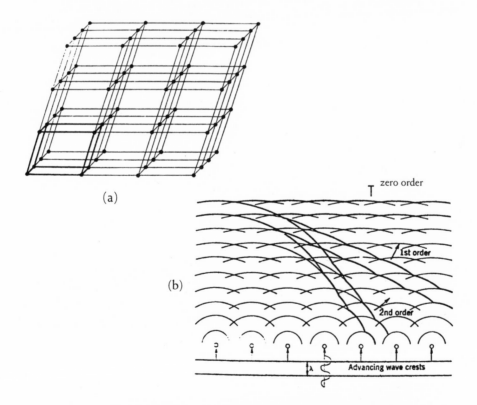

(a)

(b)

**Fig. 2.12** Illustration of (a) simple three dimensional lattice of atoms and (b) the diffraction of an electromagnetic wave by a row of these atoms to yield different orders of constructive interference.

69

If we shine a beam of x-rays into a crystal, since they are electro-magnetic waves, they interact with electrons in the atoms of the crystal lattice. This interaction causes new wavelets of EM radiation to move out into the surrounding space. At certain orientations, the wavelets add up and superpose, producing an incredibly strong signal. At other orientations, they cancel each other out. There is a tremendous amount of information contained in that diffraction pattern (see Fig. 2.12b). The intensity difference between an orientation where the waves constructively interfere versus one where they destructively interfere can be $\sim 10^{20}$ for a crystal of only millimeter size.

The next concept that needs further consideration is that of the reciprocal lattice. This is an extremely important concept in all of solid-state physics and crystallography. In the Level One model, it is not just a concept, it is <u>actual</u> at the nodal network level of space. Every lattice structure, no matter how complex, has a mathematically reciprocal structure which can be determined in the following way: starting with a set of planes in the crystal (direct lattice), you take a perpendicular line and, by going along that perpendicular a distance inversely proportional to the separation of the planes in the direct lattice, you reach a point that can be called the reciprocal lattice point for that set of planes in the direct lattice at their fundamental spacing. By following this procedure for other sets of planes in the crystal, you locate other network points of the reciprocal lattice. In this way, you obtain two lattices that may interpenetrate each other. For example, if we were to start with a crystal having a face-centered cubic lattice (see Fig. 2.13a for the direct lattice) so that there are atoms in the cube corner positions plus atoms in every face centered position, it turns out that the reciprocal lattice has active points at the corners of a cube and also in the center of the cube (see Fig. 2.13b for the reciprocal lattice) rather than in the centers of the faces. This is called a body-centered cubic lattice with a very different unit cell size. In crystallography, the reciprocal lattice is usually not real but is a kind of mathematical space with a lattice spacing that is related to the reciprocal of the crystal lattice spacing.

According to the Level One model, the ultimate space is a 10-D lattice. Its proposed nodal network structure at a 3-D analogue level is hexagonal close-packed. This means that, at 3-D, the nodal points are arranged in a hexagonal pattern as illustrated in Fig. 2.14a. Each parallel plane of nodal points is an identical hexagonal pattern but the origin of the alternate planes is shifted

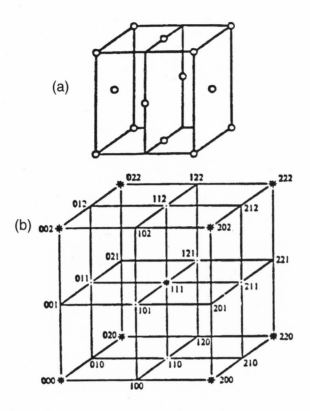

**Fig. 2.13** Representation of a direct lattice of atoms (face-centered cubic) at the top and its reciprocal lattice (body-centered cubic) at the bottom.

laterally so that one of their nodal points lies above the center of the hexagon below. This is the proposal for the mind lattice. One important aspect of this choice is that its reciprocal lattice is another hexagonal close-packed lattice but with much larger unit spacing and with the hexagon rotated by 90o (see Fig. 2.14b). Thus, the nodal points of the inverse S-T sublattice lie <u>exactly</u> on nodal points of the mind lattice although there are unique differences in the nature of the two types of nodal points.

    If we now take the inverse S-T nodal network as our primary lattice and ask for its reciprocal lattice, we find that it is yet another hexagonal close-packed lattice but with still larger spacing and with the hexagon rotated a further 90°.

Thus, the nodal points of the +VE S-T sublattice lie <u>exactly</u> on the nodal points of the inverse S-T sublattice (and also of the mind lattice). Although there are further unique differences in the nature of these two types of nodal points. With this Level One model, the structural lattice picture would be like that illustrated in Fig. 2.14c. The smallest hexagonal unit is the mind lattice, the next larger hexagonal unit (rotated by 90o) is the inverse S-T sublattice while the largest hexagonal unit (rotated an additional 90o) is the +VE S-T sublattice and it has the same orientation as the mind lattice but its size is ~$10^{20}$ times larger.

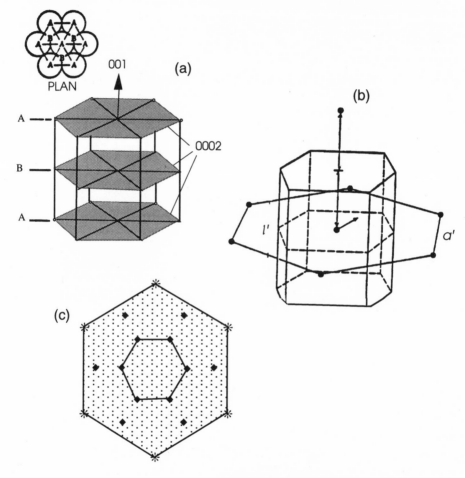

**Fig. 2.14** Various representations of hexagonal close-packed (HCP) symmetry, (a) atom locations in the direct HCP lattice, (b) hexagonal lattice with its reciprocal rotated by 90 degrees and (c) plan view of the three nodal networks from Fig. 2.7a.

One of the important things about this particular nodal point arrangement is that, since they are configured to be reciprocal lattices of each other, when waves that are traveling in the mind lattice are diffracted from its nodal network, they are directed to pass through the nodal points of the inverse S-T network (and at greatly increased intensity). Likewise, when waves that are travelling in the inverse S-T lattice are diffracted from its nodal network, they are directed to pass through the nodal points of the +VE S-T network (and at greatly increased intensity). Thus, there is a connectivity and integration of information between these three levels via the important mechanism of wave diffraction.

In the Level One model, only when the diffracted mind lattice beams exceed a critical intensity do they trigger the inverse S-T nodal network points to radiate waves into the inverse S-T sublattice. This set of response waves are of a different type and frequency band than the mind lattice waves. Thus, these inverse S-T nodal points have a transponder/transducer characteristic that is very non-linear. In a similar fashion, only when the inverse S-T sublattice beams exceed some other critical intensity do they trigger the +VE S-T nodal network points to radiate waves into the +VE S-T sublattice. As one might expect, this set of response waves are of another different type and frequency band than the inverse S-T sublattice waves. Again, a type of transponder/transducer characteristic is displayed by the +VE S-T nodal points.

**5. Diffraction:** In terms of physical domain diffraction, what happens is that, when EM radiation is diffracted off the planes of a direct lattice, the beam goes through the active (or nodal) points of its reciprocal lattice. For each diffraction beam, you get wave superposition with constructive interference only at one of these points--the beam is focussed through only one of these reciprocal points (the * points in Fig. 2.13).

Another important concept for us is that, when you have a direct space and you have another space that is the reciprocal of it, then the reciprocal space is really a frequency space; i.e., $\lambda_x \to 1/\lambda_x$, $\lambda_y \to 1/\lambda_y$, $\lambda_z \to 1/\lambda_z$ and $t_t \to 1/t_t$. Thus, these two spaces are conjugates of each other with one being a distance-time space and the other being a frequency space (or wave number space).

In the space-time frame, an object is located at the position (x,y,z,t) and we pictorally represent it in a 3-space diagram via a t-coordinate running from each (x,y,z) space point as indicated in Fig. 2.15a. We generally register the object's presence with our eyes and, interpret its nature via the aspects of physical light (photons) that enter our eyes (or other photon sensing capabilities of our body system). The important qualities of light utilized here are photon density (or flux), frequency, polarization and contrast (or pattern). These we interpret as light/dark, color, glare and shape, respectively. It is perhaps important to note that the photon registration system of the body is a multielement antenna system (see Chapter 3) capable of great discrimination.

In the conjugate frame, the frequency domain, the equilibrium counterpart to the physical object is located at $(v_x, v_y, v_z, v_t)$ and we pictorally represent it in a 3-space diagram via a $v_t$ coordinate running from each 3-D frequency point $(v_x, v_y, v_z)$ as indicated in Fig. 2.15b. In this frame, the counterpart object is magnetic in nature and radiates/scatters etheric photons which enter some sensory organ of the body (perhaps the eyes) and this is a key step in allowing one to perceive the presence of the counterpart object.

If the target physical object is physically far removed from the observer, who we will place at the origin of Fig. 2.15a, then the counterpart, frequency domain, object will be located in the low 3-D portion of Fig. 2.15b. If the target object is physically close to the observer, the counterpart object will be located in the relatively high frequency 3-D portion of Fig. 2.15b. The physical object's time behavior can be observed by focussing on that 3-D location and monitoring the time-variation in physical photon characteristics. Let us assume that the density of physical photons of a particular frequency, etc., that are received by the eye vary in time like a simple sine wave as shown in Fig. 2.16a. If so, then the conjugate etheric object will give a density of characteristic etheric photons as illustrated in Fig. 2.16b; i.e., approximately, one can expect to find the conjugate representaion of Fig. 2.15a as the <u>Fourier Transform</u> of this sine wave. The shorter is the period of the sine wave in Fig. 2.16a, the closer are the delta ($\delta$) functions of Fig. 2.16b to the origin ($v_t = v_{t1}$). The larger is the amplitude of the sine wave in Fig. 2.16a, the larger is the signal strength (amplitude of the $\delta$-functions) in Fig. 2.16b.

If the time-variation of the physical photon flux from the physical object is complex in that it consists of the superposition of many sines and cosines of different frequency, then the etheric photon flux will be represented in the $v_t$-space of Fig. 2.16b by a series of $\delta$-functions having different amplitudes that are separated from each other along the $v_t$-coordinate. As an example, for a cosine wave of frequency $w_1$ modulated by a cosine wave of frequency $w_2$ as in Fig. 2.16c, the Fourier transform approximately gives the etheric conjugate $\delta$-functions as in Fig. 2.16d.

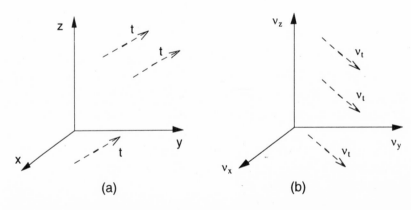

(a)                    (b)

**Fig. 2.15** Representation of the dual conjugate four-space frames, (a) the physical frame (+VE S-T) with the time-coordinate extending from each point in 3-D space and (b) the inverse or etheric frame (inverse S-T) with the $v_t$ frequency-coordinate extending from each point in the 3-D frequency domain. The origin and coordinate axes lie on top of each other.

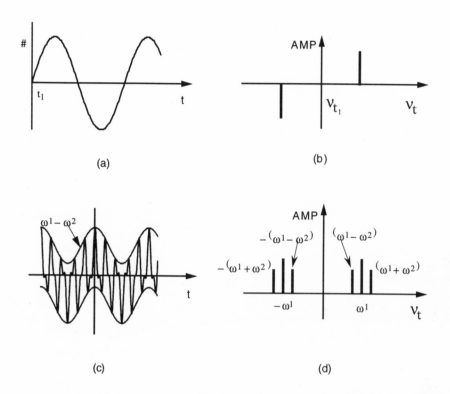

**Fig. 2.16** Illustration of the Fourier transform relationship between the direct and inverse space domains with (a) a simple harmonic physical property variation in time at a point in direct space and (b) the conjugate localization of the etheric domain property along the $v_t$ coordinate of inverse space. Another illustration of the inter-domain Fourier Transform relationship for a more complex time-variation of property in direct space, (c) a cosine variation of frequency $\omega_1$ modulated by a cosine variation at frequency $\omega_2$ and (d) the inverse space $\delta$-function conjugate representation.

One can expand this concept of the reciprocal lattice to determine the reciprocal of any geometrical shape; i.e., anything with a spatial pattern has a correlate which is a frequency pattern. For example, if you have a rod shape in direct space, it has a reciprocal which, in frequency space, is a flat disc perpendicular to the rod and vice versa. If you have a set of points along a straight line in direct space then, the reciprocal space correlate is a set of parallel planes perpendicular to the line and vice versa. If you have waves in direct space, this leads to impulses in reciprocal space and vice versa. Thus, one can begin to see how the wave/particle duality of quantum mechanics may be just the natural expression of correlated patterns in the two conjugate sublattices, +VE S-T and inverse S-T.

For more complex patterns such as a set of holes in a plate (or dots on a page), one can shine light through the holes and let the diffracted light fall on a screen placed at a particular distance behind the plate[23].

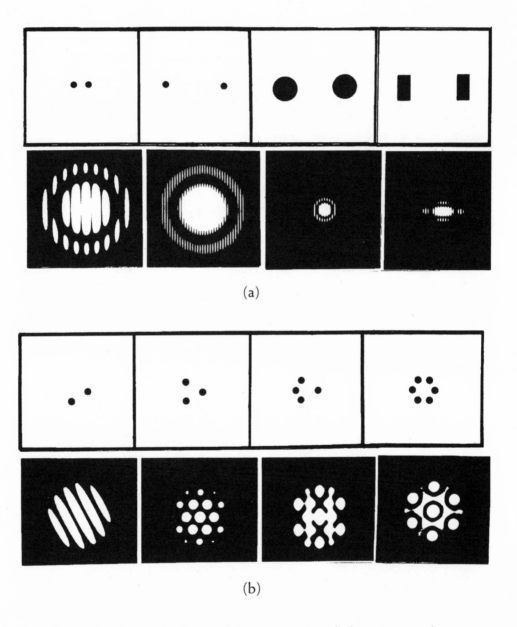

(a)

(b)

Fig. 2.17   Composite figure of direct space-time hole patterns and frequency-space diffraction patterns

These diffraction patterns will be the reciprocal space frequency patterns. When the holes are of different sizes and shapes, changes in the diffraction pattern result as can be seen in Fig. 2.17a. The diffraction pattern envelopes are circular in nature, but one can see a unique internal structure develop. Now let us look at another pair of correlates, as in Fig. 2.17b. Here we start with two holes and add a third, then a fourth and, finally, six holes in a hexagon arrangement. As this hole change occurs, the diffraction pattern changes from a parallel array of ellipses to a series of hexagonal type arrays with other information penetrating the hexagonal grid. Overall in this figure, we can see how (1) increasing the spacing between a pair of dots in direct space, increases the frequency of perpendicular intersections of the basic ring pattern from one dot, (2) increasing the size of the dots decreases the size of the segmented ring pattern, (3) rotating the orientation of the dots in one direction rotates the segmented ring pattern in the opposite direction and (4) square dots lead to rectangular rather than circular rings. If one mathematically calculates the Fourier Transfrom for a circle and for the set of circles shown in Fig 2.17, one obtains the same result as determined experimentally by the diffraction pattern. Figs. 2.18 show the diffraction patterns from a set of circular holes arranged in circular and spiral patterns. For the spiral hole patterns of Fig. 2.18b, we find a most interesting diffraction pattern. Here we see mandalas!

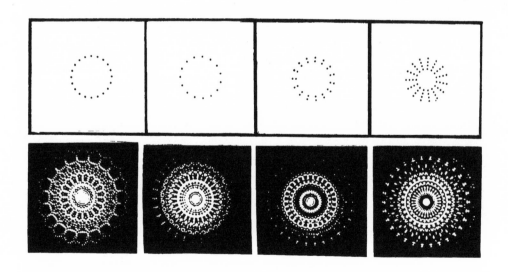

**Fig. 2.18a** Composite figure of direct-space hole patterns and frequency-domain diffraction patterns.

**Fig. 2.18b** Composite figure of direct-space hole patterns and frequency-domain diffraction patterns.

If we think of these conjugate patterns in terms of our two 4-space bodies, physical and etheric, each appears to be approximately the Fourier Transform of the other[24]. When one begins to consider the meaning of such pattern correlates in these two bodies, one can also see that, when you mentally focus on one of these bodies, you set in motion a set of waves that influence the other body and vice versa. We will return to this topic again in Chapter 6 when DNA phantom signals are discussed.

**6. Energy Bands**: This concept will be illustrated for all types of particles in a lattice by focussing on electrons in a physical crystal. We normally think of an isolated atom as having all of its electrons bound to it; however, when the atom is contained in a crystal, that is not necessarily true. To lower the free energy of the system, some of the outer electrons can be released to become waves that flow through the lattice. They will build wave packets so that they can travel, and they can travel through the lattice because they have mobility. If we apply an electric field to certain materials we will find that they are very conductive to the flow of electrons (metals). Other materials are very non-conductive (insulators) and some materials lie between the two extremes (semiconductors). The ability of electrons to flow or not flow is strongly related to the type of electron energy bands formed by the material. Let me now try to explain how these bands form.

When we evaluate the energy of a wave of wavelength $\lambda$ and construct a graph of wave energy versus $1/\lambda$ (called the wave number, k), we obtain a kind of parabolic relationship such as illustrated in Fig. 2.19a. Because there is diffraction of the electrons by the lattice of atoms it turns out that, in certain regions of Fig. 2.19a, a gap is developed representing regions of energy where electron waves are forbidden by our physical laws. We find that, between any two gaps is a zone or band of allowed energies. These zones are called energy bands. Thus, we have an energy band scheme where the electrons can travel in a wave number or frequency space but not at energies lying in the gaps. This is illustrated in Fig. 2.19b. In general, the mobility of an electron is larger the higher is the band in which it moves.

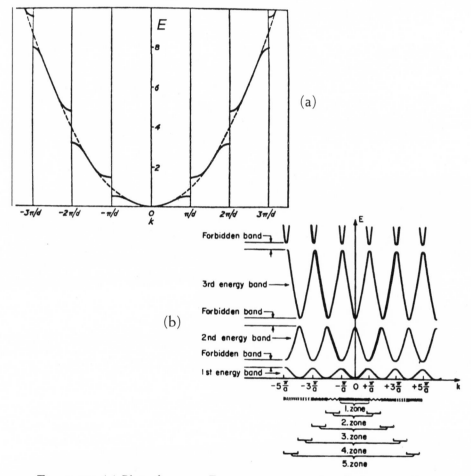

**Fig. 2.19** (a) Plot of energy, E, versus wave number, k, for a small periodic potential and (b) the energy band spectrum illustrating both allowed and forbidden domains for electron waves.

When we consider elastic waves (sound waves) moving in a crystal lattice consisting of two different types of atoms (different masses), then we again find a band-type of behavior when we make a wavenumber type of plot. In this specific case, there are three distinct allowed bands. The lowest band is called the acoustical band (low frequency) while the two upper allowed bands are called optical bands (high frequency). Thus, when we extend this concept to the three nodal networks of space, the elastic wave propagation analogy reveals the presence of many allowed bands separated by forbidden zones. Here, the lowest frequency (or energy) band will be the "acoustical" type branch determined largely by the +VE S-T nodal network (the velocity of these waves will be the velocity of light in free space, c, when no physical matter is present). The lowest "optical" type branches will be determined largely by the inverse S-T nodal network (the velocity of wave propagation in the upper branch will be c' $\sim 10^{10}$c). The upper "optical" type branches will be largely determined by the mind nodal network (with correspondingly higher wave propagation velocity).

When one treats the propagation of elastic waves in a physical crystal, one of the mathematical solutions is a longitudinal wave whose velocity is equal to $(C_{11}/\rho)^{1/2}$ where $C_{11}$ is a particular elastic constant of the crystal and $\rho$ is its density. There are also two mathematical solutions which are transverse or shear waves (perpendicular to the direction of propagation) with velocity equal to $(C_{44}/\rho)^{1/2}$ where $C_{44}$ is another elastic constant of the crystal. For various metallic crystals, $C_{11} \sim 4C_{44}$ so that the longitudinal wave velocity ~twice the transverse wave velocity. For various ionic crystals, $C_{11} = 3C_{44}$. However, if we have a cubic crystal that is elastically isotropic, then the velocity of the transverse waves is predicted to be equal to the velocity of the longitudinal wave. For our interest here, it is important to note that a fine-grained polycrystalline material behaves elastically as if it were isotropic on a macroscopic scale. Thus, it becomes very difficult to distinguish the longitudinal from the transverse modes of wave propagation. We can expect an analogous type of behavior from our various space lattices of nodal points, when the size of the grains is large enough one will be able to distinguish both longitudinal and transverse wave signal propagation.

**7. Non-Local Effects:** In the late 1960's, Bell[25] proved an extremely profound theorem with far-reaching implications for quantum mechanics. His theorem states that, after two particles interact via conventional forces and then move apart beyond the range of such force interactions, the fabric of quantum mechanics requires that they continue to influence each other instantly via some real connection joining them together no matter how far apart is their separation. This seeming paradox has a ready explanation based upon the Level One model.

Consider an event wherein two physical particles come into close contact, interact and then separate. The character of this event is informationally transferred from the particles to the +VE S-T nodal network at that physical location. The nodal network information both propogates in its sublattice at a velocity v = c and excites both the inverse S-T nodal point sublattice and the mind nodal point lattice with the information. In the former, the signal velocity is c' $\sim 10^{10}$c while, in the latter, the signal velocity is c">>c'. Thus, the information concerning both the particle interaction event and the particle separation process is broadcast ahead of the physical particles via two of the three nodal networks and then diffracted back to the +VE S-T nodal network at remote locations. This means that the remote nodal points "know" that a physical particle is coming and also when it will arrive.

This Level One model predicts that information of the pattern type, located anywhere in space-time, is represented <u>everywhere</u> at the nodal network points of both the +VE S-T and the inverse S-T sublattices as well as at the nodal network points of the mind lattice. Relative to physical reality, wave communication of information between these various nodal points seems to occur instantly because the signal velocity is so rapid compared to physical light speeds. The relativistic view of conventional physical science concerning events happening in space-time is to describe them using the Minkowski space construct illustrated in Fig. 2.20a. The origin is the "now", the upper cone is the future and the lower cone is the past. Any physical event of the future takes place inside the upper cone while events that occur at the velocity of physical light take place on the walls of this cone. That is why it is called the "light cone". Fig. 2.20b illustrates the extension of this concept to that needed to describe the Level One Model. Instead of a three-distance-time plot, we need an $(N-1)$-distance-$X_N$ plot for an $(X_1, X_2, X_3, X_4,...X_N)$ dimension space. We will represent this on a two-dimensional plot as $X_N$ versus $|S|$, where

$$S^2 = X_1{}^2 + X_2{}^2 + X_3{}^2 + ...+ X^2{}_{N-1,}$$

as indicated in Fig. 2.20b. Here the inner light cone contains physical events. The region between the inner cone and the next larger light cone contains etheric events occurring at velocities up to $10^{10}$ times faster (if that term is relevant for a frequency domain) than physical events on average. The larger cones move us into the emotional and mind event domains where the signal velocity jumps by a factor of $\sim 10^{10}$ from light cone to light cone. Thus we see that, as we proceed outwards (to higher dimensions), we are heading towards an infinite velocity and approach a condition in which we can be everywhere in no time--we are approaching omnipresence!

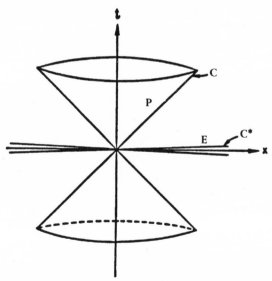

**Fig. 2.20a**  Minkowski-type diagrams, (a) for the physical light cone with v=c at the surface and the edge of the etheric light cone with v=c*>>c at its surface.

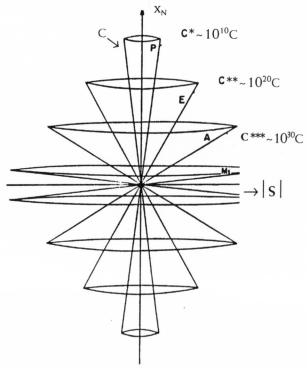

**Fig. 2.20b** A higher dimensional representaion with $X_N$ being the analogue of time, t, and $|S|$ being the analogue of distance, X, showing four light cone domains (P=physical, E=etheric, A=emotional and $M_1$=instinctive mind) with different surface signal velocities.

**8. Remote Viewing:** As just discussed in "7", information concerning patterns or events located or happening in the physical universe resides almost instantaneously at the various nodal network points. A very large number of these nodal points are located within our physical brain envelope. One must learn to access the various nodal networks and then learn how to read the information written there. I suspect that the larger the number of contiguous nodal points one can read, the sharper and more accurate will be the picture obtained. Further, one must access not only the <u>acoustical</u> band but also the various <u>optical</u> bands (higher frequency information) to obtain complete information concerning the "target". In this regard, the future-seeing portion of the information can only have a certain finite probability of being accurate because new events occurring between the "now" and the "then" may alter the patterns stored at the grid points in significant ways.

**9. Dematerialization/Materialization:** Imagine a pond surface on which little "skimmerbugs" are moving about on the surface. They have a small body and many long legs, and resemble Abbott's Flatlanders[26] in that they perceive only two dimensions. Suppose you have a skimmerbug skimming across the pond near you and you put your leg in the pond. To the skimmerbug, that is a materialization event. You then take your leg out of the pond and, to the skimmerbug, that is a dematerialization event. If you think of the number of ways in' which your three-dimensional phenomenon can penetrate its two-dimensional perception frame, you can begin to appreciate how difficult it will ever be for the science of skimmerbugdom to be able to produce a proper scientific explanation of the phenomenon. We see here that one's scientific prowess is limited largely to the level of the society's operational perception.

To dematerialize physical matter, we need to remove it from our 4-space into another or into a higher dimensional space. We thus need to take electric charges travelling at $v<c$ and convert them to magnetic charges travelling at $v>c$; i.e., an inversion mirror operation through $v=c$ in the sense of Fig. 2.10. It is necessary for us to reverse the chiral nature of the ultimate particle in the sense of Fig. 2.3. The Level One model allows for such a possibility even if most of us are unable to cause it to happen by the focus of our intentionality.

**10. Levitation:** It is fairly well known that gravity is associated with physical mass producing a local positive curvature in the 4-D space-time surface. By the same type of space-curving process, etheric mass will produce the opposite sign of curvature in the 4-D space-time surface and thus will yield a levitational force. To accomplish actual levitation of an object, it is necessary to use our intention (or some future device) to inject sufficient etheric and deltron substance into the object to overcome its normal gravitational force of attraction to the earth. The deltrons are needed so that the 4-D space-time surface can "feel" the presence of the negative mass. It is by mastering this process that one may learn to walk on water.

**11. Firewalking:** To date, tens of thousands of people worldwide have had successful personal experiences with firewalking over distances from ones to tens of meters. Their successful completion of this attempt to walk across a bed of glowing coals required the intention/belief that it was possible to complete the experiment without damage to the feet. From the present model, it is fairly straightforward as to how this might be accomplished.

From a purely physical viewpoint, foot contact with the hot coals transfers a flux of heat into the soles of the feet. In an extremely short time, this should raise the skin temperature to levels where tissue burning and serious damage occurs. However, from a physical/etheric viewpoint, we have a positive energy domain and a negative energy domain in intimate contact but normally very loosely coupled to each other. If one could somehow transfer the physical heat input from the hot coals to the etheric substance domain at the soles of our feet <u>before</u> the physical skin temperature rises to critical levels, then this increase in etheric energy could be rapidly transferred to other parts of the body and dissipated by normal modes of heat transfer (greatly increased blood flow would also help a little).

It is via our mind-directed intention and the belief to sustain this focus, that deltrons are released from the higher dimensional domain to serve as a coupling medium between the physical/etheric substances in the soles of the feet. So long as this intention is strong enough and maintained for long enough, at least one mechanism exists to allow firewalking to occur without physical damage to the cells of the body.

**12. Spirit-Initiated Physical Action:**   From the Level One model, one can readily discriminate a process path whereby spirit produces physical action.  This is illustrated schematically in Fig. 2.21.  Here, the intention imprints the desire of spirit onto the nodal network of mind.  This mind-level information pattern imprints a correlate on the inverse S.T. domain and also activates the emotion frame to inject a higher density of deltrons into the interface between the relevant physical substance and its etheric  counterpart. Thus, the etheric level information imprint is transferred from the magnetic frequency domain to the electric space-time domain and one detects materialization of the intention via our physical senses.  It is important to recognize the importance of the individual's emotional strength here, because this is necessary for a strong final imprinting on the physical domain.  Finally, it is important to recognize that action in the physical band of reality is the <u>end result</u> of a fairly significant sequence of steps initiated by <u>spirit-directed</u> intention.  The unseen is the driver, the seen is the driven.

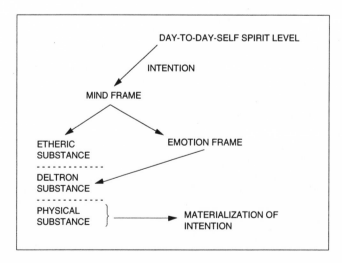

**Fig. 2.21**   Illustration of one possible process path whereby spirit produces action in the physical domain.

**13. Homeopathy:** A key postulate, here, is that the condition of health occurs when each type of physical chemical in the physical body has an etheric chemical counterpart in the etheric body at an appropriate ratio, $C_{Ej}/C_{Pj}$, for the j-species. Disharmony leading to disease is thought to occur when this ratio is out of balance. Balance may possibly be restored by manipulating $C_{Pj}$ either down or up. However, present allopathic medicine utilizes only the "increase" mode so this practice, by itself, is unlikely to restore balance in all cases. Fortunately, balance can also be possibly restored by manipulating $C_{Ej}$. Homeopathic remedies deal only with the increase mode. A potentized remedy is, in fact, the etheric counterpart of the physical constituent that has reached toxic proportions in the body and has, by itself, produced the specific symptoms. Thus, by combining both allopathic <u>and</u> homeopathic procedures in the increase mode, all values of the ratio $C_{Ej}/C_{Pj}$ are possible so that a balanced condition may always be produced.

This can also be looked at from an energy point of view in that each atom is an absorber and radiator of a specific spectrum of energies of the EM or ME variety. Thus, for optimum tuning between the etheric and physical bodies so that energy is most efficiently utilized, the proper chemical radiators must be available in each body and at a concentration level such that the absorption cross-sections for the important specific radiations (as seen through the deltron coupling medium) are properly impedance-matched. This means that, not only must the $C_{Ej}/C_{Pj}$ ratio be in the proper range for etheric/physical balance to be achieved, but $C_{Ej}$ or $C_{Pj}$ must also be in the proper concentration range to exchange radiation efficiently with the other chemical constituents of the body. This allows the body to function at a good overall power level. In summary, there are a set of radiation balances required for energy exchange within the physical body as well as between the physical and etheric bodies, and some total content pool of special chemical constituents is needed to maintain a type of stationary state level in the presence of the natural radiation losses from the body. Water is generally used as a host for the potentized remedy because a magnetic imprint can be readily transferred from the etheric domain onto these molecules via their transition to the hydronium state ($H_3O$). Our Level One model allows for the possibility of homeopathic medicine to function in a very natural way. We will return to this topic in Chapter 6 where a more detailed description of homeopathic action following the Level One model will be given.

**14. Pattern Transfer:** From what has already been discussed, we know, to a fair approximation, that a Fourier Transform relationship connects the pattern carried by the +VE S-T nodal network and the pattern imprinted on the inverse S-T nodal network. Further, we know that an additional Fourier Transform relationship connects the inverse S-T nodal network information pattern and the mind nodal network information pattern. However, nothing has been said about the pattern relationship between physical substance and the +VE S-T nodal network or between etheric substance and the inverse S-T nodal network. In the Level One model, a direct imprinting process (no transform relationship) is postulated to occur between a pattern of physical substance and the information recorded on the +VE S-T nodal network. This physical substance/+VE S-T nodal point coupling occurs via deltrons. Likewise, a direct imprinting process occurs between the etheric counterpart of the physical substance and the inverse S-T nodal network. Here, the force coupling is via a magnetic type of interaction (somewhat deltron-like but not deltron).

To illustrate these various pattern shifts, suppose that we take a triangle made from a copper plate. Fig. 2.22 shows the corresponding patterns at the different nodal networks and at the etheric level of substance. Of course, a steel, tin, silver, etc., physical triangle would yield the same set of patterns. Thus, the material aspect, as distinct from the macroscopic shape aspect, is not evident at this level of modeling. One must proceed to Level Two type of modeling to reveal the physical/etheric material correspondence. At least Fig. 2.22 shows us that the macroscopic shape distributions of these two types of substance are related by a single Fourier Transform.

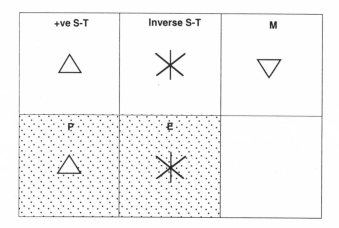

**Fig. 2.22** Representation of pattern change for a physical triangle as one makes successive Fourier Transform operations on this shape as we move from frame to frame.

**15. Human Soul/Body Relationship:** The Level One model deals with seven levels of substance: spirit, three levels of mind (instinctive mind, intellectual mind and spiritual mind which loosely relate to the three sections of the brain: the root brain, the left and right lobes, and the frontal lobes), the emotional (transitional) or astral, etheric and physical. Fig. 2.23 illustrates the collection of these substances into the indestructible part, the Being or soul, and the temporal part, or body (or simulator), in which the Being has invested itself for a period of experience. The "umbilical cord", so to speak, that connects the Being to its containment vehicle is the emotional (or astral) substance. This transitional substance also forms the outer containment shell of our Being between repeated investments in the physical realm of consciousness (reembodiment or reincarnation). As mentioned before, energy interactions occur between these different levels of substance so that, if you perturb the system at one level, a ratchet effect can cause energy trains to travel into different dimensions of this set so one can experience the phenomenon manifesting at different levels of the set. Thus, the body can be likened to an earth-sensory chamber or vehicle (or "car") that we drive during one earth-life experience while we, the Being, are the "driver" of the sensory vehicle.

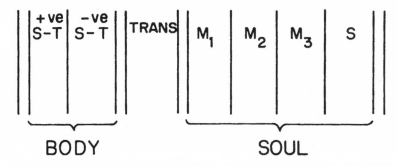

**Fig. 2.23** Representation of Being (soul) attached to the simulator (body) via the transitional (emotion) frame as an interfacing network.

**16. Consciousness Vehicles:** Although most of us don't really know what consciousness is, we tend to think that it relates to the ability of natural systems to exchange information. I tend to think that consciousness is a correlate of spirit entering dense matter (to be discussed more in later chapters) with a relationship between consciousness and the different types of energy present in the simulator being something like that illustrated by Fig. 2.24. From what has been said earlier, for each type of energy present in the various dimensions of the Level One model, it manifests in a set of allowed energy bands. One way to differentiate between the consciousness of a rock, a virus, a bacterium, a cell, a plant, an animal and a human is in terms of the types and number of different energy bands that they utilize for expression of their natures. For example, the physical consciousness of a mineral is proposed to be related to the correlation of the wave functions for the various energies flowing in its 3-D structure. The energies involved here would be at least electric and magnetic. When we consider something like a virus, we should talk in terms of energy pattern correlations in both three and four-dimensions and with several additional energy bands. As we move to a plant, increased correlations in the higher dimensional lattices and substances must be considered. For humans, we need still more energy field correlations at the eighth, ninth and tenth-dimensional levels.

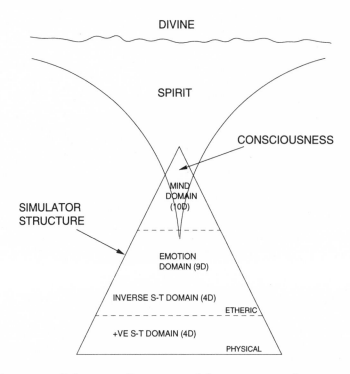

**Fig. 2.24** Schematic illustration of the connection between spirit and the simulator giving rise to consciousness.

When one considers a correlation of these various energy packets, it is the synergistic rhythmic coupling into an integrated system that is involved--a type of "divine" dance. The picture is that we have the possibility of many different energy types, expressed in many different energy bands, functioning in 8-D, 9-D or 10-D space, all interacting in a synergistically-phased way; i.e., in a partially coherent fashion. I postulate that the higher is one's consciousness, the more there are of these energy type and energy band correlations that function at higher dimensional levels as well as at the lower dimensional levels. Thus, a person who is very enlightened, compared to one who is not so enlightened, is proposed to have many more energy bands at the mental and emotional levels correlating and working synergistically with the energy fields of the various energy bands functioning at the lower dimensional levels of the individual. This allows the Level One modeling to contain the possibility for rationalizing different levels of consciousness in nature and our physical world reality.

**17. Energizing Normal Humans and Saints:** Although I have discussed how energy and information transfer through the various nodal networks, nothing has been said about how the higher dimensional energies transfer to and enliven our dual 4-D bodies. It is thought that the major component of the life energy is radiated from the nodal networks to the physical and etheric substances of the body. We will discuss radiators and antenna systems more fully in the next chapter; however, here, it is important to understand the constructive or destructive interference of the total nodal network radiation from the region within the envelope of the physical/etheric body. Just as in the theory of diffraction, where a regular array or lattice of atoms is needed to generate a strong diffracted beam through a reciprocal lattice point, a regular arrangement of properly phased radiators is needed so that the signals from each will constructively interfere to produce a strong net signal. Likewise, the larger is the size or number of regularly spaced radiators in the array, the larger will be the amount of energy and information transferred and the more vital and conscious will be the individual.

The structural character of the nodal networks are influenced by three main forces: (1) cosmological, (2) individual internal harmony versus disharmony and (3) collective humanity's internal harmony versus disharmony. When all the forces are beneficial, the nodal networks form relatively perfect lattices of very large extent (see Fig. 2.7a) and humans manifest fantastically large energy densities. When the reverse occurs, the nodal networks form an almost amorphous arrangement and humans manifest only very small amounts of life energy. In between, the nodal network structure is polycrystalline (see Fig. 2.7b) and the larger is the size of the average lattice grain, the greater will be the amount of life energy flowing through an individual.

Generally, a saint has reached a high state of inner self-management at mental and emotional levels so that the body substance radiation fields are harmonious and synchronized. This supports an ordering process to take place at the nodal network level so that grain growth occurs and the average nodal network grain size increases. Such individuals have an abundance of energy to expend in life even with negligible physical food intake. Such individuals often manifest a large "light" nimbus or halo (or aura) around the head and body. Most individuals have not reached such a level of internal harmony through self-development so their internal nodal networks are more fragmented by the sometimes chaotic signals generated by the body substance. Thus, their nodal networks have a smaller lattice size and less life energy is constructively radiated into the body envelope from the nodal points.

**18. Applied Intentionality:** The simulator is a device designed to teach us how to <u>effectively</u> use our intentionality. Since every application of our intention is an act of creation, it ultimately teaches us how to create properly, efficiently and effectively. It is our intention, as individuals or as groups, that imprints a pattern of potentials at the nodal points of the mind lattice. This, in turn, ultimately manifests in some type or types of events in our sensory world. If our intention is focussed and clear, some correlation should be observed between our act of intention and these events. If it is fuzzy and conflictory, little correlation is likely to be observed. A persistent and consistent intention, maintained with patient but focussed power, usually achieves correlated events in our 4-D frame of experience. The Level One model provides a mechanism whereby such correlations might be qualitatively studied.

**19. A Link to Astrology, Vivaxis and Feng Shui:** When an entity is born into the physical domain at a particular point in space-time, all the relative positions of the various planetary and celestial bodies are precisely set. This specific map of physical substance in space-time has a conjugate map of substance in the frequency domain via the Fourier Transform process. Likewise, the being enters life with a specific signature located mainly in a well-defined region of the frequency domain (etheric domain). Some type of local magnetic polarization can be expected to occur in the etheric domain when "life" (entrance of major spirit forces into the fetus at birth) for this entity begins. I would like to define that unique polarization field in the frequency domain as the individual's <u>vivaxis</u>, which remains at that location while the individual's physical body grows and moves from place to place in space. The companion etheric body also grows and shifts its dominance from one region of the frequency domain to another. It is the various magnetoelectric radiations from the various planetary etheric counterparts configured in the frequency domain map that interact with the magnetic aspects of the entity's etheric body in the frequency domain so as to exert some subtle-level effects on the individual. Thus, astrological forces are <u>not</u> space-time forces but are frequency-domain forces.

Feng Shui is based on the idea that subtle energies, in the form of Chi, can be influenced and directed by nature and its various elements, by the placement of objects of various shapes and colors in different configurations, by sound and by the human mind. The Level One model allows a natural rationalization of these aspects of Feng Shui via the direct space/inverse space relationship. For any particular shape placed in a room, the Fourier Transform provides its contribution to the overall intensity map in wavenumber space for the room. Changing the object's size, orientation or position in the room changes the details of the intensity map for the room. Adding other objects to the room alters this map by superposition-type constructive/destructive interference. This type of effect can be seen both in Fig. 2.18 as one adds more circular holes to the plate and in Fig. 2.A.3 in the Appendix as one changes the geometry of the slit family. The solid triangle shown on the front cover of this book yields an inverse space pattern with 6-fold arms extending towards infinite frequency. The intensity profile along one of these arms in this domain falls off continuously, without any discontinuities, as one goes to higher frequencies. Thus, one can perhaps look at these arms as some type of energy conduits from the higher subtle domains to the lower frequency regions and, from there, to any humans located in the room.

**20. A link to the Inflationary Cosmology Model:** One of the drawbacks of the standard "Big Bang" model for universe formation is that it doesn't fit with the kinetics of agglomeration of physical matter to form galaxies, stars, planets, etc. Standard physical processes are far too slow to account for the rate of formation of these celestial structures so some other mechanism must be invoked to account for their presence. A decade or so ago, Alan Guth of MIT modified the standard Big Bang cosmology by invoking an early "inflationary" period in order to eliminate magnetic monopoles. The inflation , which was proposed to occur in the time interval $10^{-35}$ - $10^{-33}$ seconds after initiation, and at speeds much greater than the speed of physical light, expanded space enormously (without violating relativity theory) and produced causally disconnected regions in space. After the inflation period, the expansion was slow compared to the light velocity. Two of the successes of the inflationary model were that it allowed space to be isotropic and it allowed speedy seeding (nucleation) of physical matter clumps into stars, galaxies, etc. Recent observations by the Cobe satellite of our early universe, at only ~300,000 years of age, provided experimental evidence for the seedlings needed for galaxy formation. Even at that early age, the physical universe had already departed from a homogeneous matter distribution and was providing evidence of "clumpiness".

From the Level One model, a Big Bang scenario would have the nodal network system develop in infinitesimal time ( much less than $10^{-35}$ seconds) and the etheric (magnetic) matter agglomerating into clumpy patterns in the frequency domain at very small times as measured by using physical domain referents (less than $10^{-35}$ - $10^{-33}$ seconds). Since this magnetic substance can move at velocities up to ~$10^{10}c$, it produces the precursor magnetic substance map in the frequency domain which, via deltron coupling, seeds the clumping tendencies for the electric substance map in the space-time domain. Although one tends to adopt the physical reference frame as the origin of events about which substance in all the other domains adjust, this is exactly backwards. Action occurs first in the subtle domains and propagates sequentially into the physical domain which adjusts towards an equilibrium force balance.

# Closing Comment

The Level One model is largely an energy band model, like the conventional physics model, rather than a consciousness model, like the direct experience models; however, the modal networks portion of the model integrates consciousness into the overall picture because it is through these structural elements that consciousness flows to generate both energies and substance. It was designed this way in order to serve as a bridge from the familiar to the strongly unfamiliar across which conventional scientists might venture. Their expertise is sorely needed in the exploration of the new terrain, because the model presented here is definitely incomplete. However, I feel that it is a useful model in that it will help us to go the next step in experimentation and theory whereby we will be able to more clearly define the higher dimensional nature of our universe and ourselves.

The proposal, here, of magnetic particles travelling faster than the speed of light accommodates the combined constraints of special relativity theory and the quantum facts utilized in Bell's theorem. Since this showed that there must be something happening faster than the speed of light, Bell postulated the existence of a deeper level to nature than our familiar four-space universe. The Level One model qualitatively expresses a rich structure of the vacuum which fulfills Bell's requirement.

The atomic picture proposed here is that of a cosmic atom containing physical, etheric, emotional, mental and spiritual parts. Our physical senses and our instrumentation, based upon designs consonant with the physical senses, have revealed a great deal of self-consistent information about the physical aspects of the cosmic atom. Experimental testing of the higher dimensional aspects of the atom awaits the invention of instrumentation consonant with latent human sensory capacities (see chapter 4). Although all the higher dimensional levels are equally important in the overall picture, the physical/etheric interface is the one most likely to reveal its secrets to focussed attention at this time. From a language/communication point of view, the glossary lays out a useful temporary nomenclature for subtle substances and subtle radiations.

# References

1. D. Griffiths, "Introduction to Elementary Particles", (John Wiley & Sons, Inc., New York, 1987).

2. Paul Davies, "Superforce, The Search For A Grand Unified Theory of Nature", (Simon & Schuster, Inc., New York, 1984).

3. J. Horgan, Particle Metaphysics, Scientific American, Feb. 1994, p. 97.

4. P.C.W. Davies and J. Brown, Eds. "Superstrings, A Theory of Everything?" (Cambridge University Press, Cambridge, 1988).

5. I.J.R. Aitchison and A.J.G. Hey, "Gauge Theories in Particle Physics", (Adam Hilger Ltd., Bristol, 1982) p. 11.

6. P.W. Milonni, "The Quantum Vacuum", (Academic Press, Inc., New York, 1994) p. 310.

7. C. Misner, K. Thorne and J. Wheeler, "Gravitation", (W.H. Freeman and Co., San Francisco, 1970) Ch. 43, 44.

8. L. Abbott, The Mystery of the Cosmological Constant, Scientific American, August (1993) p. 106.

9. M. Kaku, "Hyperspace", (Oxford University Press, New York, 1994).

10  a.A. Shearer, "Effortless Being", (Mandala, Unwin Paperbacks, London, 1989) p. 9.
    b.Swami Savitripria, "Psychology of Mystical Awakening", (New Life Books, Sunnyvale, CA, 1991).

11. A. Besant and C.W. Leadbeater, "Occult Chemistry", (Theosophical Publishing House, Madras, 1908 (lst Ed.); London, 1919 (2nd Ed.); Madras, 1951 (3rd Ed.)).

12. S.M. Phillips, "Extra-Sensory Perception of Quarks", (The Theosophical Publishing House, Madras, 1980).

13. R. McCraty, M. Atkinson and W.A. Tiller, New Electrophysiological Correlates Associated with Intentional Heart Focus, Subtle Energies, 4 (1995) 251.

14. D.L. Childre, "Self Empowerment", (Planetary Publications, Boulder Creek, CA, 1992).

15. S. Paddison, "The Hidden Power of The Heart" (Planetary Publications, Boulder Creek, CA, 1992).

16. W.A. Tiller, The Simulator and The Being, Phoenix: New Directions in The Study of Man, 1 (1977) No. 1.

17. D.R. Herriot, Applications of Laser Light, Scientific American, Inc., (1968).

18. W.A. Tiller, A Lattice Model of Space, Phoenix, 2 (1978) 27.

19. O.M. Bilaniuk, V.k. Deshpande and E.C. G. Sudarshan, Am. J. Phys. <u>30</u> (1962) 718.

20. Y.P. Terletskii, "Paradoxes in The Theory of Relativity", (Plenum Press, New York, 1968).

21. D. Bohm, "Quantum Theory" (Prentice-Hall, Engleword Cliffs, N.J. 1951).

22 R. M. Eisberg, "Fundamentals of Modern Physics", (John Wiley &Sons, Inc., New York, 1961).

23. G. Harburn, C.A. Taylor and T.R. Welberry, "Atlas of Optical Transforms", (Cornell University Press, Ithaca, N.Y., 1975).

24. R.V. Churchill, "Operational Mathematics", (McGraw-Hill, New York, 1958).

25. J.S. Bell, <u>On The Einstein Podolsky Rosen Paradox</u>, Physics <u>1</u> (1964) 195.

26. E.A. Abbott, "Flatland: A Romance of Many Dimensions", (Dover Publications, New York, 1952 (6th Ed., Revised)).

## APPENDIX 2.1

## The Fourier Transform

At the time of Napoleon, one of the greatest French scientists was J.B.J. Fourier who made many important theoretical discoveries concerning, among other things, the transfer of heat. Fourier was the first to devise a mathematical method for expressing any periodic mathematical function, or any non-periodic mathematical function restricted to a body of regular shape, as a sum of harmonic waves. Thus, the superposition of a complete set of such waves can be used to represent the form of any object. Fourier's theorem states that, in one dimension, x, any periodic function, $f(x)$, can be expressed as

$$f(x) = b_0 + b_1 \cos\left(\frac{2\pi x}{\lambda} + \theta_1\right) + b_2 \cos\left(\frac{2\pi x}{\lambda/2} + \theta_2\right) + \ldots + \tag{1a}$$

$$+ b_n \cos\left(\frac{2\pi x}{\lambda/n} + \theta_n\right) + \ldots = \sum_{n=0}^{\infty} b_n \cos\left(\frac{2\pi x}{\lambda/n} + \theta_n\right)$$

$$= \sum_{n=0}^{\infty} b_n \left[\cos\theta_n \cos\left(\frac{2\pi nx}{\lambda}\right) - \sin\theta_n \sin\left(\frac{2\pi nx}{\lambda}\right)\right] \tag{1b}$$

$$= \Re \sum_{n=0}^{\infty} b_n \exp\left(i\frac{2\pi nx}{\lambda} + \theta_n\right) = \Re \sum_{n=0}^{\infty} a_n e^{inkx} \tag{1c}$$

Here, the harmonic waves (cosines or sines) have wavelengths which are integral submultiples of the fundamental wavelength, $\lambda$, the $\theta_n$ are the phase angles of the different waves relative to the origin, $x=0$, and the $b_n$ are the amplitudes for the various waves. Equations 1b and 1c are just different ways of representing eq 1a with $\Re$ meaning the mathematically real part of the exponential expression with $i = \sqrt{-1}$. In the final expression, $a_n = -b_n e^{i\theta_n}$ is now a mathematically complex quantity. Fourier was able to show that, via his procedure, all of the $a_m$ are determined and given by

$$a_m = \frac{1}{\lambda} \int_{-\lambda/2}^{\lambda/2} f(x)e^{-i\frac{2\pi m}{\lambda}x}dx; \quad m=0,1,2,...,n \tag{2}$$

where the integral is over a single wavelength.

We can think of the Fourier Transform coefficients $a_n$ as a function $a(n)$ of $n$. Although $a(n)$ exists for only integral values of $n$, we can define it for all values of $n$ but with zero amplitude for all non-integral values. Information about the wavelength, $\lambda$, can be included in eq 2 by using the variable $k=2\pi n/\lambda$ rather than $n$ and this is usually referred to as the wavenumber that corresponds to a harmonic of wavelength $\lambda/n$. Thus, eq 2 becomes

$$a(k) = \frac{1}{\lambda} \int_{-\lambda/2}^{\lambda/2} f(x)e^{-ikx}dx \tag{3}$$

Since $k$ is proportional to $1/\lambda$, the space whose coordinates are measured by $k$ is called reciprocal space as contrasted to direct space with coordinates measured by $x$. The extension of this mathematics to higher dimensions than one is straightforward.

To illustrate how the foregoing procedure leads to the <u>Fourier Transform</u>, we consider how $f(x)$ and its conjugate, $a(k)$, change as we allow the wavelength, $\lambda$ to increase to infinity. This change is illustrated in Fig 2.A.1, where we see that the periodic array of this shape in direct space is represented by a set of spikes in reciprocal space. As $\lambda$ increases, the spikes approach one another but the envelope of the tips of the spikes remains invariant. In the limit of $\lambda \rightarrow \infty$, the spikes are infinitesimly close to one another, and the function $a(k)$ has just become the envelope which we call the Fourier Transform (FT). In mathematical terms, the Fourier Transform of a function $f(x)$ is

$$a(k) = \int_{-\infty}^{\infty} f(x)e^{-ikx}dx \tag{4}$$

so $a(k)$ is the continuous function representation in frequency space of the specific shape $f(x)$ in direct space. As such, they are conjugates of each other and represent two aspects of the whole. For a variety of different planar aperture patterns in direct space, their FT conjugates are shown in Fig 2.A.2. In Fig 2.A.3,

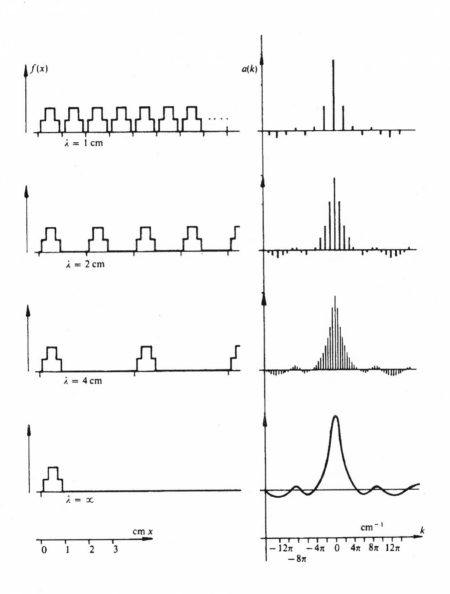

**Fig. 2.A.1** Illustrating the progression from Fourier series to transform

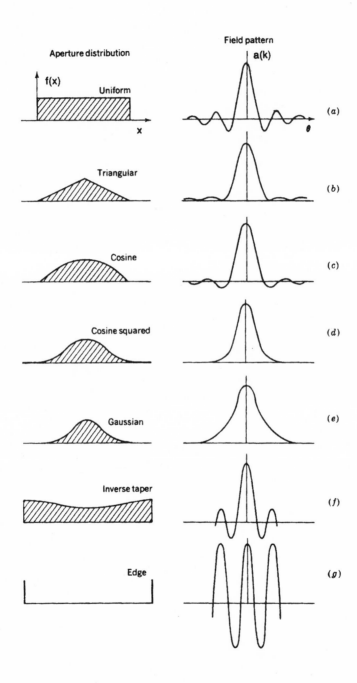

**Fig. 2.A.2** Seven different antenna aperture distributions with associated FourierTransforms.

DIRECT SPACE SHAPE          RECIPROCAL SPACE SHAPE

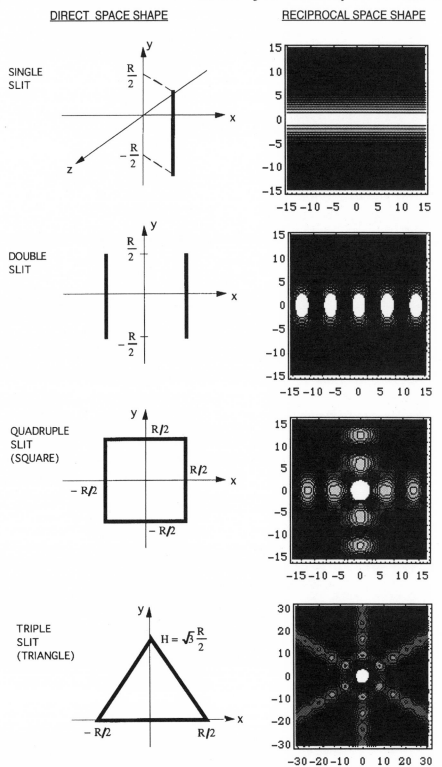

**Fig. 2.A.3** Conjugate shape patterns in the spectral domain corresponding to four direct space slit patterns.

the direct space/reciprocal space conjugate shapes are given for four physical slit configurations.

   Some discussion of Chapter 4 (Appendix 1) indicates that Karl Pribram has already pointed out that the human brain converts optical information from the space-time domain to the frequency domain prior to physical level information processing. It is the Fourier Transform (Gabor Transform) that is the mathematical mapping vehicle from one domain to the other. In this chapter, I am proposing that these frequency domain processing procedures of the brain be extended beyond the physical cognition limits to the various subtle levels so that cognition of subtle level radiant information patterns can occur via these extensions. From the Fourier Transform mathematical formalism, it is immediately obvious that, for any subtle level radiant signal that would be travelling at velocities, $v'$, much greater than $c$, similar information conversion processes can obtain by choosing $v'/v \sim$ constant. Thus, the subtle domain information can be stored in the Bio-Mind at successively higher octaves in inverse space or wave number space than the physical level storage. The energy band picture of Fig. 2.19 illustrates an aspect of this concept. A simple replacement of $-1$ for $+1$ converts a positive energy domain to a negative energy domain. It is interesting to note that if one takes the amplitude, $a(k)$ from equation 4 and looks at its square which is proportional to the intensity of substance( or its energy) in the frequency domain, the result is a negative quantity. The standard procedure to avoid such an unphysical result is to take the product of $a(k)$ and its complex conjugate. Here, we want the negative sign.

# CHAPTER
# 3

## BODY RADIATIONS, ANTENNAS AND AURAS

*Our bodies, sculpted from dense matter,*
*Are filled with light -- in such glorious forms*
*And colors and movement that one weeps*
*With joy at beholding such beauty.*

This chapter focusses mainly on radiations, physical and subtle, and on the information and energy content inherent in a field of such radiation. We also ask "how does patterning of this radiation come about and does it have any relationship to what has been called the human aura?" We also want to see how some of the various major structural elements of the body interact with incoming radiation signals to access subtle information and how the internal radiation fields of the body interact with the chemical fields of the body. We will thus obtain a better picture of how energy medicine differs from and complements chemical medicine. Finally, we want to see how the development of an internal "dowsing" type of body reaction opens an access window to information at the subtle levels leading to enhanced intuition in both our daily lives and in medical diagnostics. The best place to start for unravelling this overall picture is with the origins of electromagnetic radiations from atoms, molecules, cells, etc.

## Electromagnetic Energy Emission and Absorption

In order to provide a slight background perspective on radiators, absorbers and radiation, the simplest place to begin is at the level of the atom. A simple model of the atom is that of a nucleus of positive charge surrounded by a number of electrons, each of them being in well-defined but different energy states. Other possible states for these electrons exist but, in the atom's equilibrium state, they are not filled by electrons. In Fig. 3.1, some of these energy levels are schematically illustrated using the simple Bohr model for a hydrogen atom[1]. If we stimulate this atom (with a photon, for example), we can cause an electron to shift to one of these unfilled or excited levels. Eventually, the electron will shift back to its equilibrium level. This event is associated with the emission of electromagnetic (EM) radiation--generally a photon in the ultraviolet or visible range of the EM spectrum.

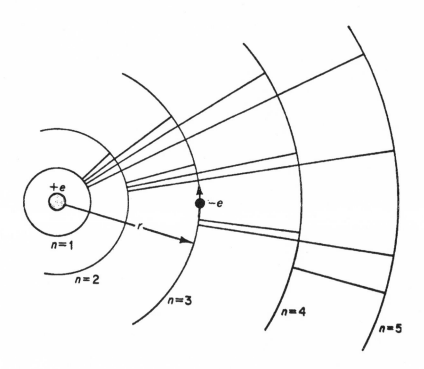

**Fig. 3.1** Circular orbits of the hydrogen atom showing the electron in the n=3 orbit plus possible energy transitions between orbits.

A useful model for simulating the electron level change is the "classical harmonic oscillator" model. Here, we say that a charged particle of mass M is bound to a position of equilibrium with a spring by a force of interaction, G, (known as the force constant of the spring) as illustrated in Fig. 3.2. When the particle (electron) is displaced from its equilibrium position and released, it is found to oscillate around this equilibrium position at its resonant frequency, $v_o$, given by the simple equation

$$v_o = \frac{(G/M)^{1/2}}{2\pi}$$

while the amplitude of oscillation decays with time because of the frictional damping in the spring; i.e., it acts something like the familiar tuning fork. For the charged particle, the initial displacement may be caused by an exchange of energy with another atom or by the absorption of some EM energy.

This provides us with a very simple model of a light source[1]. The vibrating charge will create an EM field oscillating in a narrow frequency range, $\Delta v$, about this resonant frequency as illustrated in Fig. 3.3. Here, $I(v)$ is the intensity of the radiation from the source at frequency $v$ (the intensity is proportional to the square of the wave amplitude so it is the power inherent in the wave at frequency $v$). In general, a given type of atom will exhibit a spectrum of such frequencies; i.e., a series of such lines at different frequencies, where each line is associated with a particular electron transition from one orbital energy level to another.

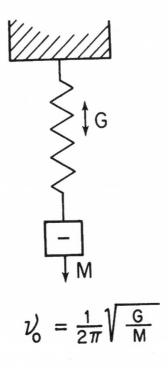

$$v_0 = \frac{1}{2\pi}\sqrt{\frac{G}{M}}$$

**Fig. 3.2** Weight on a spring representation of a simple harmonic oscillator of resonant frequency, $v_0$.

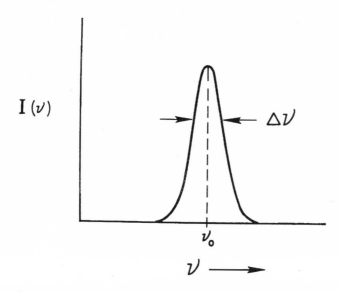

**Fig. 3.3**  Intensity versus frequency plot for a single electron transition.

If we consider groups of identical atoms, the foregoing describes the situation so long as the atoms are far apart and isolated from each other. They each give identical spectra with lines of the type illustrated in Fig. 3.3. If we allow two of these atoms to come closer together so that they begin to exert an EM force on each other, they become coupled so that G in Fig. 3.2 is no longer a constant; i.e., the motion of one exerts a force on the other and vise versa. For these two atoms, their resonant frequency changes from a single value, $v_o$, to two values, $v_1$, and $v_2$ which depend upon their distance of separation as illustrated in Fig. 3.4. These values of $v_1$ and $v_2$ diverge from each other as the two atoms become closer and closer together and interact with a tighter coupling force. We complete the picture by bringing more and more of these atoms close together so that they interact strongly with each other. This, in turn, produces a whole range of resonant frequencies which cause the single resonant line of Fig. 3.3 to broaden into the resonant band of Fig. 3.4. Each resonant line in the spectrum of an isolated set of identical atoms (gas phase) broadens into a unique resonant band of states when they are brought close together (condensed phase--liquid or solid). In such a situation, $I(v)$ is given by a curve like that illustrated in Fig. 3. 5 rather than that given in Fig. 3.3.

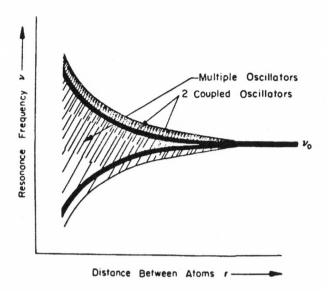

**Fig. 3.4**  The effect of oscillator coupling on the broadening of their frequency band.  The example used here is that of a gas of varying density, each molecule or atom representing an individual oscillator. At low gas densities (large separation distances, r) coupling is negligible and all atoms radiate (or absorb) within the same narrow frequency interval.  As two atoms are brought closer together, they form a coupled resonant system at two diverging frequencies (black regions). When more atoms are added to the coupled system, additional frequencies appear, favoring the upper region (indicated by the degree of shading).  The frequency distribution at the smallest r represents the density of states for a solid, liquid or a very dense gas.

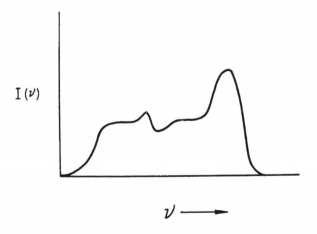

**Fig. 3.5**  Intensity versus frequency plot for an idealized physical solid (many atoms interacting).

There are a variety of important characterisitcs associated with these electronic vibrational states of matter. First, every atom, molecule, cell, gland, animal, etc., has at least one resonant EM energy band of some bandwidth, $\Delta v$, at which it will both emit energy (EM radiation) in some pattern and also absorb it; i.e., they are both the same for a particular system. Thus, each system is in communication with the outside world (transmitting and receiving) via its resonant frequency spectrum. Second, this particular spectrum is like a unique fingerprint via which one can identify the specific material.

If we look carefully at the human body with EM detectors, we will find EM energy radiated from the body not only as a result of electron orbit changes but also as a result of physical rotations and vibrations of the molecules, flexure of cell membranes, pulsation of organs and body movement in general. In time, we may even come to detect natural $\gamma$-ray and x-ray emission from the body. Each of these processes generates EM radiation in a different frequency range as indicated in Table 3.1. From conventional science we know that the movement of any electric charge involves the emission of electromagnetic waves. Thus, the movement of electrons in atoms leads to emission in the ultraviolet, the movement of atoms in molecules creates emission in the infrared, the movement of molecules in cell membranes leads to emission in the microwave region while the movements of cells in muscles and body organs generates emission in the radar and radio frequency ranges. The larger is the entity causing electric charge displacement, the lower is the frequency of the EM emission.

**Table 3.1** BODY EM RADIATIONS

| MATERIAL SCALE | | FREQUENCY, EM EMISSION RANGE |
|---|---|---|
| Atom-electron | $\rightarrow$ | Ultra-violet |
| Molecule rotation | $\rightarrow$ | Infra-red |
| Membrane flexure | $\rightarrow$ | Microwave |
| Organ pulsation | $\rightarrow$ | Radio frequency ($10^4$-$10^6$ Hz) |
| Body movement | $\rightarrow$ | Low frequency (1-$10^3$ Hz) |

Besides the foregoing, an additional indirect mechanism exists for emissions from the body. Here, the primary stimulus comes from the sound spectrum (also called the phonon spectrum) of the body's cells, muscles and organs associated with their relative motion. The sonic resonances for a particular body part occur in a significantly lower frequency range (by a factor of ~1 million to ~10 million) than its EM resonances. This is so because the sound wave velocity through tissues is about 1 million times slower than the EM wave velocity. Because collagen, tissue and bone are all piezoelectric materials, the small stresses produced by the sound wave patterns generate associated electric field patterns and thus emit EM wave patterns. Thus, movements of a particular body part give rise to two emitted EM wave pattern signatures. One signature occurs at very high frequency due to direct ion movement while the other occurs at low to intermediate frequencies via electrically neutral mass movement coupled to the piezoelectric response mechanism. For example, the indirect sound pattern to EM wave pattern resonances for body cells are in the 1 million to 10 million Hertz range while the direct EM emission from these same body cells occurs in a frequency range about a million times higher. For any type of wave, a fundamental relationship exists between the wave velocity, v, the wave frequency, $\nu$, and the wave length, $\lambda$, i.e.,

$$v = \lambda\nu$$

Thus, for a given sized body part (~ $\lambda$), if v changes then so does $\nu$.

From the foregoing, the body can be thought of as a type of transmitting/receiving antenna. Incoming EM waves of a particular frequency range will stimulate movement of the appropriately sized body part, either by direct EM-coupling or by piezoelectric transduction to sound-coupling. If there is no correlation between the movements of the various sized body parts, there is no integration in the system and the out-flowing radiation has no pattern. It is called "white" noise. The greater is the degree of correlated movements between different sized body parts, the more pattern-like is the total emission, the greater is its information content and the more integrated is the system. It is to standard EM antenna theory that we look next in order to better understand the informational aspects of the EM patterns. However, before doing so, it is important to recognize that every level of substance, physical and subtle, will generate characteristic radiations in much the same way as already described for EM radiation. From the Level One model discussed in Chapter 2, and from the subtle energy phenomena touched on in Chapter 1, we can expect some radiation intensity spectrum, $I(\nu)$, like that illustrated in Fig. 3.6, to be present in nature. Here, P, E, A, $M_1$, $M_2$, $M_3$ and S stand for physical, etheric, astral (emotional), instinctive mind, intellectual mind, spiritual mind and spirit, respectively. Each of these domains is unique and each may contain several key radiations rather than just one. Thus, Fig. 3.6 is just a metaphor, consistent with Fig. 3.5, to illustrate the overall concept. These spectral distribution curves should really be plotted on individual axes, as indicated via the insert, since we are discussing different <u>kinds</u> of radiations for each level of substance. However, for pedagogical purposes, there is value in having them represented on one axis. It is from this diagram that we may see the basic radiation components that comprise the human aura. As discussed in Chapter 2, as we proceed to higher and higher dimensionality of the subtle domain, the signal propogation velocity increases in jumps of ~ $10^{10}$; thus, for constant wavelengh, $\lambda$, at each of these levels, the previous equation shows us that a constant ratio $v/v$ is required for these waves so that $v$ must also increase in jumps of ~$10^{10}$. We interpret this as jumping to higher and higher frequency bands as we proceed through the subtle domains.

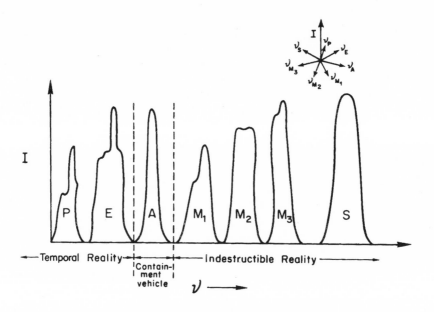

**Fig. 3.6**  Schematic spectral distribution curve illustrating, along one coordinate, relative radiation characteristics for the seven levels of substance discriminated in the Level One model.

# Antennas

**Simple Antennas:**  We are all familiar with the television receiving antennas perched on the top of most houses. Transmitting antennas are very similar. They both consist of just a few long strips of metal, perpendicular to the main shaft, designed to radiate (or receive) EM energy as effectively as possible. To begin to understand what is actually happening here, let us consider a radio frequency generator connected to a transmission line of closely spaced wires and of length equal to a quarter of a wavelength, $\lambda/4$, of the EM signal produced by the generator (see Fig. 3.7a)[2].

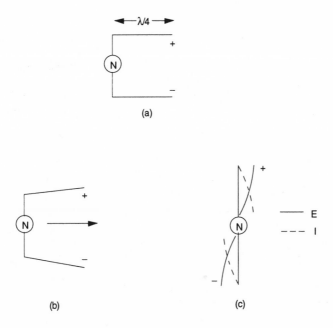

**Fig. 3.7** Evolution of a half-wave dipole antenna from a transmission line, (a) generator connected to a quarter-wave transmission line, (b) ends of transmission line partly opened and (c) transmission line completely opened forming a half-wave antenna.

In this open-circuited transmission line, the electrical current amplitude is zero at the open ends while the voltage is a maximum, and perfect wave reflection occurs so that the current and voltage profiles in one wire are standing waves and are exactly opposite to those in the other wire. Since the transmission line wires are physically close to each other and parallel to each other, each creates a field that is cancelled by the other so there is no radiation of energy. However, if the ends of the transmission line are opened outwards as in Fig. 3.7b, there will be the radiation of some energy as the wire separation approaches or exceeds the wavelength, $\lambda$. In Fig. 3.7c, the transmission line is now opened maximally so that the two wires are in a straight line. Now there will be maximum radiation of energy since the fields in the two wires are no longer opposing each other. While one wire is positive, the other wire is negative so that the two fields are now aiding each other yielding maximum energy transmission. This represents the fundamental half-wave or dipole antenna.

The pattern of radiation from an antenna can be modified to suit the type of service desired. The actual EM radiation pattern of the fundamental half-wave dipole is that of a toroid or doughnut shape with the antenna aligned centrally along the axis of the doughnut (see Fig. 3.8a).

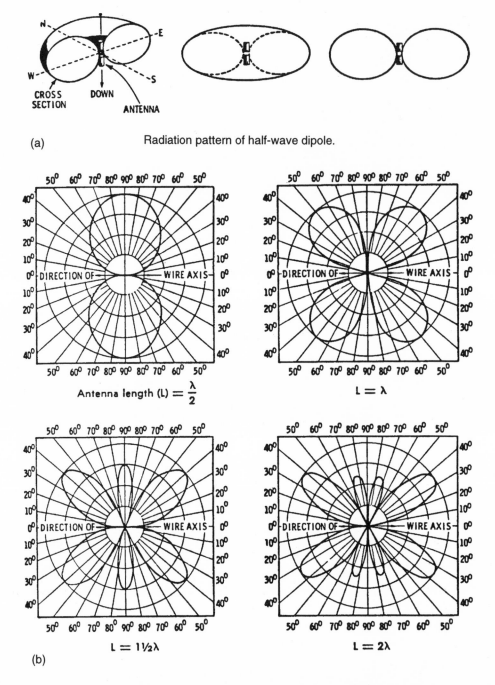

(a)  Radiation pattern of half-wave dipole.

Antenna length (L) = $\frac{\lambda}{2}$

L = λ

L = 1½λ

L = 2λ

(b)

**Fig. 3.8** (a) Toroidal radiation pattern of a centrally aligned half-wave dipole and (b) typical radiation pattern sections for the same dipole antenna (now horizontally aligned) at four different frequencies of operation.

This field intensity falls off with distance away from the antenna. If we increase the frequency of the signal to the antenna, we initially lose the standing wave pattern of voltage and current illustrated in Fig. 3.8a. However, at double, triple and quadruple, etc., the initial frequency, we again have an antenna length, L, that is an integral number of half wavelengths, $\lambda/2$, of the EM signal. What changes in this case is the directivity of the antenna patterns as illustrated in Fig. 3.8b for L = $\lambda/2$, $\lambda$, $3\lambda/2$, and $2\lambda$. In general, the higher the signal frequency for a fixed L, the more loops will there be in the antenna pattern. Each loop direction will be a direction of major receptivity or transmissivity of the antenna while the directions between the loops will be null receptivity/transmissivity directions.

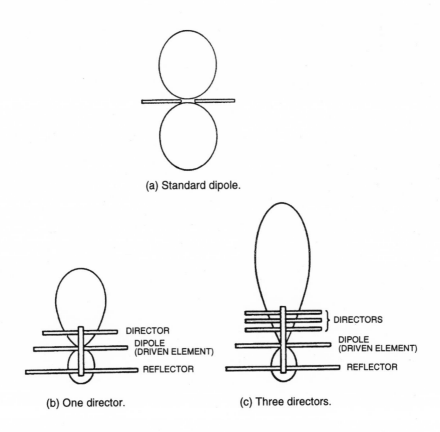

(a) Standard dipole.

(b) One director.

(c) Three directors.

**Fig. 3.9** Illustrating the effect of adding reflector and director elements on the antenna pattern, (a) standard dipole, (b) one reflector and one director and (c) one reflector and three directors.

The gain of an antenna means the amount of increase in signal voltage induced in the driven element of the antenna in question relative to the voltage induced in a reference dipole placed in the same location and with the same resonant frequency. The gain of an ordinary dipole can be increased by the addition of additional elements (called parasitic elements) either in front of or behind the driven dipole element. These parasitic elements are called directors or reflectors depending on their length and position with respect to the driven element. Although they are not connected directly to the driven dipole element, signal energy induced in them is coupled to the dipole through induction and radiation fields. In general, any antenna having one active element and two or more parasitic elements is known as a Yagi antenna and it is one of the highest gain antennas yet developed. Fig. 3.9 illustrates the effect of additional directors on the antenna response pattern.

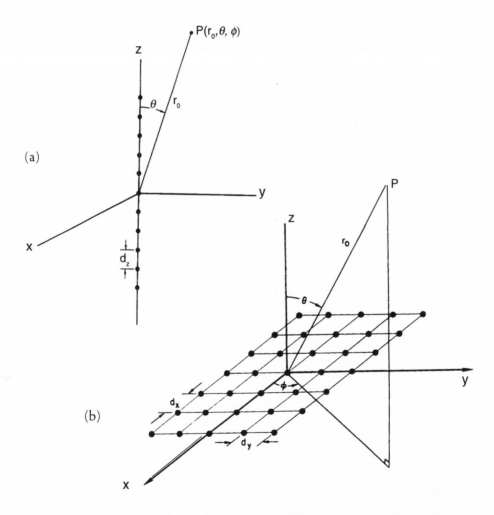

**Fig. 3.10.** Two array geometries for multiple antenna elements superposing their signals at point P, (a) a linear array and (b) a planar array.

**Antenna Arrays:** When one sets up a number of identical antennas in some geometrical pattern and controls the relative phase (or timing) of their signal transmission/reception, the actual signal strength at some position (x, y, z, t) in space-time is given by the superposition of the signals from each of the antennas in the array. This is illustrated for a linear array in Fig. 3.10a and for a planar array in Fig. 3.10b. One could also go a step further and consider a volume array which would be a 3-D lattice of antenna elements. Just by controlling the spacing, number of elements and the type of element, one is able to produce very different antenna patterns. In Fig. 3.11, we see the effect of using point sources of equal amplitude leading to a broadside array pattern and an end-fire array pattern from two arrays of almost equal length[3]. For the broadside array, the pattern is disk-shaped with a small beam width in the plane of the figure, but the beam width is 360° in the plane perpendicular to the page.

On the other hand, the pattern of the end-fire array is cigar-shaped both in the plane of the page and in the plane perpendicular to the page. If the antenna type is changed to the dipole-type, then superposition leads to an interferometer type of field pattern within the overall antenna pattern. This is illustrated in Fig. 3.12a for a simple two-element interferometer. In Fig. 3.12b, a two element interferometer using 40-point source end-fire arrays is illustrated. In radioastronomy applications, an interferometer is used for receiving radiation from celestial sources as they drift across the sky through the antenna pattern. The detection and location of these sources are facilitated by the small beam widths of the individual lobes in the overall antenna pattern. In the broadside array of Fig. 3.11, all the sources are in phase with each other ($\delta = 0$) while, in the end-fire array, the progressive fixed phase difference between elements is proportional to their separation distance, d. Actually, the beam maximum can be tilted in any arbitrary direction, $\theta$, relative to the array axis by suitable adjustment of the fixed phase difference between adjacent elements in the linear array. Thus, by time-dependent controlling of the phase difference, $\delta(t)$, between elements of the array, the beam angle can be adjusted or <u>scanned</u> without moving the antenna. Such arrays are called <u>scanning</u> arrays and the moveable beam pattern may be as illustrated in Fig. 3.13a for a linear array. Planar arrays can be utilized to generate a moving pencil beam with some alteration of beam shape with scan position as illustrated in Fib. 3.13b. Electronically steered radar utilizes both the interferometric and scanning capacities of a multielement antenna array (100 to 1000 elements) to detect and simultaneously track many objects hundreds of miles away that are moving at many hundreds of miles per hour even when the objects are quite small[4]. A wide variety of antenna elements from monopole and dipole to spiral and helical and from metallic to dielectric provide an amazing spectrum of waveforms and frequencies that can be generated or responded to.

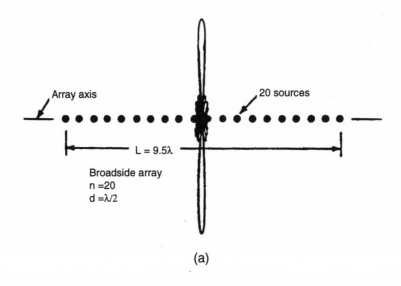

Array axis

20 sources

L = 9.5λ

Broadside array
n =20
d =λ/2

(a)

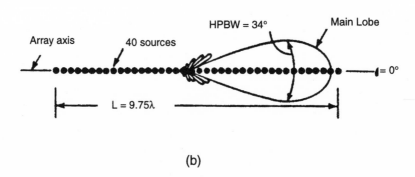

Array axis

40 sources

HPBW = 34°

Main Lobe

= 0°

L = 9.75λ

(b)

**Fig. 3.11** Broadside array field pattern from 20 point sources of equal amplitude and with λ/2 spacing and (b) end-fire array field pattern from 40 point sources of equal amplitude and λ/4 spacing.

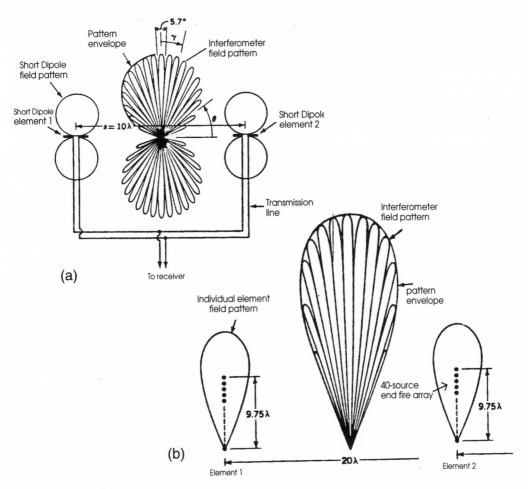

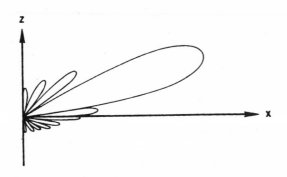

**Fig. 3.12** Interferometer field patterns for (a) a simple 2-element interferometer using short dipoles spaced 10λ apart and (b) two 40-point source end-fire arrays spaced 20λ apart.

**Fig. 3.13(a)** Scanning beam from a linear array

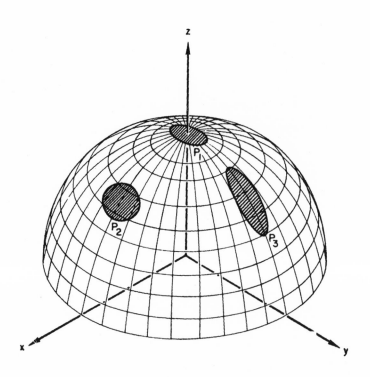

**Fig. 3.13(b)** Beam shape versus scan position for a pencil beam from a planar array.

## Antennas in The Biological Kingdom

Every one of the physical senses in humans probably functions via a special sensor array. This is certainly true of sight where the rods and cones of the eyes respond to EM radiation in the optical frequency region. More will be said about this antenna system in Chapter 4. Animals and even insects are endowed with such antenna arrays. Callahan[5] has provided us with a beautiful description of such arrays in moths. After he built an infared detector based on a crystal of the pyroelectric material triglycine sulphate, he

116

discovered that insects emit a coded infrared signal which contained a unique navigational message. He showed that the trichodea sensilla of the Cabbage Looper and the Corn Earthworm Moth are arranged in a log-periodic sizing so that they would function well as log-periodic antennae (wide frequency band capability). He also pointed out that a conical type of antenna was to be found on the Florida Scarab Mite and that thin tapered helical-type dielectric sensilla are found to serve as antennas on many species of wasp. It seems to be a reasonable assumption that all living organisms utilize antenna arrays of varying degrees of complexity as a major portion of their information gathering and sending apparatus.

Returning to the human, we have learned that EM antennas can take many forms. All that is necessary is a source of EM energy and a waveguide whose dimensions are first smaller and then finally larger than a half-period of the travelling wave. For a receiving antenna, we just need to replace the energy source by a detector/amplifier system. The human body has this capacity in the autonomic nervous system (ANS) as a signal carrier, via both the sympathetic and the parasympathetic branches, which influences secretion, smooth muscle response, blood vessel response, electrocardiogram, heart rate variability, respiration, etc. It also serves as an excellent waveguide via the myelin sheath surrounding each nerve axon to conduct a travelling wave to a multitude of end points just under the surface of the skin. This same marvellous nervous system functions also as a signal conductor in a detection mode of operation.

One set of antenna elements in this system are thought to be the acupuncture points (A.P.) of the body. Since these number in the thousands, they would provide an exquisitely rich array with capabilities exceeding the most advanced radar system available today. These sensitive points are coupled to the ANS via the fourteen known acupuncture meridians. Fig. 3.14 shows some acupuncture meridians (channels) and some acupuncture points of the body. Just to concretize the picture being painted here, we will sketch some of the details shortly; however, for the overall picture, the important things to know are that the human body's antenna system could function over a wide range of wavelengths and could produce a directed scanning beam of circularly polarized radiation (the wave is expected to have this type of polarization at launching because the myelin sheath appears to act as a helical waveguide--see Chapter 4).

It is now well known that an electrical resistance of about 50,000 ohms exists between any two A.P.'s while, over the same length of normal skin, the equivalent resistance is a factor of ~20 times higher. Most of this resistance is

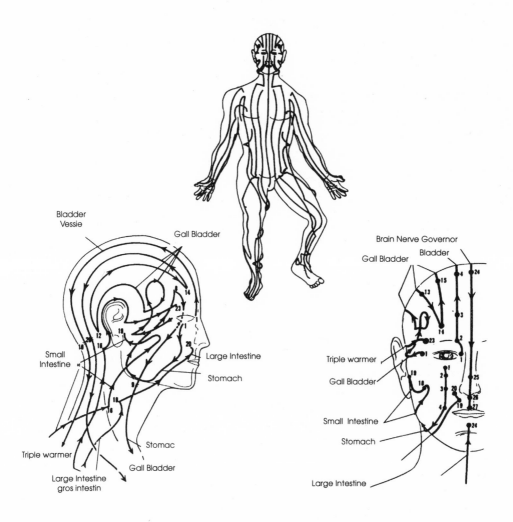

**Fig. 3.14** Some meridian circuitry and some acupuncture points in the body.

in the outer surface layer of the skin (called the stratum corneum--see Fig. 3.15). This A.P. resistivity changes strongly with hypnogogic state, increasing by a factor of ~2-3 during sleep[6a] and, in the case of emotional excitation, the points are observed to increase in area to the ~5 (millimeter)[2] range (as revealed by the area of high conductivity). It is very interesting that only slight histological (cellular) difference appears to exist between an A.P. and the surrounding skin even though the local resistance is reduced by a factor of 10. As Helms points out[6b], A.P.s are situated in surface depressions located along the cleavage planes between two or more muscles. It is located in a vertical column of loose connective tissue which is surrounded by the thick and dense connective tissue of the skin, itself not a good conductor. Placing small electrodes of different materials (different electron work function) on two A.P.s, a voltage difference is developed between the points of magnitude increasing as the electron work function difference increases. For a nickel/silver electrode pair, the potential difference is ~50 millivolts while the current developed is ~1 to 10 microamperes. This current shrinks to almost zero between two skin points that are not A.P.s. Using a ganged-electrode technique, Becker, et al.[7] have provided conductance maps around several A.P.s and have observed small electrical potential variations along the meridian channels.

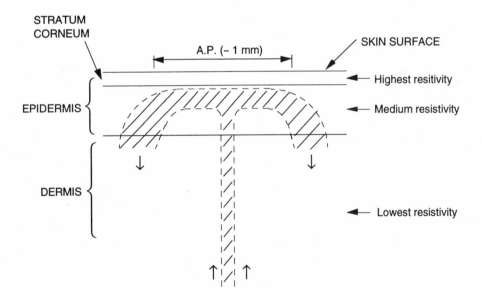

**Fig. 3.15** Schematic illustration of ion pumping along the meridian locus via chi-induced A(t)-field followed by fountain-like broadening of excess ions at the skin surface. This broadening of the high conductivity zone at the A.P. satisfies the conditions needed for antenna transmission/reception at the A.P.

When measuring the electrical resistance between symmetrical points on the left and right sides of the body, one often finds that the resistance is different in the forward direction (R) than when the electrodes are reversed (R'). When a person is healthy relative to the organs associated with that meridian, these two resistances will be the same (R=R'). However, if pathology is developing in one or more of these particular organs, R will be different than R' ($\Delta R=R-R'>0$). As the degree of pathological advancement increases, the magnitude of $\Delta R$ increases. This difference has been called the semiconductor effect[6a] which is the electrical correlate of the well-known heat response time difference between A.P.s when pathology is present[8].

It has also been noticed that, when a serious imbalance exists in the meridian circuitry, and as an acupuncture needle is placed in the appropriate point, a suction-like force holds the needle in place so that, if one tries to withdraw it, the skin pulls up around the needle and it is not easily withdrawn. However, after the needle has remained in the point for the proper length of time so as to bring about a temporary balance to the circuit, the needle may be withdrawn with no effort and the skin does not pull up around the needle. This suction force, which is probably due to an osmotic pressure difference, $\Delta P$, between the points, seems to be proportional to $\Delta R$. For the pathological condition, an electrostatic potential difference, $\Delta\phi$, is also noted between the points[9]. Because the connective tissues are thermoelectric[10], application of heat leads to electric current flow and associated electrical potential changes. Thus, the left side/right side imbalance of an A.P. reveals itself via $\Delta R$, $\Delta P$, $\Delta\phi$ and $\Delta K$ where $\Delta K$ is the thermal conductance difference for the two sides between the skin surface and the local nerve ending. At this point, it is useful to note that acupuncture-type treatments utilize any and all of the following stimulation methods: pressure, chemical heat (moxa), needles, electric current and laser light to alter $\Delta P$, $\Delta K$, $\Delta R$ and $\Delta\phi$. This stimulation is now known to generate the chemical, endorphines, in the blood stream which, in turn, generate the chemical, enkephalines, in the brain--all natural opiates of the body. Seratonin has been found to be one of the most important mediators for acupuncture analgesia in both the brain and the spinal cord. More recently, pain killing and analgesic effects have also been noted when a magnetic field is applied to an A.P. A D.C. magnetic field of strength > 500 Gauss was found to produce local analgesia and a mild magnetic field (~20 Gauss) applied continuously to a specific A.P. was observed to generate a meridian effect[11].

Using the equations of Chapter 1 and the insights of Chapter 2, my views of this antenna system are: (1) The primary structural elements of this antenna system are located at the etheric substance level rather than at the physical substance level in order to explain the lack of major histological difference between A.P.s and surrounding tissue. (2) Subtle energy wave flow along the etheric meridians yields a transduced flow of magnetic vector potential, A, waves along the physical locus of these meridian channels (sometimes nerve fibers).

(3) Such A-flow means an electric field, E, is generated along this channel which pumps ions along the channel and, if large enough, produces electrolytic dissociation of water ($H_2O \rightarrow H^+ + OH^-$) to greatly increase the ionic conductance of the channel[12] and increase the electrical conductivity of the A.P. at the skin surface (as is observed). (4) Because the surface of the skin blocks the continued outward passage of ions, they must fan outwards in a radial direction much like a fountain (see Fig. 3.15) and then work their way back into the sub-epidermal tissue while recombining ($H^+ + OH^- \rightarrow H_2O$) since they are no longer in the high field region. (5) The size of the charge fountain head is appreciable larger in diameter than the channel of charge feeding into the surface so the conditions needed for EM radiation emission and reception are fulfilled by this A.P. and (6) This charge pattern will certainly function as a monopole antenna with overtones of helical character depending upon the detailed shape of the fountain head.

This model allows the external EM and subtle energy environment to communicate with the internal physical and subtle substance of the body via a network of points on the surface of the body. At the EM level, one should be looking for information exchange in the millimeter range of the EM spectrum. At the etheric level, this network probably represents the "subtle nadi" of the ancient Hindu teachings[13a]. Even more subtle levels of energy and substance may be involved in this antenna structure. It should be pointed out that, if for some reason the flow of Chi in the etheric meridians becomes partially or completely blocked then, at the physical level, A decreases causing E to decrease so that electrolytic dissociation does not occur and the A.P. resistivity increases, etc. When one perturbs the A.P. by one means or another so that ion flow is restored at the physical level, this generates an increased value of A which reacts at the etheric level to unclog the meridian flow channel. With this kind of a picture, we can also begin to see why a D.C. magnet can influence A.P. behavior. With this general approach, one can also begin to rationalize small psychokinetic events such as triggering remote glowing of fluorescent tubes or remote movement of objects on a table. Even from just the EM level, phased radiation pulses from the A.P. antenna array could be built up to a sufficient magnitude to cause such effects. In Appendix 3.1, the topic of acupuncture, its strong connection to the nervous system and its general utility for treatment of both physical and psychological ailments in humans is expanded upon.

A second major body antenna system, that is undoubtedly connected to the A.P. and meridian system, is the endocrine/chakra system. In the physical body, the master glands that manufacture the major hormones and thus control all the chemical factories of the body are the endocrine glands. These are also the locations of the major spiritual centers of the body, called the seven major chakras, which function at the etheric and more subtle levels. Thus, we should think of the individual chakra-endocrine pairs as transducers of energy from the subtle levels to the physical level. In Fig. 3.16a, we see the relative location of these centers while Fig. 3.16b provides a representation of a chakra-endocrine

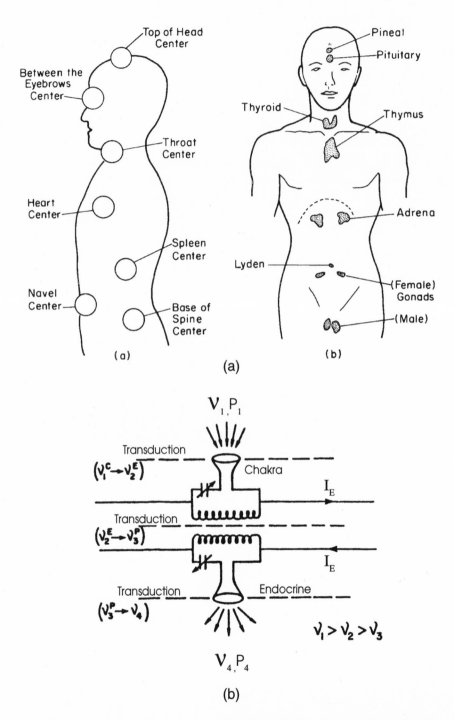

**Fig.3.16** (a) Location of the seven major chakras at the etheric level of substance and the seven major endocrines at the physical level of substance and (b) a schematic illustration of tuning and transduction aspects of a chakra/endocrine pair for tapping power from the cosmos.

pair as a tuned circuit via which one may tap energy from the cosmos. One can tune this circuit and produce magnetic current flow in the etheric circuit. Via deltron coupling, electric currents are caused to flow in the physical body and then back to nature both via direct radiation from the physical body and via back-flow to the etheric body and then radiation from that level to the environment. Fig. 3.17 illustrates a side view of the chakra system with their root stems located in different neural plexi. Table 3.2 shows the connections to the various physiological systems of the body. Figs. 3.18a and b show a theosophical perspective of the chakras with their "light" channel connections and the types of psychoenergetic or superphysical phenomena associated with each center[13b, 13c]. From an antenna perspective, Fig. 2.21 of Chapter 2 shows us that a circular or spiral array of monopole antennas at the physical level leads to mandala-like patterns at the etheric level. Such patterns have much in common with the theosophical descriptions of the chakras. By properly phasing these monopole elements, one expects that selected regions of the etheric mandala patterns could be made to rotate at various frequencies. Other geometrical arrangements of monopole and dipole elements could be utilized to generate petal-like radiation patterns with rotating elements much like the descriptions given for various chakras by those with the sensitivity to perceive these centers.

**Table 3.2**  THE HUMAN CHAKRA/ENDOCRINE/NEURAL PLEXUS SYSTEM

| CHAKRA | ENDOCRINE | NEURAL PLEXUS | PHYSIOLOGICAL SYSTEM |
|---|---|---|---|
| 1.   Sahasrara | Pineal | Cerebral   cortex | Nervous system, organs & tissues of entire body |
| 2.   Ajna | Pituitary | Hypophysis diencephalon | Autonomic nervous system & hormone system of entire body |
| 3.   Visshuda | Thyroid | Cervical, ganglia, connecting medulla oblongata with spinal chord | Respiratory   system |
| 4.   Anahata | Thymus | Heart plexus in sympathetic trunk | Circulatory   system |
| 5.   Manipura | Adrenal | Solar   plexus | Digestive   system |
| 6.   Muladhara | Cells of Lyden | Sacral  } | Genito-urinary connecting left and right  sympathetic nervous system |
| 7. Swadhistana | Gonads | Coccygeal | |

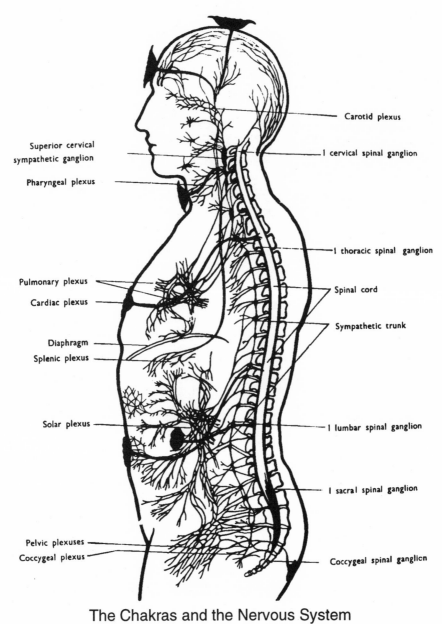

The Chakras and the Nervous System

**Fig. 3.17** Sideview of neural plexi and the seven major chakras.

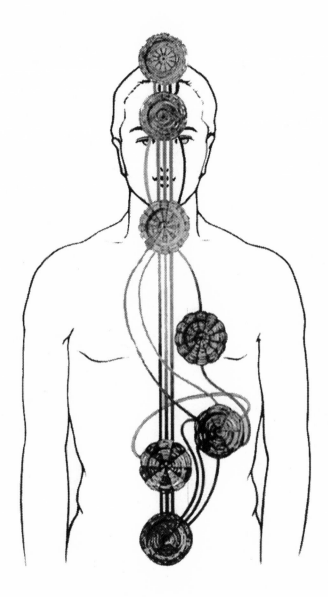

**Fig. 3.18(a)**  Schematic illustration of the different morphological character associated with the different chakras.

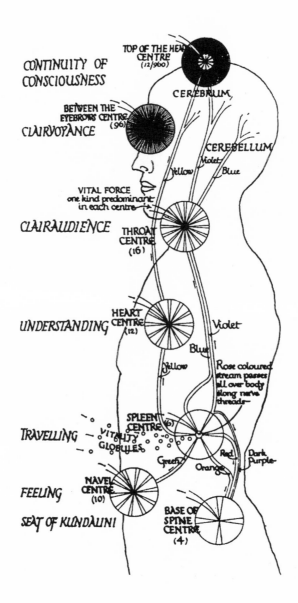

**Fig. 3.18(b)** Main types of psychoenergetic phenomena associated with each center.

126

These two major antenna systems of the body operate in conjunction with each other. The chakra/endocrine gland/neural plexus system transfers subtle energies of various types to our 4D- bodies via a power step-down and field transduction process. These energies fuel the hormonal factories of the endocrine glands and vitalize the central nervous system. Analogous processes occur at the etheric level and these interact closely with the acupuncture meridian system. The overall process is designed to vitalize all the body's organs and systems at the 4D level so that it functions as an integrated and harmoniously balanced vehicle for human experience. At the physical level, this requires that the proper distribution of major and minor chemical constituents be present to both feed the various chemical factories of the body and to provide the necessary internal photon spectrum for catalytically activating all these chemical change processes. A similar requirement is expected on the etheric side of the 4D health equation and, finally, balance between the physical and the etheric sides of the equation is crucial to keep the biological machinery humming in fine tune.

**The Human Aura:** One very important piece of the antenna picture remains to be discussed and this relates to the physical interpretation of the mathematical aspects of the EM emission process. In Fig. 3.19, the EM energy emission from a short dipole is illustrated for both the region very close to the antenna (the near-field) and the region very far from the antenna (the far-field)[3]. In the far-field, the energy flow is mathematically real; i.e., it is always radially outwards. This energy is radiated, it doesn't come back to the antenna, and it is a maximum in the $\theta=90^\circ$ direction. In the near field, the energy is mathematically imaginary and is largely reactive; i.e., the energy flows out and back twice per cycle without being radiated. In Fig. 3.19, the arrows represent the direction of energy flow at successive instants.

I now propose that we call this near-field region of the EM antenna the EM aura of the antenna. If the antenna was moving, this aura would move with it (with some minor variations due to its local environment). Thus, we can consider it to be a part of the antenna. If we insert a sizeable metallic or dielectric object into this EM aura region of the antenna, the electric and magnetic standing waves will be altered and the effect would manifest as a power fluctuation on the meters monitoring the voltage, current and power delivered to the antenna from its power source. Conversely, via the use of small electric and magnetic field probes inserted at various locations in this near-field region, one can run a diagnostic study on the functional state of this dipole antenna.

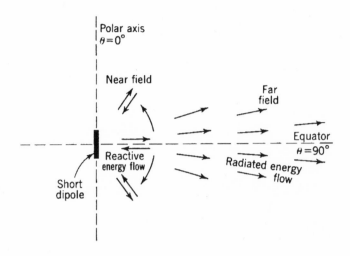

**Fig.3.19** Energy flow in both the near-field and far-field regions of a short dipole.

As we have discussed earlier and schematically illustrated in Fig. 3.6, subtle levels of substance exist in the body and they each give rise to radiation emission in much the same manner that physical substance generates EM emissions. Likewise, just as the physical body has major antenna systems associated with it, the etheric body and our more subtle bodies have special antenna systems associated with them. Thus, each of these antenna systems is expected to have a transduced A-field correlate manifest at the physical level and its near field radiation pattern will be a standing wave field, or <u>auric field</u>, representation of that subtle body. This means that an auric sheath should be present around the physical body for every subtle body the human has. Further, if we have materials that interact with or resonate with a specific level of subtle substance, and if one or more of these substances are placed in the appropriate auric sheath, a response to this disturbance of the particular standing wave field will manifest both in that subtle body and also in the physical body. If this response can be detected, it would make a useful diagnostic tool. An illustration of the multiple auric sheaths around the human body is given in Fig. 3.20.

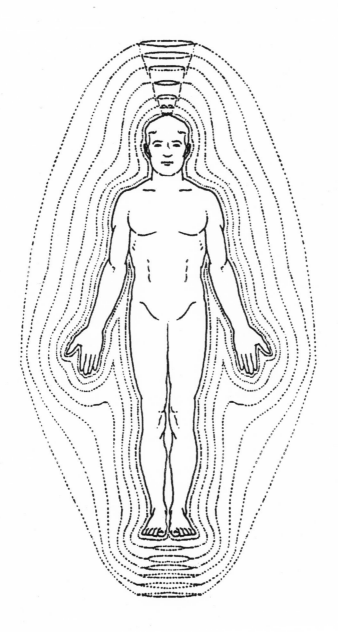

**Fig. 3.20** Schematic illustration of multiple auric sheaths surrounding the physical body.

# The Muscle Connection

Some osteopaths and chiropracters have observed that distinct muscle reactions are found to be associated with placing small permanent magnets over specific A.P.s. They have begun to use this technique to diagnose organ condition and to treat various ailments with the analgesic effects of D.C. magnets at A.P.s discussed earlier in this chapter and with the magnetic field effect on myosin phosphorlyation mentioned in Chapter 1. It is the field of applied kinesiology that has done the most to evaluate body function through the dynamics of muscle testing[14]. It has been clinically found that structural, chemical and mental factors can be detrimental to muscle function. In applied kinesiology (AK), a clear association is found between specific muscle weakness and possible organ involvement. It appears that the nervous system controls the strengthening and weakening of muscles in an organized manner.

Scopp[15] performed objective muscle tests via six trained practitioners using hand-held dynamometers and ten subjects. The data revealed a 91% positive correlation between the six examiners, indicating that muscle testing is reliable on an interexaminer basis. Scopp also evaluated nutrient recommendations for specific muscle weaknesses via a double blind nutrient/placebo testing. He found a statistically significant increase in muscle strength, at the $p<0.05$ level, for the nutrition versus the placebo group.

Early on in the development of AK, Goodheart[16] observed a fairly consistent relationship of specific weak muscle groups with specific organ or gland dysfunction. From A.P. studies, a meridian can be out of balance via having either too little or too much energy flow. Goodheart found that (a) when the energy level in the meridian is low, an associated muscle will test weak and (b) when the energy level is excessive, the muscle will test excessively strong, sometimes to the point of hypertonicity. The triad of health links that AK explores is shown below.

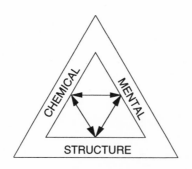

A variety of challenges are given in AK to test these various links: (1) a physical challenge can be placed into a muscle articulation to determine if the articulation and its associated proprioceptors can accept the stimuli without adversely affecting body function. Muscle proprioceptors are somatic sensory organs located at strategic points in the muscle to secure inside information and effectively bring about cooperation and coordination between muscles. For the proprioceptors and the interconnecting nerve network, it is physiologically necessary to consider <u>arrays</u> of several types of sensory endings which act in concert to provide information about the forces and influences acting on a particular locality to be analyzed together in the central nervous system. The function of the neuromuscular spindles (a major part of the muscle proprioceptor) is entirely on a <u>subconscious level</u>, giving no conscious sensory perception. They have both afferent and efferent nerve communication which proceeds to the spinal cord and cerebellum for control of the muscle in which they reside, as well as for integration of the muscular system in general.

(2) The chemical side of the triad shown above can be evaluated via the administration of nutrition as a positive aspect, causing improved resistance of an involved muscle -- or it can be via the administration of detrimental chemicals which cause weakening of the muscles. For chemical testing, the substance is placed on the tongue while muscle testing (it is not necessary to swallow).

(3) The mental side of the triad can be evaluated by challenge with positive and negative thoughts. A patient can be tested to determine the influence of a negative emotional experience by having them concentrate on the experience; an adverse effect on the body can be observed by a weakening of the muscles. This is more obvious in specific muscles that equate with certain aspects of the autonomic nervous system, such as the stomach, adrenals, etc.

It appears that AK sometimes deals with very subtle energy patterns of body function. It seems that some individuals can apply seemingly therapeutic approaches and obtain results that cannot be accomplished by others. Although such procedures are valuable to that practitioner, they often cannot be taught to others who presumably do not have the same inner capabilities and mental matrices. In this category, four procedures are of interest: (a) placing a chemical substance in a jar, and then placing the jar on the body surface adjacent to the organ under question, can either strengthen or weaken the appropriate muscle response depending upon the nature of the chemical in the jar; (b) the practitioner touching the A.P. of a weakened organ will find a weakened muscle response if tested within ~15 seconds, but will find no change in muscle response if a waiting period of greater than 20 seconds is used before testing; (c) if, in (b), the practitioner mentally fixes his attention on the patient's weakened organ throughout a waiting period of ~60 seconds before muscle testing, then the muscle will still exhibit a weakened response and (d) if the practitioner moves his/her finger downwards along the locus of a particular meridian, in which the energy is expected to flow upwards, but keeps his/her finger a few inches from the body, the appropriate muscle is found to be weakened by testing. From these four observations, one may conclude that the practitioner's energy field (auric field) has become part of an overall practitioner/patient interaction that clearly influences the patient's muscle responses. It seems likely that subtle energies are involved in this information exchange. Certainly that must be true in (a) since the EM radiations of the chemicals in the jar will not significantly penetrate the walls of the jar. It is almost as if the subconscious mind of the patient, acting via the muscle proprioceptors, is communicating essential information about the patient's condition to the conscious state of awareness via the muscle response. Somehow, the particular subtle energy field development of the practitioner facilitates this information transfer process. This is an important extension of the standard "dowsing" response to be discussed in the next section.

**The Dowsing Response:** The most common example of human response to external radiation fields is dowsing (finding underground water without digging--sometimes called water-witching). Harvelik[17] reports that one Mr. de Boer was extraordinarily sensitive to EM radiations. As Mr. de Boer walked over a test course, his hand-held "Y" rod yielded a weak dowsing response even when the D.C. electric current flowing in the test course wire, buried several feet underground, was reduced to one millionth of an ampere. This current would produce a magnetic field strength at the dowser's hand level of about one-ten billionth of the earth's magnetic field strength. Two conditions caused Mr. de Boer to receive no signal as he walked over the wire: (1) having his heart side facing the positive electrode and (2) having metal rods attached to his right forearm. Mr. de Boer responded fairly uniformly to A.C. signals over the entire frequency range from 1 Hz to 1 million Hz (1 Hz = 1 cycle/second). EM wave generators operating in the 7- meter and 5-centimeter wavelength bands, at 1 watt and 0.2 watts, respectively, were used to show that he reacts to the <u>magnetic</u> vector of the EM wave and especially to horizontally-polarized EM radiation. He reacted regardless of whether the beam struck him directly or by reflection from some surface and from all sides of his body. When a metal belt covered his adrenals, no dowsing signal was observed as he walked through the high frequency beam. The signal was also suppressed when he wore a metal crown around his head even though the beam reached his waist which was not shielded by a metal belt. However, when de Boer wore both the metal belt and the metal crown, he not only developed a dowsing signal when he crossed the beam (waist high) but he seemed to be even more sensitive to the high frequency field of the beam (Bird[18] indicates that surgical loss of the adrenal glands in a particular dowser led to the loss of his dowsing ability). Using his "Y" rod in the Washington D.C. area, Mr. de Boer has been able to stand at one spot and, by rotating himself, locate the angular direction between himself and several specific radio stations, given only their operating frequencies.

Generally, in the early afternoon, Mr. de Boer's sensitivity to EM signals dropped by a factor of ~1000. Because of the sun's position, early morning or late afternoon were best for him. He was also most sensitive after he drank two glasses of water (an increase by a factor ~50).

Maby[19] has pointed out that one of the most convincing proofs of the reflex physiological nature of traditional radiesthetic and dowsing responses is to be seen in the consistent numerical relationship between a randomly varied physical stimulus and the neuromuscular response to it. The radiesthetic reactions (like dowsing) nicely obey Weber and Fechner's classical (logarithmic) law for ordinary physical sensations; whereas, if the response were psychological (e.g., imaginary or auto-suggested), we would find no such precise numerical relationship. For dowsing, Bird[18] reports on a Canadian study showing an electrical signal developing in the muscle just prior to the contraction reaction associated with the dowsing wand movement.

In ordinary field dowsing, it is always discontinuities in the generalized surrounding medium and sharp changes in the local field, that cause the traditional rod reactions. In a state of rest, nothing much normally happens. One must move through the local "field of manifestation" of the selected objective, or else the field must move or alter in strength or polarity. Otherwise, to obtain clear responses, the radiesthetist must be confronted by, for example, intermittent alternating currents, pulsating magnetic fields, impinging corpuscular radiations, etc.

There are basically two categories of dowsing, (1) local field dowsing and (2) remote dowsing (see Chapter 6). In the former, a sensitive human takes a rod or pendulum out into the field and obtains a motion reaction to a spot under the earth while located over it. Such a person could be walking, riding in a car, flying in an airplane, etc., and would still react when located over the spot. On the other hand, remote dowsing has three subclassifications, (1) remote field dowsing, (2) map dowsing and (3) information dowsing. In remote field dowsing, the sensitive individual operates while sitting in a truck on the edge of the area to be dowsed. In map dowsing, the dowser may be sitting at home by the kitchen table, working from a good map of the area to be dowsed. Information dowsing resembles map dowsing except that no map is used. Here, the dowser asks specific questions of the "universe" and reads the answers by observing the specific motions of the wand or pendulum, having foreknowledge of the code of these motions. Once again, we see the ability to access subtle information channels available in nature by the use of a simple device linked to the human muscle system/muscle proprioceptors/the central nervous system and some subtle antenna array detector of our body. This dowsing response system allows unconscious information to reach the conscious awareness level via wand or pendulum movement detectable to the eye.

## We Are Also Light Machines

Although great care and attention has been given to the chemical nature of our bodies, much less effort has been devoted to the photonic or "light" nature of these same bodies. Most, if not all, of the key chemical factories of the body are thought to consist of catalytic reactors wherein simple chemical feedstocks (A and B, say) are brought together on especially configured surfaces and stimulated to an activated state so that a specific new molecular species (C) can form via the reaction

$$A + B \xrightarrow{h\nu} (A + B)^* \rightarrow C + D$$

Here, the * represents the activated state, $h\nu$ represents the photon energy and D is a biproduct of the reaction. The stimulation process for this low temperature reactor is most likely to require an incident photon of frequency in a specific range $\nu_o \pm \Delta\nu$ so that it can be absorbed by this especially configured surface producing either an excited electronic, vibrational or rotational energy level. The presence of this excited state, in turn, provides the energy activation needed for the species A+B to surmount the energy barrier involved in the formation of C. Without the presence of this incident photon, the raw materials A and B would just sit there on the substrate surface for a very long time without forming C. The presence of this specific substrate is also critical because of its geometrical, photon absorbtive and activated state properties. Thus, from this overly simplified description, we see that, in order for the body to produce a given ensemble of chemicals, there must also be present a given spectral distribution of photons. Further, in order to produce these same chemicals at a given rate (because the body consumes them at some rate), there must also be a sufficient flux of the key photons. Calling $J_j$ the flux of species j, our typical rate equation becomes

$$J_A + J_B + J_{h\nu} \rightarrow J_{(A+B)^*} \rightarrow J_C + J_D$$

Thus, from this simple reasoning, we see that, for stable body function, we not only need a special soup of chemicals being created in a dynamic fashion but we also need a companion family of photons of sufficient intensity to keep the pot bubbling efficiently.

Ultra-weak photon emission from various living systems is a common phenomenon for all plants and animals with the radiation intensity being on the order of a few hundred to a few thousand photons per second[20]. For mammalian cells this has been estimated to be about 1 photon per cell in ~3-20 minutes[21]. The spectral range of the photon emission spreads at least over the region from the infrared to the ultraviolet with the mitochondria in cells appearing to be the localization of the radiation source. In contrast to bioluminescence, ultra-weak photon emission becomes increasingly important as we move from the simplest organisms to the more complex ones. Cells mainly emit photons before mitosis so that proliferating cell cultures radiate more intensely than do those in which growth has ceased[22]. Cancer cells are intense radiation sources with peak intensities, without spectral shifts, increasing by a factor of ~100 after treatment with toxic agents[20].

It is interesting that the human photoreceptor, the flavin molecules, are not limited to the retina of the eye but are ubiquitous, being found in virtually every tissue of the body. In addition, flavins are not the only photoactive molecules in the body: carotenes, melanin and heme molecules, such as hemoglobin and bilirubin, plus a great variety of metalloenzymes are also photoactive. Thus, the key difference between chlorophyll and hemoglobin, where iron in hemoglobin replaces magnesium in the molecular hub of chlorophyll, begins to take on special significance. As one might expect, the blue light range, 300 to 400 nanometers, corresponds to the absorption and action spectra of many extremely vital biomolecules (see Fig. 3.21). Such absorption always precipitates chemical reactions. Much of the longer wavelength radiation, and particularly the red, can be traced to certain activated molecular species (principally carbonyl and singlet oxygen) which arise from the breakdown of peroxy radicals formed during oxidative metabolism[21].

From the period 1975-1985, Zheng, while still in China, studied ultra-weak photon emission from human fingertips[23]. Using a blue-end sensitive photomultiplier tube, she found the following results: (1) using a test group of 361 healthy individuals, she found that the counting rate increased with age with a regular variation of counting rate between different fingers. A seasonal variation was also observed (a factor ~2-3 higher during the summer months). (2) For a male subject who fractured his right leg in an accident, the counting rate was very high during the period of severe pain and dropped abruptly by a factor of ~10 between the fifth and seventh day and then slowly dropped by an additional factor of two as the pain disappeared and (3) A group of coronary heart disease patients were divided into two groups according to their serum lipid concentration. The hyperlipemia group showed a significantly higher counting rate than either a normal group or the hypolipemia group showing that the photon counting rate correlated with the lipid concentration.

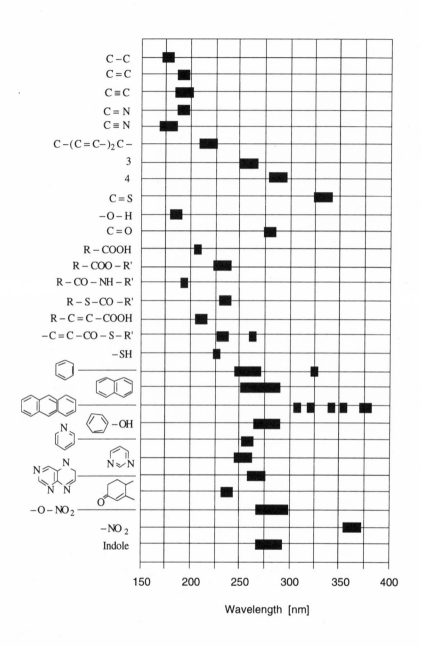

**Fig. 3.21** The absorption spectra of major biomolecules. These molecules absorb at the wavelength indicated irrespective of the biological system in which they are located, plant or animal.

Most of her data indicates that an increase in blue photon counting rate, everything else being equal, connotes a loss of vitality or a growing pathology with respect to the body systems represented by the measured finger.

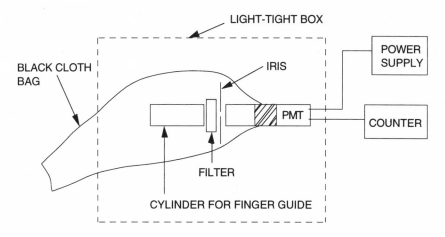

**Fig. 3.22** Schematic illustration of the experimental set-up used in the Stanford Biophoton Emission Studies.

When Dr. Zheng moved to the San Francisco area, this author and Professor C. Bates, conducted some photon emission experiments with her at Stanford because she is also a Qigong master. We set up an apparatus of the type illustrated in Fig. 3.22. The general testing protocol was to sit in front of the device in a relaxed fashion for 10 minutes with the room darkened and at constant temperature (about 22.5° C). The hands, which had previously been washed, were placed into the double-layered bag for five minutes. Then, each fingertip was measured for 10 seconds and repeated 5 times. After subtracting the background counting rate to adjust for random photon emission from the environment, the number of counts per 30 seconds was recorded for each finger. The absolute magnitude of these counts indicated that we were dealing, here, with ultra weak photon emission. The counting rate with the finger was only ~10%-20% above background so the experiment would have benefitted from having a cooler laboratory or, preferably, a cold photomultiplier tube (PMT). Our results showed that the emitted photon count in the blue end of the spectrum was substantial and that 2-3 times as many photons were emitted at the red end of the spectrum (for a similar $\Delta v$) with a dip in the middle range. Another study of human bioluminescence was recently published[24]. Their PMT was kept at a constant temperature of -23° and they monitored the abdomen, lower back, heart, forehead and hand. They recorded ~170-600 photon counts per second per (centimeter)$^2$, depending on anatomical location. They also found emissions to be strongest at the red end of the spectrum but falling below detectable levels in the ultraviolet. Significant variations were observed between individuals in both photon rate and spectral profile and, for a single individual, significant rate variations occurred with time of measurement.

In these two studies, the mainly red photon emission agrees generally with what others have found from mammalian tissue as being attributed to oxidative production of chemical radicals. Both experiments probably underestimate the shorter wavelength emission because of strong tissue absorbtion. However, the finger monitoring experiment is likely to suffer from less tissue absorption because of the thinner stratum corneum layer on the finger tips. It is also possible that Qigong masters emit a higher blue and ultraviolet photon flux than do normal individuals. From all of the foregoing, it seems reasonable to conclude that cells are photoelectrochemical devices and that our physical bodies, as collections of such cells, are light machines as well as chemical machines.

# References

1. M. Garbuny, "Optical Physics" (Academic Press, New York, 1965).
2. A. Lytel, "ABC's of Antennas" (Howard W. Sams & Co., Inc., New York, 1971).
3. J.D. Kraus and K.R. Carver, "Electromagnetics" (McGraw-Hill Book Company, New York, 1973).
4. E. Brookner, Scientific American 252 (1985) 94.
5. P.S. Callahan, "Tuning In To Nature", (The Devin-Adair Company, Old Greenich, Connecticut, 1975).
6a. W.A. Tiller, in "Galaxies of Life", Eds. S. Krippner and D. Rubin (Interface, New York, 1973, pp. 71-112).
6b. J. Helms, "Acupuncture Energetics; A clinical Approach for Physicians", (Medical Acupuncture Publishers, Berkeley, CA., 1995).
7. M.A. Reichmanis, A. Marino and R.D. Becker, IEEE Trans. on Biomed. Engrg. BM013, 533 (1975).
8. Y. Manaka and I. A. Urquhart, " The layman's Guide to Acupunture" (Weatherhill, New York, 1972) p 93.
9. H. Motoyama, Private Communication, 1977.
10. A.R. Liboff and M. Furst, Ann. N.Y. Acad. Sci. 238 (1974) 26.
11. M. Tany and S. Sawatsugawa, Am. J. Acupuncture, 3 (1975) 58.
12. J.L. Crowley, R.A. Wallace and R.H. Bube, J. Polymer Sci., 14 (1976) 1769.
13a. A. A. Bailey, "Esoteric Healing, Vol iv, a Treatise on the Seven Rays" (Lucis Publishing Co, New York, 1977)
13b. A.E. Powell, "The Etheric Double", (The Theosophical Publishing House, London, 1960).
13c. C.W. Leadbeater, "The Chakras", (The Theosophical Publising House, Wheaton, IL, 1969).
14. D.S. Walther, "Applied Kinesiology, Vol. 1" (SdC Systems DC, Pueblo, Co, 1981).
15. A.L. Scopp, J. Orthomolecular Psychiatry, 2 (1978), No. 2.
16. G.J. Goodheart, Jr., "Applied Kinesiology" (Privately published, Detroit, 1964).
17. Z.V. Harvelik, American Dowser, 13:3 (1973) 85; 14:1 (1974) 4.
18. C. Bird, "The Divining Hand" (E.P. Dutton, New York, 1979).
19. J.C. Maby, American Dowser, 14:2 (1974) 69.
20. G.M. Barenbiom, A.N. Domanski and K.K. Turoverov, "Luminescence of Biopolymers and Cells" (Plenum Press, New York, 1969).
21. R. Van Wijk and D.H.J. Schamhart, Experientia, 44 (1988) 586.

22.  A.I. Zhundavlev, O.P. Tsylev and S.M. Zubkova, Biophysics, <u>18</u> (1973) 1101.

23.  R.R. Zheng, Shanghai Journal of Traditional Chinese Medicine, <u>5</u> (1983) 44; J. of Luminescence, <u>40-41</u> (1988) 825.

24.  R. Edwards, M.C. Ibison, J.J. Kenyon and R.B. Taylor, Int. J. of Acupuncture and Electro-Therapeutics, <u>15</u> (1990) 85.

25.  M. Austin, "Acupuncture Therapy", (ASI Publishers Inc., New York, 1972).

26.  K. Matsumoto and S. Birch, "Hara Diagnosis: Reflections on The Sea", (Paradigm Publications, Brookline, Mass, 1988).

27.  A.P. Dubrov and V.N. Pushkin, "Parapsychology and Contemporary Science", (Consultants Bureau, New York, 1982).

28.  R. Voll, in "Electroacupuncture According to Voll", Am. J. of Acupuncture, <u>6</u> (1978) 5.

29.  W.A. Tiller, in "Energy Fields in Medicine", (The John E. Fetzer Foundation, Kalamazoo, Michigan, 1989) p 257.

# APPENDIX 3.1

## The Outside/Inside Interface

In the original literature on acupuncture, the human body and its inter-action with its environment were considered largely in terms of an energy balancing process. Illness was considered as a disturbance of some material processes in the body and the cure was considered to be a control mechanism which returned these material processes to their balanced state. Energy was thought to enter the body from the outside environment via a stream of bipolar particles. One polarity of particle stimulated the organs and systems of the body while the other polarity of particle had an inhibitory effect. These were the yin and the yang of the energy substance called Chi. Thus, the concept of illness developed as a disturbance in the balance between the processes of excitation and inhibition; i.e., all illness can be classified into two categories, (1) illnesses due to over-excitation (excess syndrome) and (2) illnesses due to over-depression (insufficiency syndrome). The cure attempts to restore the Chi polarity balance in the organism by stimulating the biologically active points on the skin surface. These points are located along special lines called meridians.

At present, fourteen meridians are recognized and each meridian serves a different organ or major body system. They are the main channels along which the Chi flows. They branch out into smaller channels which, in turn, branch out into still smaller channels like capillaries which cover almost the entire skin surface. Each meridian consists of two parts, that at the surface of the skin which collects energy and that which services the internal organs by transporting the energy to the organ or body system sites. All meridians are also classified as excitatory or inhibitory according to the polarity of the Chi energy that they control. Similarly, all the organs are either elements of the excitatory or inhibitory energetic process. For this reason, inserting needles into points along a specific meridian may affect, not only the organ linked to this particular meridian, but also other body systems that may be far removed physically from that organ. This bioenergy flows through the organism in rhythmic cycles, with one full circulation being completed in 24 hours[25,26].

Because the peak amplitude of this bioenergy passes through one body system after another, each system achieves its peak receptivity for treatment at a particular time of day. Knowledge of the circadian rhythm of this bioenergetic process is necessary in order to treat a particular disease effectively. For instance, the best time to treat the liver system is between 1:00 and 3:00 AM, for the respiratory system it is between 7:00 and 9:00 AM and, for the heart, it is between 11:00 AM and 1:00 PM. For twelve of the fourteen meridians, the flow path is I. Heart (Yin)  II. Small Intestine (Yang)  III. Bladder (Yang)  IV. Kidneys (Yin)  V. Circulation (Yin)  VI. Triple Heater (Yang)  VII. Gall Bladder (Yang)  VIII. Liver (Yin)  IX. Lungs (Yin)  X. Large Intestine (Yang)  XI. Stomach (Yang)  XII. Spleen (Yin)  I. Heart (Yin).  The heart line (I) begins on the thorax, travels along the upper limb to the fingertips carrying yin predominance energy.  At the fingertips the polarity changes, becoming a Yang predominance energy.  It now travels along the small intestine line (II) to the head and, from the head, it travels on the bladder line (III) to the feet (toes). At the toes, the polarity changes from yang to yin. From the toes the yin predominance energy follows the kidney line (IV) to the thorax and then, still yin, follows the circulation line (V) to the fingertips where, once again, a reversal of polarity occurs.  As we proceed along the circuit, at the extremities of the upper and lower limbs, the polarity of the vital energy undergoes a reversal. In the central area, head and thorax, although the energy passes from one meridian to another, there is no polarity change.  These energy polarity reversals are most easily influenced at certain points, called <u>command points</u>, near the extremities of the limbs.

During fetus development, when the meridians and acupuncture points are initially being formed, it is found that the skin and the nervous system form from the same embryonic tissue; thus, it is felt that the two should have a strong interrelationship.  Insertion of a needle into an active point generates an impulse of Chi which travels along the meridians to the organs and corresponding body system.  This impulse is also thought to affect centers in the autonomic nervous system, releasing their physical energy, to bring the organism's state back to balance.  This special relationship between the nervous system and A.P.'s is demonstrated by the efficacy of acupuncture treatment for various neurotic and psychotic disorders as well as numerous neurological disorders[27].

Acupuncture is found to completely eliminate such symptoms of neurasthenia as psychological weakness, fatigue, fears, anxiety, compulsive behavior, etc.  It is also effective for such disorders as psychasthenia and hysteria.  In the neurological disorder area, children who receive acupuncture treatment at an early state of poliomyelitis may be able to regenerate damaged nerves so that, not only the range of motion in an arm or leg but also the muscle mass of the disabled extremity can be restored.  Acupuncture has also been successfully used to treat neuritis of the auditory nerve which usually leads to deaf-muteness and which cannot be cured by traditional medicine.

From an abundance of experimental data[27], it appears that the skin is a channel through which the energy, which supports psychological activity, enters the human body.  Since this energy ultimately comes from the universe, the skin is the link which ties the organism and the universe together. This function of the skin is closely related to the function of the brain system which controls the galvanic skin response (GSR). GSR lowers the electrical resistance of the skin in response to events calling for cognitive or motor activity of the person. After numerous experimental and clinical studies, it can now be considered an established fact that the electrical resistance of the A.P.'s is directly related to the status of the appropriate internal organs[28]. From such electroacupuncture studies, it is interesting to note that, by merely restoring the command A.P.'s to their proper electrical resistance range by electric charge injection[29], health is restored. Of course, more than one rebalancing treatment is usually needed to produce ultimate stability of the A.P.'s electrical properties.

The remaining question to be touched on here is "can electrical stimulation of A.P.'s affect the activity of the brain?" The answer has been found to be "yes" via using an electroacupuncture apparatus to measure the conductivity symmetry of symmetrical A.P.'s while simultaneously recording the brain blood supply via rheoencephalography (REG) and brain electrical activity via electroencephalography (EEG)[27]. REG and EEG were measured both before and after recovery of symmetrical point conductivity (SPC). The electrical activity of the brain was compared with the initial asymmetry of the skin points and the symmetry recovery time.

Preliminary experiments showed that the SPC recovery improved the subject's performance on a variety of tests[27]; they all completed the tests faster and with fewer errors. There was a marked decrease in subject tension while working on the tasks <u>after</u> stimulation of the A.P.'s. Further, electrical stimulation of these points changed the shape of the REG wave, indicating an increase in the activity of the cerebral cortex. Analysis of the rheograms showed that the flattening out of the REG wave occurred mainly in the left (dominant) hemisphere. In subjects of excitatory type, stimulation of the A.P.'s led to an increase in delta wave amplitude in the EEG while, in inert subjects, stimulation led to an increase in the fast wave component (the beta rhythm). Perhaps the most important result of these experiments was a correlation between the parameters of the initial asymmetry of SPC and the symmetry recovery time on the one hand and the EEG indicators of some parameters of brain control on the other[27]. The data show that electrical stimulation of A.P.'s affects not only isolated parameters, but the <u>entire nervous system</u>. The data also indicate an increase in the activity of the higher control centers of the cerebral cortex.

Although REG is a method for measuring the supply of blood to the brain (via pulsation of brain blood vessels), it can also be utilized to record the activity of various components of the thinking process. Problem solving occurs in the cerebral cortex and the various parts of the cortex can be recorded to learn something about the various elements that control thinking. For example, when a subject is task-oriented and concentrating on a problem's solution, there is a REG response from the parietal-temporal region whereas, a REG response in the frontal cortical region is more likely to indicate an increase in general personality tension. Conscious mental activity occurs when both the personality region <u>and</u> the cognition region are active. When these two regions function separately, unconscious psychological processes are thought to occur.

In closing this appendix, it is important to note that the goal was not to have the reader understand all the inner workings of acupuncture and its treatment modalities. Rather, the goal was to broaden the concepts developed in Chapter 3 concerning A.P.'s and meridians without breaking the flow of the picture being painted there.

# CHAPTER
# 4

## INTENTIONAL DEVELOPMENT OF THE BODY'S EXTENDED SENSORY SYSTEM

*The play of magnificent energies, physical and subtle,*
*That dance through the universe,*
*Reach out invitingly to our responsive neural and nadi networks*
*To entrain us in their rhythms. Yet muted to our ears,*
*The finest instruments in the celestial orchestra*
*Wait patiently for subtle synapses to form in us.*

Nature is a vast interpenetrating and interacting ensemble of substance at all ten dimensions of the universe. And each individuation in each dimension is radiating and absorbing energy and information in both a multiple variety of forms (sonic, EM, subtle, etc.) and over a wide variety of frequency ranges. Thus, these different spaces pulse with currents of different kinds of energy and information that flow back and forth between the different manifestations of substance. Sometimes the flow is gentle and sometimes it is turbulent; but always, it is our environment. The ability of humans to sense and discriminate this information is essential for their survival and for their evolution.

It has often been said that human evolution is characterized by and limited by the penetration of spirit into dense physical matter so that the more spirit there is present in the dense body of an entity, the higher is its consciousness.[1] The entity applies that in-dwelling consciousness, through its focussed intentionality, in the various acts of its daily life. By the entity's actions, thoughts and attitudes, transformational changes eventually occur in the dense and subtle matter of the body which can produce a refined structure allowing a greater inflow of spirit (or produce a degraded structure which does the opposite). The greatest example we have of this process in action is the gradual refinement of the homosapian over time via the initial embodiment of human spirit into the mammalian ape. The transformation process appears to involve the iterative cycle (1) recognition of a new principle, (2) testing and utilization of the new principle, (3) adaptation of internal structures via the repeated utilization of the principle which actualizes its potential, (4) new structural development allow-

145

ing new levels of function which leads to the recognition of another new principle, etc. In support of this view, let us first look at some research findings regarding sensory system development. We need to know something of how our bodies sense environmental information, how some of it becomes consciously registered in our brains while some of it stays at the unconscious level, how we might access this unconscious information and how it all becomes integrated into a personal view of reality.

## How Do We Consciously Sense Environmental Information?

By early in the 20th century, scientists had discovered what were initially interpreted as four separate types of nerve receptors in the skin, corresponding to four skin-based senses: warmth, touch, pain and cold. Later work indicated that there is a whole continuum of receptor types of which the above four types are merely the most exaggerated forms. In addition to the above, there are itch, tickle, vibration and different types of pain (burning/searing, throbbing/aching, stabbing, sharp, etc.). It was discovered that all skin nerve receptors are sensitive to at least some kind of pressure and pressure change suggesting that different sensations were distinguished by different code-like patterns of neural signals on the multiple neural channels[2].

This research also uncovered four separate nerve pathways to carry the information back to the spinal cord and thence to the brain. Neurons carrying information about pain were shown to first pass through clusters of nerve cells in the spine (ganglia) where they made contact with nerves controlling the muscular system. In this way, urgent information ("take finger out of fire")[2] could be acted on immediately rather than wait the seconds that might elapse before the pain message could get to the brain and be registered as "pain". We might call this process <u>unconscious</u> muscle signalling to the proprioceptors as discussed in Chapter 3.

Structurally, then, we see four strands of nerve cells forming the nerve cable that connects the skin sensors to the brain via a composite structure of nerve "wire" segments connected by synaptic junctions. Signal passage in the wire segment occurs via an electrical depolarization mechanism while signal passage across a synaptic junction occurs via the availability of uniquely specific chemicals detaching, transporting and attaching again to specific receptor sites (via a lock and key mechanism). Thus, photoelectrochemical forces are involved at these junctions. It was also found that signals of sufficient strength in one of the strands can inhibit signal passage in adjacent strands (a very non-linear process). Complete information passage is registered via both time-phased signals moving in one nerve strand and correlated signals moving in adjacent strands.

At least in the case of pain signals, the brain can generate its own set of key chemicals (serotonin, etc) which can transport <u>down</u> the nerve cable from the brain and, if present in high concentration, produce lateral inhibition to block pain signals from travelling <u>up</u> the spine to the brain--so the pain is not felt. This is how human intention can be utilized to control the sensation of pain!

Turning for a moment to the sense of smell, when air flows up the nostrils, molecules of odors are attracted to and held by a particular binding site whose chemical composition forms a temporary bond with the odor molecule. This bond changes the cell's ability to pass sodium and phosphorus through the cell wall and a correlate of this event is the development of an electrical spike in the nervous system[2]. A coding scheme is probably operating here just as it does in the sense of taste. If one receptor is sensitive to molecules A, B and C while another receptor is responsive to B, D and E then, only when the two fire simultaneously will the message "molecule B is present" be transmitted[2]. Like the other senses, part of the sense of smell is conscious and it can be trained to be more discriminating. Virtually anyone can become more sensitive to perfumes and odors and can be trained to pick out the components of more complex aromas[2].

Early evolutionary life forms such as reptiles had a special set of nerve endings in the brain reserved for olefaction, and these made contact with the nerves governing the most instinctual types of behavior. As evolution progressed, the "reptilian" brain, or "instinctive" brain, together with the olefactory sense and its nervous system connections, was incorporated into the brain structure of emerging life forms such as birds and mammals[2]. Via primative mammals and then to primates and then to homosapians, this selfsame instinctive brain with its olefactory sense and central nervous system pathways is a part of the human brain today. The identical "instinctive" part of the brain that incorporates olefaction also contains the nerve center that controls involuntary nonconscious muscular activity such as breathing, heartbeat, pupil size and genital erections. The neurophysiological association between sex and smell is apparently one that goes back all the way to the beginning of human evolution[2].

## How Sensory Systems Develop in the Newborn

The newborn appear to have a rich template of neural possibilities in the brain but only a few are actualized by environmental stimulation and the unused remainder atrophy. Amazingly, it appears that all children are born with the ability to echolocate even though most never use it since other cues are available. However, like a bat, babies who are blind from birth will sometimes emit sounds which then bounce off an object and reflect back (much like sonar)[2].

The kitten is born with the innate ability to learn how to visually discriminate horizontal and vertical patterns. However, unless it comes into contact with features of its environment that somehow <u>activate</u> these innate abilities, this innate sense will not develop. Since there are distinct neural pathways for horizontal and vertical components of vision, the stimulation of both is required for normal sight[2].

It is now thought that map area formation in the brain is a two-stage process. First, nerve fibers innately find their way to the correct part of the brain through a general coding scheme that directs chemicals on the nerve fiber to within the general quadrant of the brain where they are to form synapses. Second, only those nerves that are actually stimulated repeatedly form lasting synapses, strengthened by neurochemical processes; the other synapses simply dissolve. Here we see that experience itself critically tailors the sensory mechanism used for its perception[2].

It has been proposed that a child is born with a set of innate language learning abilities centered in a small area on the brain's left temporal lobe. Like sensory systems, however, the innate language learning ability must be stimulated at the proper age--at which time the child develops its actual ability to speak and understand its native language. It is probably the acquisition of language itself that results in the differentiation of left and right brain hemispheres and spoken language, therefore, has a profound effect on the experience of sensory phenomena. This has been borne out by studies on deaf children who are not taught sign language in infancy--they fail to develop the various left and right hemisphere specializations found in normal children. On the other hand, deaf infants who are taught sign language develop a normal differentiation between left and right hemisphere activities, with the language center in the left hemisphere developing quite normally[2].

The important implication in these observations is that the very structure of the brain is somehow influenced by actual experiences of the world. They suggest that the environment itself is partially responsible for determining which sensory systems will be important to the species, and which pathways within those systems will be reinforced and therefore survive[2]. This data also suggests that a very different array of stimulation and reinforcement signals, applied to newborn infants in an artificial environment, could produce a greatly altered human species.

Present day studies in neurobiology[3] find that "supervised learning" trains nerve cells and controls brain function. In computers, this strategy compares the actual output of a program with the desired output and then modifies the program if the actual output is wrong. Actual laboratory studies of frogs, monkeys, owls and other animal systems show that supervised learning controls brain functions ranging from the development of motor skills to memorization skills. Any activity in which the brain uses feedback to adjust its response can benefit from supervised learning. For example, when a person tries to hit a ball and misses, the brain generates an error signal in one group of nerve cells that will prompt the nerve cells to adjust their connections appropriately. Then, with repeated trial and error, most people learn to hit the ball[3]. In all this, we see (1) the <u>recognition</u> of an unwanted deficiency of function, 2) the <u>intentional</u> exercise and <u>stimulation</u> of the process with the view to correcting the deficiency and (3) the <u>structural transformation</u> in the involved neural networks that then produces the desired level of function.

## Reality, Illusion and Mindsets

The typical information pattern to brain perception process seems to be (1) external data set sensed by sense receptors, (2) propagation of an electric signal train along the nerve cable to the brain, (3) registration of the signal train in the brain, (4) comparison of signal information content with internal data banks for interpretation and (5) a decision on what has been perceived in the event. We generally take this decision as the <u>reality</u> of the event and accept it without question. However, what about dreams, ecstatic visions, hallucinations, delerium tremens, etc.? How do these real phenomena fit into this logical and linear picture? Some of them appear not to be related to signal trains impinging on our sense receptors from outside of our body and some strongly challenge our internal data banks "view of reality". Recent studies of "lucid" dreaming show that the sleeper can consciously enter and direct the flow of the dream, which we normally think of as an unconscious level process[4]. In some cases, the brain transforms the data into an acceptable image to conform to what it thinks it ought to be sensing; in other cases, it just denies the existence of what it is sensing because it violates the prevailing mindset too much. Once the barriers (step 4 above) defining normal perception have been broken down, it then becomes possible to perceive and experience all manner of unusual phenomena--or the same phenomenon as usual, but in a different way.

One of the most striking experiments concerning step 4 above was carried out in the mid-1930's by Slater and involved the use of "upside down" glasses[5]. Subjects were asked to continually wear these glasses that distorted perception so that the wearer saw everything in an upside down configuration. It was very destabilizing for the wearer but after ~two weeks, the brain made an internal structural change and the wearer now saw everything "right side up". After this point in time everything appeared "normal". Then, when the subject permanently removed the glasses, the world was upside down again for about two weeks while the brain restructured its networks into the old configuration and then the subject's normal vision was restored. Here, we see the power of the subject's mindset to make the needed changes for restoring the subject's prevailing view of <u>reality</u>!

Shamans and medicine men, schizophrenics and others thought to be mentally ill, all take leave of their senses on a regular basis. This is far from simple chicanery. Whether the result of an optical illusion, a natural chemical imbalance or a drug-related experience, this appears to be an experiencing of alternate or metastable state possibilities in the perception domain. Perhaps, just as atoms and molecules have both ground states and a multiplicity of excited states, then so too can large collections of physical plus subtle substances, combined to form an event, display a spectrum of possible collective states that can be directly experienced.

It is interesting that the many different forms of illusion and hallucination appear to share some striking similarities. Experiments have revealed that four types of clear images have been found in a large number of hallucinatory experiences: (1) a grating or lattice form, (2) a cobweb-like form, (3) a tunnel, funnel or cone form and (4) a spiral form. Not only are the forms themselves similar, but they occur in a natural progression from the lattice shapes to the spiral as the hallucination progresses. Color changes also manifest in this form progression, shifting from blue at the beginning of the experience to yellow, orange and reds in the later stages of the experience[2]. Appendix 4.1 shows how the process of physical sight involves the Fourier transform relationship discussed in Chapter 2 and how this has led Pribram[6] to propose a holographic model for brain processing.

## Conscious and Unconscious Thought Processes

Subliminal perception deals with stimuli below the threshold of ordinary neural sensing. Because subliminal stimuli are not consciously perceived by the ordinary sensory apparatus doesn't mean that they are not perceived at all. It would seem that subliminal perception works at the level where the primary thought processes of unconscious activity originate (the instinctive brain) while the conscious processes are secondary thought processes because they involve higher order processing (in the cerebral cortex or intellectual brain). We now know that two completely separate neurological pathways exist in the brain. One, with fast-conducting nerve fibers, is the well understood "ordinary" sensory data pathway whereby tactile, visual and auditory information proceeds directly from the sensors to the cerebral cortex and then to higher-order information-processing centers. These stimuli immediately become conscious and are actually perceived. Data from sense receptors also proceed along a second pathway to the reticular network system of the brain, an arrangement of constantly branching, highly interconnected nerve cells arranged in a column that runs through the middle of the intellectual brain[2].

To illustrate the difference between the two pathways, let us suppose that you are awakened by a loud sound but can't remember what woke you. This is because the sound has travelled rapidly from the ear, along the fast-conducting fibers, to the cortex where it has been identified as a sound and responded to accordingly. However, the message along the second pathway to the reticular center is the one that actually causes the wakefulness and this signal train travels much more slowly so that, by the time you wake up, the information about what woke you has already come and gone from the cortex[2].

In animal experiments, if one blocks the classical sensory pathway to the cortex, a sleeping animal can still be awakened by touch or sound even though no cortical activity is registered. However, in the reverse situation, where the reticular activating system is blocked but the classical cortical activating system is not blocked, the animal cannot be aroused from sleep[2].

Even though these two systems are separate, it is their interrelationship that defines the state of waking consciousness. The stimulus that affects the reticular portion of the brain can also, if it is strong enough (a non-linear switch), cause the transmission of nerve impulses that make the cortex part of the brain lower its threshold for conscious registration of stimuli arriving from sensory receptors. When the cortex is asleep, its firing threshold has risen to the point where normal sounds do not cause alarm or a waking reaction. From this we see that a subliminal perception can be defined as one for which the level of the stimulus is simply not strong enough to activate the reticular system to send a consciousness-arousing message to the cortex[2].

Just as the nerve impulses from the sense organs split into two separate pathways, one fast and one slow, so too does the brain process information in two separate ways: consciously and unconsciously. Both kinds of thought occur simultaneously and both are in progress most of the time. The conscious processes are described as secondary thought processes because they involve higher order processing and require a larger signal amplitude than the primary thought processes of unconscious activity. Conscious thought, responding to these large strength signals, normally dominates the brain's functions. However, as soon as conscious thought levels diminish, as happens in sleep, or the level of the stimulus drops below the firing threshold for conscious perception, as with subliminal perception, then the unconscious thought processes take over[2].

This model helps explain what happens in sensory deprivation experiences wherein conscious stimulation is intentionally eliminated so that the subject's inner thought processes can come to the fore. The experience of meditation, as well, deliberately turns down the level of secondary thought processes so that the inner processes can be heard[2].

As we close this section, it is useful to emphasise that (1) all three of the inner self-management modalities, discussed briefly in Chapter 2, are designed to turn down the level of the secondary thought processes so that the primary process can be worked with and structurally organized, (2) direct sensory registration of subtle energy correlates is likely to be via the subliminal signal pathways to the reticular network and to the brainstem containing the nerve center that controls involuntary nonconscious muscular activity. For conscious perception of such signals, training is needed to alter the activation of the non-linear behavior of the reticular system so as to more readily send a consciousness-arousing message to the cortex, (3) several of the images observed in hallucinatory experience have a striking resemblance to Figs. 2.14-2.18 and (4) from modern information theory[7] it seems clear that we no not perceive reality but only gain some information about reality; we can never <u>know</u> reality using our presently developed sensory systems. As Emanual Kant said long ago, time and space are merely our vehicles for perception--they are not reality itself.

## Biomechanical Transducers As Subtle Information Detectors

From the previous section, we learned that unconscious level information received by the body appears to go to that primary processing system that controls <u>involuntary nonconscious muscular activity</u>. Let us now see how various types of muscle response can transduce this subliminal information into conscious level information. Besides the applied kinesiology and EM dowsing responses discussed in the last chapter, other important biomechanical transducers are the hand-held pendulum, the vibrating wand and the vascular autonomic reflex system (VAS). All three involve a type of radiesthetic response of a portion of the body to a subtle stimulus. Maby[8] has pointed out that one of the most convincing proofs of the reflex physiological nature of traditional radiesthetic and dowsing responses is to be seen in the consistent numerical relationship between a randomly varied physical stimulus and the neuromuscular response to it. He has shown that the radiesthetic reactions nicely obey Weber and Fechner's classical (logarithmic) law for ordinary physiological sensations. On the other hand, if the response were psychological (e.g. imaginary or auto-suggested), one would find no such precise numerical relationship.

My first-hand experience with this topic was with a dowser who I will refer to as WC. He was the main human subject in a year-long study that I conducted in the early 70's. Although I (WAT) was not initially able to function as an effective human transducer using a hand-held wand, I was eventually able to do so and some joint studies will be reported on to illustrate commonalities and variances.

WC, in his water dowsing, generally utilizes three types of instruments which are illustrated in Fig. 4.1. The full length of the instrument in (a) is about 36 inches, and the copper handles are mainly for comfort. To hold the instrument, the hands are held palm up with forearms bent at roughly right angles out in front of the body (arms relaxed). The fingers are wrapped around the copper sleeves with the thumb on the side of the rod (pointing back towards the body). This is generally used first in the sequence to locate the general vicinity of an underground stream.

The second step in the sequence is to utilize the angle rods illustrated in Fig. 4.1b. These are about 1 foot long with 6-inch open sleeves that rest on a half-nut stopper joined to the welding rod by epoxy or silver solder. An angle rod is held in each hand by gripping the copper sleeves and holding the sleeves vertically in front of the body at the same distance from the body with the tips slightly depressed below the horizontal. Thus, the rods extend horizontally in front of the body and are free to swing in a horizonal plane. These rods are used to locate the edge positions of the stream (by automatically crossing when you cross one border and uncrossing again as you cross the other border) and to map out the detailed locus of the underground stream.

The third step in the sequence is to utilize the counter rod illustrated in Fig. 4.1c. It consists of a 1/16-inch diameter spring steel rod about 26 inches long with a small half-nut epoxied on one end and a 1/2-inch diameter, 5-inch long, thick-walled steel tube epoxied to the other end. This device is held in the right hand (for a right-handed person) and is used for indicating both the depth of the stream, its linear rate of flow, its volume rate of flow and the direction of flow (all are wand oscillatory responses to the specific mentally-asked question).

In our study, we were not involved in the location of water but in the study of subtle fields around specific materials and around humans. For our studies, we utilized only the counter rod as depicted in Fig. 4.1c; however, for a special experiment, a handle such as illustrated in Fig. 4.1d was attached. The experimental procedure was generally to grasp the wand with the right hand, which is firmly braced against the right side of the body, with the left hand held either free of the body or touching the left side of the body above the waistline. The wand tip is located in the immediate vicinity of the object or human body under test and the motion of the tip observed.

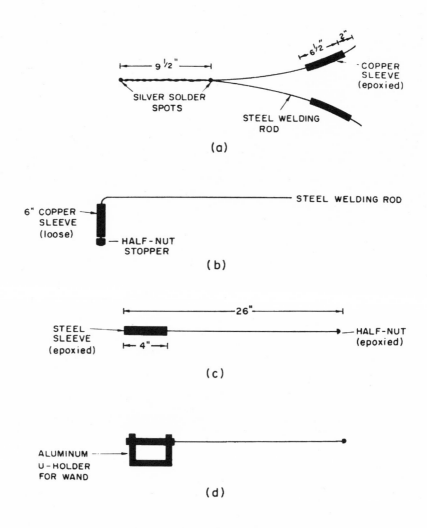

**Fig. 4.1** The different types of sensing devices used by a dowser.

The general mode of the tip motion is elliptical with either clockwise or counterclockwise steady rotation or oscillatory rotation. In the extremes, this leads to the five distinct periodic modes of wand tip motion indicated in Fig. 4.2--clockwise circular rotation, counterclockwise circular rotation, oscillatory circular rotation, vertical linear oscillation and horizontal linear oscillation. On a finer scale of tuning, information discrimination is also present in the specific angle of linear oscillation relative to the horizonal and in the degree of ellipticity of the tip motion (aspect ratio of the ellipse). This fine scale tuning is only for accomplished practitioners and so I restricted our information modes to the five illustrated in Fig. 4.2.

In our study of different materials, we have found that they fall into four unique categories which have been designated as (1) bipolar, (2) unipolar (positive), (3) unipolar (negative) and (4) oscillating. In Appendix 4.2, it is shown how all these modes of motion can be understood via the superposition of right-handed and left-handed circularly polarized waves.

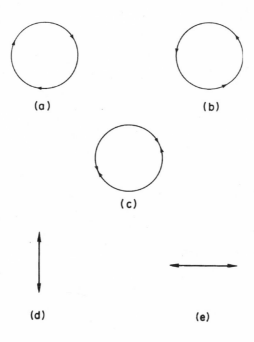

Fig. 4.2 The five most distinctive types of wand tip motion.

**Bipolar Materials:** This is the most common material response and, for the wand held in the right hand and the tip placed close to the object as in Fig. 4.3, it yields a right-hand (clockwise) rotation (Fig. 4.2a) on the right side of the material, a left-hand (counterclockwise) rotation on the left side of the material (Fig. 4.2b) and vertical oscillations directly over the top of the material (Fig. 4.2d). With the wand held in the left hand, the directions of rotation are reversed. If the wand is held on the same side (right side, say) of the material for too long a period of time then, after rotating clockwise for a period, the motion becomes erratic, the operator begins to feel tension in his arm and his body begins to feel strange. Next. the wand begins rotating counterclockwise and he finds his body polarity has been reversed (see below). Most household objects and materials fall into this category.

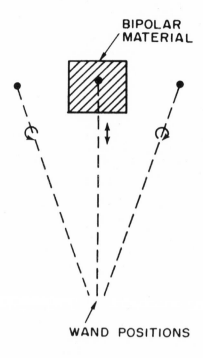

**Fig. 4.3** Illustration of a unique wand tip motion pattern near a bipolar material.

**Unipolar Materials:** For this kind of material, the wand exhibits only clockwise rotation (positive) or only counterclockwise rotation (negative) no matter what the location of the wand relative to the material object. Most unipolar materials were found to be of the positive variety and generally are beneficial herbs like ginseng, gotukola, fo-ti-ting, etc. WC related to me that the male gonads and male sperm were also found to be of this polarity. The only unipolar materials of the negative variety that he ever found were the female gonads and the corresponding secretion. He stated that the two secretions combined on a glass slide yielded the familiar bipolar response.

**Oscillating Polarity Materials:** With this class of material, it does not matter where the wand is spatially located with respect to the material object (so long as it is close), one observes that the tip rotates to the right, and then stops and rotates to the left and then stops and reverses its direction of rotation again, etc., ad infinitum. In this category, we find materials such as mercury, lead, arsenic, cadmium, poisons like rattlesnake venom, diethylstilbesterol, etc. In all these studies, if the wand is in the right hand, the left hand needs to be held within ~6 to 16 inches of the object in order to have any motion generated at the tip. The exceptions to this are when the operator either holds some of the material in his/her left hand or it is in contact with his/her body (either outside or inside).

**Table 4.1**  Wand Responses to Different Materials by Two Different Operators

| MATERIAL | WC OBSERVATION | WAT OBSERVATION |
|---|---|---|
| Peg leg mineral   (1) | Bipolar, body circuits OK | Bipolar, body circuits OK |
| Isotone  (2) | Positive polarity, " | Positive polarity, " |
| Discharge material   (3) | Oscillating polarity, " | Oscillating polarity, " |
| Peg leg + discharge material | Oscillating      " " | Oscillating      " " |
| Peg leg + discharge material + isotone | Positive      " " | Positive      " " |
| Azurite | Oscillating      " " | Positive      " " |
| Lithium (Li) | Positive      " " | Positive      " " |
| Molybdenum (Mo) | Positive      " " | Positive      " " |
| Azurite + Li | Positive      " " | Positive, but less than azurite above |
| Azurite + Mo | Zero      " body circuits knocked out | Positive, and stronger than azurite + Li |
| Azurite + Li + Mo | Zero      " body circuits OK | Zero, and body circuits knocked out |
| Isotone + Azurite + Li + Mo | Zero      " body circuits OK | Postive polarity |
| Diethylstilbesterol | Oscillating polarity, all body circuits oscillate; feel shaky in body, etc. | Oscillating polarity, all body circuits oscillate and one feels shaky. |

(1)  A large number of powdered minerals in a jar.
(2)  A number of beneficial herbs in a liquid solution in a jar.
(3)  A number of poisons and dileterious substances in an epoxy block.

A general comment that should be made at this juncture is that, although WC and WAT obtained identical responses for most materials tested, there were some materials that always produced different responses between us. One example is the mineral azurite (hydrated copper carbonate) which always yielded a positive polarity for WAT (and always strengthened him) but which always yielded an oscillating polarity for WC (and always weakened him).

Finally, the polarity results obtained with combinations of different materials are worthy of comment. It was found that two-material combinations, produced by placing jars of each side by side, can lead to a wand response that may be the same as one of the members or different than either of them. For three member combinations, the same options hold. In Table 4.1, the results for WC and WAT testing a variety of material combinations are given.

**Some Human Body Polarity Results:** The polarities of all individuals studied fall into two categories: (a) macroscopically bipolar and (b) macroscopically unipolar (positive) with wand motions as illustrated in Fig. 4.4. For these results, the experimenter was facing the subject and holding the wand in his right hand. For most people, one finds that the left sole, left palm and left eye exhibit a positive polarity while the right sole, right hand and right eye exhibit a negative polarity. In 1% to 2% of the cases, the polarities are reversed. Along the centerline (front and back) of a bipolar person, a vertical oscillation (Fig. 4.2d) was observed. No such centerline effect was observed with a unipolar person.

Although we didn't find any significant hand polarity reversals related to gender differences, a friend who is also a healer/clairvoyant finds that at least one primary circuit is reversed between the two genders. For example, she finds that, in women, the strongest healing hand is usually the left whereas, in men, it is generally the right. In addition, it may be useful to recall the copper-wall study mentioned in Chapter 1 where it was found that the magnet suspended over the subject's head was a key part of their transpersonal experiencing and that a reverse orientation was observed between the two genders for the maximum effect.

In our study, it was possible to determine the directions of energy flow in a bipolar body by the following simple experiment. If we pick up the jar of oscillating polarity material in our left hand and hold it for a moment before setting it down, then, with the wand in the right hand and the tip close to the oscillating polarity material but the left hand far removed

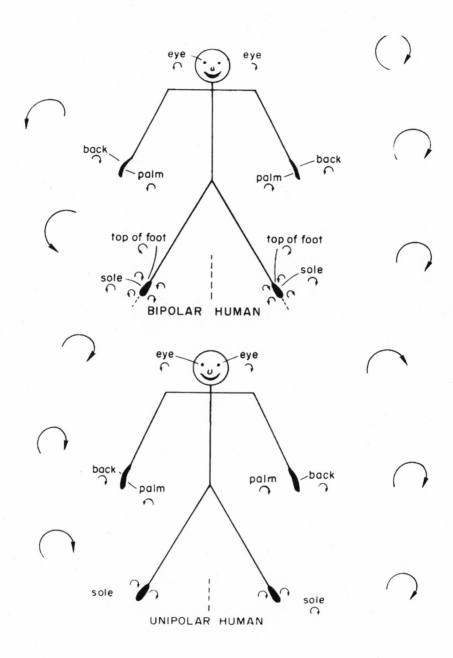

**Fig. 4.4** Polarities around the human body detected by wand tip motion for (a) a typical bipolar human and (b) a unipolar human.

from the material, we still obtain the proper tip motion and, after several minutes, the amplitude of oscillation gradually dies down to zero. This suggests that initially holding the material in the left hand allowed a certain amount of the key energies to enter the body.

If we repeat our experiment but this time pick up the jar with the right hand and then, after having set it down again, we test for wand motion while the left hand is held far away, we find no wand motion. This confirmed that the energy entered the left hand and exited from the right hand. A large variety of similar experiments were carried out with various parts of the body[9] with the ultimate conclusion that three main energy circuits were present in the body: (1) a leg circuit, (2) a trunk circuit and (3) a head circuit. The connection for the leg and trunk circuits is at the groin while that for the head and trunk circuits is at the neck. For the lower circuit, the main energy stream appears to enter through the sole of the left foot, travel up the left leg to the groin and generally travel down the right leg to exit via the sole of the right foot. However, this energy flow can be induced to cross over into the trunk circuit at the groin and exit via the right hand[9]. For the trunk circuit, the main energy stream appears to enter via the palm of the left hand, travel up the left arm to the shoulder, into the trunk of the body and across to the right shoulder, down the right arm and out the right hand. This energy stream can also be induced to enter the lower circuit near the groin and exit via the right leg or enter the head circuit at the neck and exit via the right eye[9]. For the head circuit, the main energy stream enters via the left eye and exits via the right eye. Likewise, this stream can be induced to cross over into the trunk circuit at the neck, etc.

From the foregoing, we find that the wand response is not just a function of the material under study but is also a function of the stability of the energy circuitry of the wand holder. We found that, when conducting studies with certain unknown materials, new shape configurations or just extended sequences of tests, one or several of the operator's three main circuits often temporarily ceased to function; i.e., give no wand response whatsoever. With time and practice, we learned a number of techniques for restoring normal function to these circuits and so could go on and repeat the "fuse blowing" experiment. Interestingly, on many occasions, WC could be experimenting on one side of the lab while WAT was sitting ~12 feet away writing down the observations. Then, one of WC's circuits would go out and WAT would suddenly feel a strange sensation in his own body. By checking his own circuits, WAT would find that his same circuit would be out also. Thus, not only were WC and the material under study part of a unique energy circuit, but WAT from 12 feet away was part of the circuit as well. When an energy surge blew the fuse box in WC's circuit, it tripped that in WAT's too. With further study, it was found that members of the same family generally exhibit a similar energy circuit connectedness.

Whatever kind of energy we were dealing with, it seemed to connect all members mentally and/or emotionally involved in the experiment as part of the human component of the measuring circuit. With experience, we found that these energy circuits became fatigued after several energy reversals so that, if insufficient time was allowed between repeats of a particular experiment, the results were not found to be reproducible. I found it remarkable that, after only ~4-6 hours of this type of seemingly easy experimentation with many blown and restored circuit events, I was totally exhausted and my urine had turned a dark brown with a strong ammonia smell. Clearly, something substantial happened at a physiological level during such experimentation!

**Postulated Mechanism of Device Operation:** In this overall study, five key observations were made that allow one to speculate on the essential elements of a mechanism. These are: (1) if the wand is gripped by its handle (Fig. 4.1d) in a vise while the fingers are wrapped around the steel sleeve and objects are carried into the vicinity of the tip--no motion of the tip is observed. However, if the vise is detached from the edge of the bench and placed on a resilient material which, in turn, rests on the bench top, then one begins to see a slow buildup to a large amplitude of motion (one also sees very small undulations of the vise on its flexible cushion). (2) If the wand without the handle (Fig. 4.1c), is held with fingers wrapped around the steel sleeve and pointed directly at the center of the object (along a radial line), then negligible motion of the wand is observed even when the wand tip is almost touching the object. However, if a finite perpendicular exists between the object and the wand axis, then tip motion is observed. (3) The type of motion of the wand tip is independent of the spatial direction of approach to the object by the subject; i.e., N, S, E or W. (4) If a specific element is brought up to the wand and this same element is contained in the body to a measurable degree, tip motion ensues even though the left hand is held away from the sample. If the specific element is not contained in the body to a sufficient degree, no tip motion is detected. If someone then places the specific element in the left hand of the subject, tip motion ensues and increases in amplitude to a level above that seen in the first case above. (5) The tip motion results determined by different operators studying the same object are sometimes different even though the results are consistently repeatable for the same operator.

Observation (5) suggests that different operators may have energy sensing circuitry that is different in detail and that energy passage through the operator is needed for wand response. Observation (1) suggests that energy passage through the operator triggers a process within the operator that eventually leads to organized movement in the small muscles of the hand. Observation (2) suggests that more than energy passage through the operator is needed for wand tip motion, i.e., the energy must react directly on the wand tip to produce some type of small periodic force on the tip that can move the tip laterally by a small displacement. It is fairly well known that, for bistable systems (the wand is a bistable system) subject to both small amplitude periodic forcing and random noise forcing, an increase in the input noise can result in an <u>improvement</u> in the output signal-to-noise ratio (a typical characteristic of non-linear systems)[10]. This has been called stochastic resonance. Observation (3) suggests that the type of energy being sensed by the device is being emitted radially by the object. Finally, observation (4) suggests that a type of resonance develops between the energy signature on the wand handle/human body side and the wand tip/object side and that this is crucial to large amplitude motion.

Two main reservations should be stated about the repeatability and reliability of this type of sensing: (a) the motion of the wand can also be influenced by the operator's conscious mind through voluntary muscle action rather than by the operator's unconscious mind through involuntary muscle action and (b) we seem to be an adaptive organism whose essential circuits for this type of measurement may still be in the process of change so that wand motion results obtained on the same test a year or two apart may be slightly different. When I first began to obtain wand motion, it was extremely easy for me to make the wand move in either direction by only slight mental concentration. It is not at all surprising that this should happen and that mentally generated voluntary muscle signals could swamp out the sensor signal--generated <u>involuntary</u> muscle movement. Fortunately, with practice, the magnitude of the sensor signal seemed to increase and the ease of "mentally" cheating decrease. It is extremely important to try to remove any mental bias during a measurement because it is relatively easy to let voluntary muscle control slip in if we are looking for a preconceived result. Conversely, if we approach a measurement with a detached mental state, we can obtain clear and unambiguous readings.

**Other Examples Of The Dowsing Response:** It has long been known that, using a pendulum held from the hand by a string or a chain, one is able to obtain a set of involuntary pendulum motions which confer information. These motions correspond closely to those illustrated in Fig. 4.2 except that, because the pendulum "bob" moves in a horizontal plane, a richness of angular information can also be accessed. The pendulum responds to the same set of energies that stimulate the wands illustrated in Fig. 4.1 and utilize the same involuntary muscle movement mechanism to transfer the normally unconscious level information to conscious awareness. Many more people exhibit sufficient body conductivity to utilize the pendulum technique than the wand technique and, in many ways, it is easier to use for accessing energy and other special types of information. And it has been utilized to enhance one's intuition in a wide variety of professional areas; e.g., medicine, science, engineering, business, human relations, etc. Little more will be said, here, about this technique as many satisfactory books are already available on the details and uses[11-15].

As indicated in Chapter 1, the gentleman who produced the remarkable photographic results shown in Figs. 1.10-1.13, utilized a dowsing response in his 7th cervical and 4th thoracic vertibrae to time his camera action. Others have utilized a specific throb in the throat or a twitch of the eye, etc. All of these are associated with an involuntary muscle response. A slight variant of the above that is achieving great utility by a number of forward-looking medical practitioners is called the VAS (Vascular Autonomic System). Let us look at it a little more closely.

**The Vascular Autonomic System (VAS):** In kinesiology, skeletal muscle reflexes (which are controlled by cerebral cortex centers) are utilized for the monitoring of pathological states and the homeostatic conditions of patients. On the other hand, smooth muscle (which sheathes arteries and intestines) is innervated by the autonomic nervous system originating in the hypothalamus. It is relatively isolated from the cerebral cortex and can thus be utilized to identify subtle energies.

The vascular autonomic signal (VAS) was a fortuitous discovery by Nogier[16]. He documented changes in sympathetic and parasympathetic tone of the autonomic nervous system that correlated with specific stimuli to the ear via monitoring a change in the amplitude of the palpitated pulse of the radial artery on the wrist. He called this response the Auricular Cardiac Reflex (ACR). Kenyon[17] used the ACR to determine which foods and chemicals a particular person cannot tolerate. Navach[18] discovered a therapeutic window which is a positive-VAS lasting between 9 and 15 seconds. The window facilitates the decision about which treatment vehicle is the one of choice.

One utilized the therapeutic window in the following way: for the manual VAS technique, a sample of the substance being evaluated is brought to a distance of about 6 cm from the patient's ear and, simultaneously, the VAS is read by palpating the patient's radial artery. A positive-VAS response indicates, in a general sense, that the patient can function in homeostasis with that particular substance at that volume and concentration. If the VAS remains positive for between 9 and 15 seconds, the particular dosage under test has therapeutic potential and, the closer to 12 seconds, the greater the therapeutic potential. If the VAS responds negatively to a very small amount of substance, it indicates that the food, fabric, medication, etc., is being rejected[19].

With respect to the VAS technique it is important to realize that the ear is innervated by branches derived from the trigeminal, facial, glossopharyngeal, vagus, major auricular and minor occipital nerves. Of these, the vagus nerve is the most important (see Fig. 4.5)[20]. Probably the major basis for the effectiveness of ear acupuncture is the fact that the concha of the ear is the only place on the surface of the body where one can easily stimulate fibers of the vagus nerve. This nerve reaches many of the major viscera of the body and therefore represents a parasympathetic homeostatic regulatory mechanism.

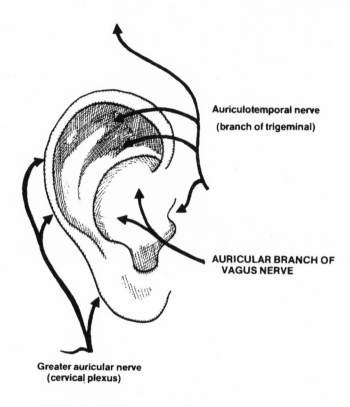

Auriculotemporal nerve
(branch of trigeminal)

AURICULAR BRANCH OF
VAGUS NERVE

Greater auricular nerve
(cervical plexus)

**Fig. 4.5** Innervation areas of the ear.

When the body and its auric field are stimulated by a weak energy to which it can adapt, the radial artery pulse tension increases for a few beats. Nogier[16] named this more tense pulse beat the "VAS". An abruptly diminished pulse tension having its onset triggered by a weak energy to which the body cannot adapt is called the "negative"-VAS. The three functional modes of the pulse are: the basal state, the VAS and the negative-VAS. The practitioner observes the reflex by a method of palpation of the radial artery at the wrist (Fig 4.6a.) and the pulse signal must be observed as it occurs (Fig. 4.6b). It is the change from one pulse mode to another as it occurs that must be observed[21]. Once the pulse change occurs, the new mode (VAS or negative-VAS) lasts only a few beats ( ~5-20) and then fades back to the basal state (see Fig. 4.6b).

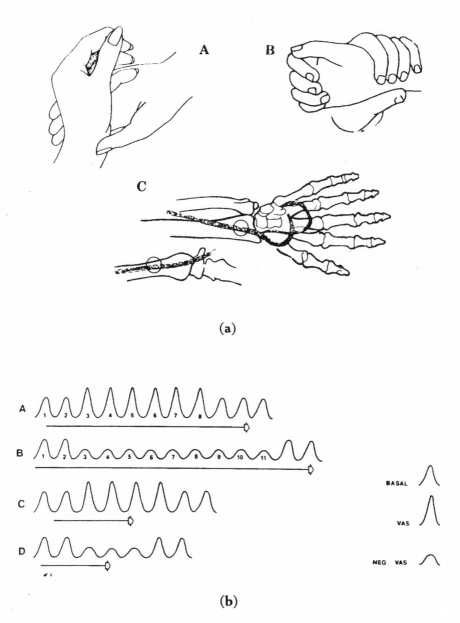

**Fig. 4.6** (a) Measurement of the Vascular Autonomic Signal (VAS) by palpating the radial artery. Either the thumb (A) or fingers (B) can be used to monitor the pulse while the circle (C) indicates the ideal site over the artery for palpation. (b) The VAS beats feel sharper, more peaked and more firm than the regular basal beats while the negative-VAS beats feel rounded and diminished in amplitude.

The sensing of the signal that eventually leads to the VAS is thought to occur via an electromagnetic induction response (a Van der Walle type of dynamic molecular polarization) to the sample held near the ear. Biochemical receptors located at sites containing neurohormones (which are EM-sensitive compounds) are induced to resonate by the stimulus they receive. The geometrical configuration of the neurohormone molecule changes and thus so does the surrounding biochemistry. Navach[18] sought the chemical basis of the rapid information transfer inherent in homeostasis and looked to the biochemistry of aromatic compounds and their characteristic nuclear magnetic resonance properties. Neurohormones, it would seem are the chemical foundation for the transfer of EM information. A single neurohormone cluster inside the skin may be induced to resonate by an outside EM source. Navach proposed that this causes a change to occur in messenger RNA in nearby cells, as well as in nearby hormones and neurotransmitters. These resonating neurohormone clusters, in turn, may stimulate secondary and tertiary neurohormone clusters in the same location and then in distal locations.

Navach[22] showed via the use of a variety of instrumentation, and in particular a 20 MHz ultrasonic Doppler System, that the VAS could be recorded. He showed that a positive-VAS response was produced by a retrograde arterial pressure wave accompanied by an increase in sympathetic tone and a concomittant decrease in the forward pressure wave. The converse occurred for a negative-VAS response. His experiments appeared to confirm that we are dealing here with a helical standing wave on the radial artery with the positive-VAS being correlated with a clockwise helix rotation and the negative VAS being correlated with a counter clockwise helix rotation. Perhaps this indicates some connection with the clockwise and counterclockwise wand tip rotations for human energy fields illustrated in Fig. 4.4. and discussed in Appendix 4.A.2.

In Navach's orthopedic practice, he routinely incorporates the phenomenon of the VAS response to various substances to reliably prescribe medications and dosages for patients. Thus, the ability to choose the appropriate antibiotic with the optimum response for an orthopedic infection without having to wait for the subsequent culture and sensitivity tests to be performed has significantly reduced hospitalization. Further, the ability to determine whether patients are allergic to medications such as antibiotics and, more importantly, the ability to predict whether patients will have adverse reactions to substances like methyl methacrylate implants in total joint replacement, have greatly reduced complications.

## Self-Healing By Energy Field Pumping And Balancing

I have used the energy field insights described in the last section for the past two decades to produce self-healing and preventative medicine for myself and my family and am pleased to be able to share what I have learned. For me, I have found great benefits in following these procedures but I do not know how universal such results might be for others.

Before describing the experimental findings, it is perhaps useful to lay out my personal theoretical perspective on this issue. First, the properties of a material giving rise to its unique wand motion are thought to come from its etheric components. Likewise, the specific wand motions found around a person's body also come from a pattern of etheric-type flow of the radiation variety. This type of flow is a little peculiar in that, if it slows down too much, it can become very viscous so as to partially convert to etheric atoms and molecules and form a gel-like state that blocks the energy flow. The body joints, because they are density discontinuities in the system, are impedances in the flow so etheric energy flow stagnation is most likely to occur at these locations. This flowing radiation field is like an etheric catalysis atmosphere for the etheric substance of the body, either creating or disassembling etheric chemical counterparts needed to balance the physical chemicals present. The palm chakras are part of the secondary chakra system that pump this radiation into and out of the body.

Second, whatever healing or major change is going on at the etheric level of the body, it is coming from the mental level by directed intention. It is directed from the higher levels of mind that cause the changes in the etheric and consequently in the physical. The wand motion is merely an indicator that the process is either still going on or that it is complete. The specific type of motion is a result of the personal code used by the operator and has no absolute meaning in and of itself.

During my experiments with WC, I recognized a possible correlation between our three proposed main energy circuits in the body and the Eeman's Relaxation Circuit[23]. Eeman's experimental arrangement is illustrated in Fig. 4.7a and consists of an individual (clothed) plus copper mats and copper wires. The back of the head and the right hand were found to be of one polarity. The base of the spine and the left hand were found to be of the opposite polarity. The individual is aligned along the magnetic flux line with head to the north and feet to the south (ankles crossed). If he/she is energy right-handed and connected in this way, he/she will just relax in this particular circuit and this brings about a balancing of the energies in his/her body. If the hand connections are reversed, a tension circuit is built which right-handed people find almost unbearable after a little while. If the individual is left-handed (energy-wise), the situation is reversed. In the experiments I have personally carried out with this type of circuit, I have utilized a slightly simpler circuit illustrated in Fig. 4.7b. Each copper mat

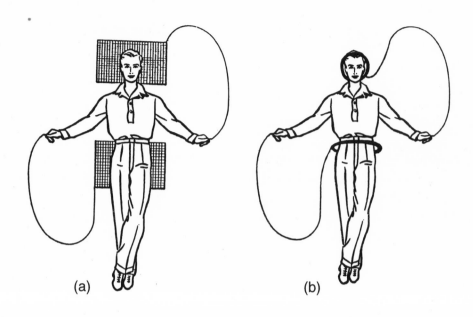

**Fig. 4.7** (a) Illustration of the Eeman's Relaxation Circuit and (b) Tiller's modification of Eemans' design.

has been replaced by a simple copper loop; one around the head making contact at the base of the brain and looping over a region ~3" above the eyebrows and the other looping around the waist at the base of spine level. When lying on top of a bed in the Fig. 4.7b circuit connection, I note a strong subjective feeling of energy flowing through my body, sometimes quite intensely in certain parts of the body before they relax. After a one-half hour session in the circuit, I feel greatly relaxed, energized and mentally centered for the following six to ten hours. Years ago, I found this so effective that I would even take it on business trips to ensure that I was able to deliver high quality performance.

From the point of view of our dowsing wand results, I would attribute the utility of the Eeman's circuit to an equalization of some "biological" etheric potential within the three main body circuits. The left hand draws energy from the head circuit, feeds it through the trunk of the body and out the right hand into the leg circuit. One might hypothesize that, in this way, the three main circuits are essentially "shorted out" to equalize their potentials and it is this which allows the body to relax.

If this line of speculation was close to the truth, then the copper serves only as a conductor of this energy and one should be able to obtain similar results by just using the bare hands. I have tried this and found it to work for me using the following simple protocol: lie on a bed, couch or floor, somewhat on one's left side, with the left hand at the back of the head (base of skull), the right hand at the base of the spine and left ankle over the right. The body orientation with respect to north does not seem to be strongly critical. In about 15 minutes, the head thoughts have disappeared and the body has progressed into a deeper and deeper relaxation state. This procedure has been most beneficial for me on those nights when I have found it difficult to drop off to sleep because too many ideas are bouncing around in my head. It has also proven to be therapeutic for the elimination of female menstrual cramps by having the female lie face-up on a couch and, kneeling on the floor, I place the left hand under the base of her skull while the right hand is placed under the base of her spine. Besides copper, silk appears to be a good conductor of these bioenergies[24] and a commercial product of the Eeman design is available in either copper or silk[25].

All during the 1960's and early 70's, I had a severe lower back problem and would generally visit my favorite chiropractor every winter when the weather turned cold. The severity was such that I would go three times a week for the first month (diathermy, manipulation, etc.), twice a week for the second month and once a week for the third. In the early 70's I decided to try an experiment on myself using my own hands to heal this problem. Every day, first thing in the morning and last thing at night, I would sit erect and place my hands on my back (overlapping my spine) and start as high up on the back as I could reach. Initially, I would leave the hands there for ~1 minute or so and then shift them a palm-width lower for the next minute or so and then progressively lower them until I reached my tailbone. The whole process would take ~ 5-10 minutes wherein I could first feel warmth and then relaxation of the muscles in my back. It seemed as if my right hand was acting like an energy hose injecting energy into the back, which stimulated the neural system and activated the vascular system, while the left hand acted like a vacuum to return the stream to the internal pumping source. I didn't miss a day of this practice and found that I suddenly didn't need to visit the chiropractor at all--for the next 15 years.

This energy pumping system works in all of us to some degree but, to readily see a cause/effect relationship with what one does with the hands, one needs to be able to achieve and exceed a minimum pump current of this energy. I reasoned that we all had internal resistance to this energy flow, just like electrical resistance in the wires of an electrical circuit, and this is what partially limits the biological current flow. If this internal resistance could be reduced, the current level (for a fixed etheric potential source) would increase and more speedy healing would occur. I eventually found that, by sitting with my palms held face to face in contact (the prayer configuration), I could feel the energy flowing around the arm circuit and, the longer it flowed, I felt as if the more organized became the channel of flow and therefore the lower was the flow resistance. Doing this while one is sitting and watching television is a relatively painless way to enhance one's energy flow current in the trunk circuit. With continual practice, my capability for pumping energy via my hands became better and better. To enhance the current flow in the leg circuit, sitting with the soles of the feet in direct contact seems to work. I didn't put as much effort into lowering the resistance of that circuit as I did for the trunk circuit and I didn't put any effort at all into doing likewise for the head circuit. It is really a type of "muscle" building so, the more you practice with intention the more energy pumping can you do.

Over the years I have found it possible to reduce and often eliminate the stress from a certain region of the body by placing the hands on the body in such a placement as to enhance the natural etheric energy flow. For example:

(1) <u>Sore Left Thigh</u>--Place the left palm on the thigh closer to the groin and the right palm closer to the knee, thus bracketing the sore region.

(2) <u>Sore Right Thigh</u>--Place the left palm on the thigh closer to the knee and the right palm closer to the groin, thus bracketing the sore region.

(3) <u>Indigestion After Eating</u>--Place left palm on or below stomache and right palm higher up on chest, both being centrally located on the body.

(4) <u>Sore Throat</u>--Place left palm on upper chest just below the throat and right palm on throat up under the chin.

(5) <u>Headache</u>--Place left palm on forehead and right palm at back of the head at base of brain area.

My advice is to just experiment with yourself to find out what works well for you. In all of these procedures, as the energy form causing the initial pain passes out of the region and through the trunk circuit, a type of energy polarization seems to develop in the wrist joints and this diminishes the current flow. Thus, periodically, it is beneficial to rotate the wrists which seems to discharge this polarization energy (often with a sharp "crack" sound) allowing the energy current to increase to its initial level.

A second mode of etheric energy adjustment is the one-handed mode. For example, by placing one's left hand on one's own body or someone else's body, etheric energy of this particular type can be removed from that location. By using the right hand, this energy can be introduced into the body. If an individual has a pain at a particular location in his/her body, then he/she or someone else can diminish the pain by placing the left hand on the location with the right hand held out from the body to release the energy stream into the atmosphere. The left palm (secondary chakra) acts something like a suction pump to pull an energy stream from the subject's body at that location and this is eventually passed through the practitioner's body and out the right palm. It appears that this energy stream carries with it some quantity of the energy form causing the pain. If one makes contact with the acupuncture me-ridian and acupuncture points for that pain area, the treatment time is decreased. If one presses on these acupuncture points with the finger tips (even through clothing), the treatment time is further decreased. Although one can discharge the energy into a variety of media, the energy polarization effect discussed above appears to limit the process. The best type of <u>sink</u> for this energy discharge found to date is an oscillating polarity material. A combination of oscillating polarity materials, presumably providing a much broader frequency band than any single member, seems to be the most efficient.

A third mode of subtle energy adjustment, and perhaps the most effec-tive for beginners, is to place the wand of Fig. 4.1c in the right hand with the tip held ~4 to 6 inches from a jar of multiple oscillating polarity materials. Then, with the left hand, locate those relevant acupuncture points that seem tender to the touch. An oscillating motion will appear at the wand tip with the radius of the circle being directly related to the pathological energy current flow and the severity of the condition. The left finger (or fingers) is maintained on the A.P. until the amplitude of motion dies down to zero (which may take several minutes). Often the finger touching the A.P. may feel painfully hot and often the hand holding the wand will respond in a similar fashion. It is beneficial to break the circuit every few minutes and rotate the wrists to eliminate any in-ternal polarization that may have been set up. This procedure is continued periodically until no further oscillatory wand motion is noted, indicating that the source of the oscillating polarity has been reduced to negligible strength.

From the personal experience to date, almost any subject can relieve many of his/her aches and pains by using the wand technique. Even though the individual may not initially be a good conductor of these energies, holding the wand in the right hand and letting the tip touch the oscillating polarity jar seems to be sufficient for producing a small leakage of the pain-producing cur-rent from the body. The discharge sink should always be placed on the right side of the body and at least 18 inches from the body (and handled by the right hand only). This overall procedure of using the wand has also been found to be effective for burns. In this case, one holds the left hand over but not touching the burned skin and discharges through the wand tip until the skin has cooled. It then will be possible to touch the skin and continue the treat-ment until the energy discharging stops.

Over the years, I have found it extremely therapeutic to just hold a jar of positive polarity material in my left hand or place it on my body at the lo-cation of the malady (sore eyes, upset stomache, shoulder muscle ache, etc.). Whether this just strengthens the etheric energy flow field in my aura or con-cretizes my intention, I don't know--it just works! Similar advantages some-times occur via using the bipolar mix jar, but they never seem as profound as with the unipolar material jar. It has also been found that placing a jar of such material on a computer or television set or in a fluorescent light fixture appears to eliminate the body stress normally generated by such devices. I always keep a jar of each on my desk, near my bed and in my travelling kit should a particular need for their use arise.

## From Maintained Intention To Body Structure Changes

As discussed in earlier chapters, our body structure at the physical level is stable and sustained by a type of chemical homeostasis or chemical pattern which, in turn, is kept stable by a pattern of electrical and magnetic potentials and other positive space-time patterns of potential. These positive space-time patterns of energy are themselves kept stable by specific inverse space-time patterns of potential which are themselves stabilized by energy field patterns at the mind level of the universe. At this point, it is useful to recall Wolf's Law of Bone Structure: If one of our bones receives a non-uniform stress for an extended period of time, the bone will grow new trabeculae (a type of bone girder) in the exact location needed to maximally support this stress distribution. The physical strain field probably interacts with the electrostatic field of the system (via the piezoelectric effect) producing certain field changes, and these changes cause ions and molecules to be carried to specific locations where they can agglomerate into the specific tissue and structural components of the trabeculae.

Carrying this idea further, we can think of mental field patterns as acting like a stress to influence the magnetochemical potential of the etheric molecules at the inverse space-time level of the body. Via the deltron potential link, this pattern produces the required correlate at the positive space-time level of physical chemicals and thus finally to influence the physical structure of the body.

It is important to realize that, when we remove the body stress that created a certain pattern of trabeculae in a bone, the trabeculae do not dissolve at once. Rather, they may dissolve only very slowly (under the proper regime of physical exercise) because of the detailed molecular dynamics involved and they may maintain the body in a distorted shape for a very long time even though the initial cause has been removed. The same is true for physical structures generated by emotional or mental stress. However, when these unharmonious patterns, which scatter energy from the main flow at the various levels already discussed, are finally removed, more energy will be available for body function.

To illustrate further how maintained intention can produce structural changes in a body gland or organ to enhance its level of functioning, consider one process for making a magnetic material in the laboratory. Let us say that we are going to make a strong magnet out of a metallic alloy called permalloy. One way is to heat the solid up to a high temperature where the magnetic precipitates in the alloy go into solution in the solid (very much as salt or sugar would go into solution in water as you heat the water). Then, after soaking at the high temperature for some time, you cool the material through a critical temperature range, and you find that little particles of a magnetic material come out of solution (again, very much as salt or sugar would come out of a hot solution if you cool it enough).

172

Now, think of these little magnetic particles as being like needles with a field-direction arrow on them. They precipitate out of solution and the arrows are pointing in all kinds of different directions as illustrated in Fig. 4.8a. The total or net magnetic field, $H_{net}$, of this material, would be the sum of all the components of these arrows pointing in a particular direction. Of course, because the individual arrows are almost randomly oriented, the sum in any particular direction is very small. Thus, although we have made a magnetic material, it is not a very good one! All right, now what can we do about that? Suppose we think "let us apply a strong external magnetic field to this material during its cooling stage". That is, apply a magnetic field, $H_{imposed}$, directed upwards along the axis of the bar as illustrated in Fig. 4.8b. Now, with this imposed magnetic field present, as the magnetic particles come out of solution both their birth and growth are influenced. Now, instead of being randomly oriented, they align themselves closely with this applied field. After you cool the sample down and take away the imposed magnetic field used during the processing, you find that your bar now has a very strong net magnetic field when you add up all the little arrows. You now have a material with a very large internal magnetic field.

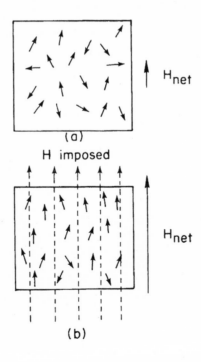

**Fig. 4.8** Schematic illustration of the formation of a magnet by the precipitation of a magnetic phase from solution under (a) no applied field and (b) the influence of an applied field, $H_{imposed}$.

Basically, you have processed the material in such a way as to increase its polarization in a particular direction: that is, its useful polarization in this direction. You have done it via the influence of an applied external field during the birth and growth process of these magnetic precipitates. Now that we have this physical picture firmly in mind, let us see how it can be done with a gland in our body.

I first want to postulate that a key part of the glandular functioning is related to subtle level polarization of the cells making up the gland. Thus, the gland functions the way it does largely because of its structure on a cellular level. What we want to do is alter that essential structure at the subtle levels. We make this alteration by the sustained application of a specific mind field; that is, we decide what is the ideal behavior and we mentally apply that image to the gland!

As an illustrative example, let us pick the thymus as the gland we wish to alter. We want to make sure it is polarized so as to much more easily radiate via the love mode than the hate mode. Thus, we take our highest conception of what is the expression of love and we intentionally apply that to the thymus and literally hold that image on the gland. Metaphorically, we can now think of this gland with some intention field pointing in a particular vector direction that represents "high expression of love". In the gland as in other parts of the body, millions of cells die and new ones are born every moment. Now we have a very similar situation to the magnetic material example of Fig. 4.8. We have a situation wherein cells are born in the presence of this influence field, this polarization field, and so orient or polarize themselves to be more closely aligned to this influence field rather than to the field of the unconstrained gland. Think of the influence of this intention field as that of putting a constraint on the gland so that it functions more easily when it operates in the "love" expression mode. However, it is still difficult for it to function consistently in this mode because its easy groove of operation is the habit groove, and that may not be a very high expression of love. However, if persistent application of this specific intention field is continued, eventually all the cells in that gland will have been born under the influence of that field. So, with the passage of time, the gland is basically restructured in the presence of this specific intention field. The gland is eventually able to function in its new habit mode when it expresses this new image of love. Then the intention field may be removed and that portion of the consciousness can be directed to work elsewhere, because the gland will now respond automatically in this new ideal way with respect to its expression of love.

Of course, with further passage of time, the individual will grow further in consciousness and, by so doing, develop an even higher ideal for the expression of love, and thus one needs to go back to the drawing board (or visualization board) and once again apply a specific intention field to again restructure the gland according to this new ideal.

This same procedure is the one responsible for the generation of the vital circuitry between the glands or between the etheric sensory system and the brain; that is, this is how the key linkages are made at the neural level of the physical and etheric bodies. The repeated act of trying to do a particular thing focusses the intention on the unconnected nerve ends that are important for successful fulfillment of the act. This intention field is ultimately manifest at the physical level as a voltage gradient between these nerve ends. The electrical stress polarizes the intervening cells so that they are eventually organized into appropriate nerve cells and the connection between the nerve endings is made. Electrical pulses can now flow and information can be transferred along this new transmission line so that the brain may now know of the message that the sensory receptors have been trying to get through for so long. It seems to be a continual "muscle-building" type of process, wherein greater and greater degrees of organization are developed in our bodies, allowing us to function with ever-growing capabilities. This is indeed the path of conscious evolution!

## Storing The Potential Of The Cosmos

In the science of thermodynamics, one talks about two important quantities, <u>energy</u> and <u>entropy</u>. Most people are familiar with the concept of energy but not the concept of entropy. This latter quantity, which was mentioned in Chapter 2, is used to measure the amount of disorder in a system (the amount of lost potential in the system). For example, if I take a jar of black marbles and a jar of white marbles and mix them together, I have increased the entropy and lowered the potential of the universe (since I would have to do work to separate these marbles again). Scientists have been able to prove that, in any non-equilibrium process whether it be the human consumption and digestion of food, a humming auto engine or the cooling of a hot cup of coffee, the rate of entropy production is positive so that the entropy content of the physical universe continually increases while its potential continually decreases with the increase of time. Until quite recently, we thought that all aspects of entropy were positive and this meant that chaos must continually grow with time so that civilizations must inevitably degrade and decay. However, in the past 50 years, we have begun to recognize that the <u>information</u> gained in a particular event or process is <u>negative entropy</u> and that, although in the course of evolution, the potential of the physical universe continually decreases, the content of information continually increases.

The information content spoken of here can be in two forms: it can be in the form of physical order or organization of an internal structure of an entity or it can be in the form of knowledge (a different kind of organization). Thus, as an organism grows, it ingests chemicals in a disordered array and transforms them into an ordered arrangement in its own structure or body. Higher organisms do the same sort of thing with mental concepts or ideas to produce a conscious organization of knowledge.

The more information gained in an event or process compared to the energy expended in the operation, the more efficient are we being with the consumption of potential in the physical universe. For example, if two people talk to each other and transfer only foregone conclusions already known to both of them, and in the exchange, they do not transfer any subtle energy, then the information content was not increased in the process. On the other hand, it cost one person energy to transmit and it cost the other person energy to receive the message; that is, this particular action created entropy and dissipated potential with no gain in information (an aspect of consciousness).

I tend to equate information (in the sense discussed above) with one facet of consciousness and feel that the aim of life is the growth of consciousness and this relates to the growth of information in the very broad sense. We will come back to a deeper discussion of consciousness in the last chapter. For now, let us consider the amount of information inherent in a situation, an atom, a person or a group of persons and see how this relates to the frequency spectrum of the particular item under consideration.

Let us first consider the information capacity inherent in a typical electrical communication system and then proceed to apply these general engineering concepts more broadly. The first element of the standard communication system, illustrated in Fig. 4.9[26], is an information source (a taped symphony, for example). The output of the information source is called a <u>message</u> (the music). The next element in the system is a transmitter which transforms the sound into electrical impulses, places these impulses on what is called a "carrier wave" via a process called mixing and modulation and then radiates this into the next element of the system, the communication channel. The input to the transmitter is the message and the output is the signal. The channel, which may be air, an electric cable or an optic fiber, is the medium used to transmit the signal from the transmitter to the receiver. While going through the channel, the signal may be altered by noise or distortions (thunderstorms or other electrical disturbances). The output of the channel is called the received signal, supposed to be in some sense a faithful representation of the transmitted signal. The next element is the receiver (radio, TV, etc.) which operates on the received signal and attempts to reproduce from it the original message. It will ordinarily perform an operation which is approximately the inverse of the operation performed by the transmitter. The two operations may differ somewhat, however, because the receiver may also be required to combat the noise and distortion in the channel. The input to the receiver is the received signal and the output is the received message (the sound patterns of the symphony). The last element of this communication system is the destination (the ear of the listener, etc.)[24].

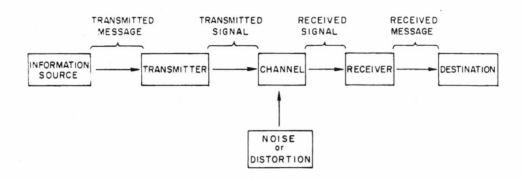

**Fig. 4.9** Important components in a standard communications system.

Another communication system with which we are familiar is that of the mind of one person (information source) communicating through a second person (channel) to the mind of a third person (destination). We can readily appreciate the opportunities for noise and distortion to enter this system! Perhaps the most significant communication system for each of us is the following: the higher forces of nature (source) working through ourselves (channels) into the human environment (destination). Here, the noise arises largely from our fears, uncertainties, insecurities, jealousies, ego, impatience, etc.

In the general communication system, noise may not only be generated in the channel but in the transmitter and receiver as well. An example that illustrates this aspect arises from the technological efforts made to automate the translation of foreign languages. The premise is simple--since we have dictionaries for each language, it seems reasonable that we could faithfully map a word or phrase from one language into a corresponding word or phrase of another language. This can, indeed, be done; however, the intended "sense" of the communication is often not faithfully reproduced by this translation procedure. On reflection, we begin to realize that a spoken communication has two major components. One is <u>knowledge</u>, which can be exactly mapped from one language to another because it is a linear quantity. The other is <u>understanding</u>, which is an integration of all the subtle factors of environment, heritage, mood, etc., all very non-linear aspects of the speaker. At present, we know only how to transform the knowledge component of the message into a signal that can be faithfully transformed at the receiver. Thus, since the total information content of the message was not transformed into a signal in the transmitter, we must state that the transmitter, in this case, introduced noise into the communication system.

From communication theory we find that, for the simple system of Fig. 4.9, the maximum ability to communicate information is determined by the channel capacity, C, which is given by

$$C = \Delta v \, \log_2 (1 + P/N)$$

In this equation, $\Delta v$ is the channel bandwidth (in this case it is the bandwidth, or effective frequency range, of the transmitter), P is the signal power of the transmitter and N is the noise level of the channel for the transmitter. The ratio P/N is called the signal to noise ratio. The mathematical function $\log_2 A$ is called the logarithm to the base 2 of A, and is just a number which varies as the magnitude of A (here, A = 1 + P/N) in the simple fashion illustrated in Fig. 4.10.

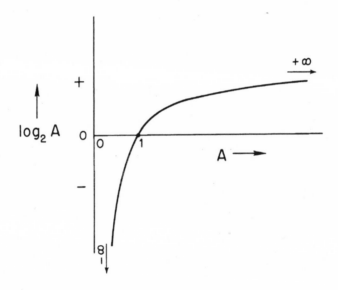

**Fig. 4.10** Functional variation of the logarithm (A) as a function of A.

For an atom as a transmitter, the channel that limits the communication is generally the air or atmosphere between the atom and a detecting instrument. For a person as a transmitter, the channel that limits the communication is generally the human being himself/herself.

To maximize an entity's capacity to act as a channel for the evolution of humanity, or for any other purpose, this equation tells us that he/she must grow in consciousness to increase $\Delta v$; he/she must increase their ability to generate or conduct a high-power signal, P, and he/she must quiet their fears and uncertainties to reduce the noise power, N.

From electrical engineering, we find that $\Delta v$ (video) is ~1000 $\Delta v$ (audio) because the carrier frequency is so much higher for video. Thus, the channel capacity and information transferred for a video transmission is about 1000 times that for an audio transmission (which may be the basis for stating that one picture is worth a thousand words). One finds, in general, that the higher is the frequency, $v_o$, of a resonating system, the larger is $\Delta v$ and, thus, the greater is the channel capacity and information transferral potential. For a human entity, this translates to "the greater is the inherent level of consciousness".

Following this line of reasoning further, as systems couple together, or organize themselves, $\Delta v$ is found to increase so that the information capacity also increases. Thus, a molecule has a greater information capacity than an atom and a small crystal, containing many coupled atoms, has a greater information capacity than most molecules (see Fig. 3.4). In fact, if we have 100 harmonic oscillators rather than one, and all are transmitting at the same power, P, the channel capacity increases perhaps by a factor of ~2 for P/N ~100 if they are uncoupled. However, it would increase by a factor of ~100 if they are strongly coupled together. This same augmentation of information capacity applies to 100 people acting independently versus their acting as a cooperatively coupled unit. Thus, we see that the level of human consciousness can increase quantitatively in a spectacular and predictable way as they cooperatively couple their fundamental frequencies.

A personal example of this "band broadening" effect that had a profound impact on me occurred on several occasions when I was acting as a technical consultant to a certain U.S. company. An individual scientist would be describing his research and relating where he was blocked in his current project. I would be listening carefully, even when the technical area was not one where I was truly expert, and would be simultaneously radiating emotional support and encouragement to him. On these special occasions, it was as if I could tap his knowledge banks on the subject and suddenly his bandwidth, $\Delta v_1$, and my bandwidth, $\Delta v_2$, coupled to produce a resultant bandwidth of $\Delta v_1 + \Delta v_2$. Then, a cascade of new ideas relevant to his project would appear in my head. As we talked further, these ideas usually formed the vehicle for unblocking his project, allowing him to move forward with renewed confidence and vigor. For me, it was a joyfully creative outpouring and I basked in the flow knowing that it was unlikely to have occurred without the broader bandwidth of our cooperative mode being available for the information flow process.

Returning to more conventional examples, from our knowledge of television, we recall that a high frequency carrier wave is used to transmit the information. The information is in the form of video (picture) and audio (sound) which is of lower frequency than the carrier wave. They are placed on the carrier wave by processes called mixing and modulation. By these processes, the maximum bandwidth can be made to be approximately the carrier wave frequency (although somewhat smaller) at which point the maximum amount of information has been placed on the carrier wave.

Let us construct a similar analogy for people by assuming that each individual has a God-given frequency which is the carrier wave of the individual (it is unchanging). The evolution of this individual is characterized by their growth in consciousness, or the fulfilling of the information capacity inherent in his/her frequency. His/her consciousness, at all the subtle and physical levels of manifestation, ripples the carrier wave with the collective information content of their being. Further, the higher the frequency of the fundamental wave (carrier wave), the greater is the inherent bandwidth and thus the information storage and communicating capacity of the entity.

We thus see that the greatest amount of information capacity occurs at the spirit level. However, we may not learn how to store information at that level without starting at the physical level. It appears necessary for us to learn what it is all about and our experience over the past several hundred years of evolution of the physical sciences have provided us with useful models for future gathering of reliable information concerning the other six dimensions. This appears to be the function of the "simulator" discussed in Chapter 2--to allow us to weave all the essential information concerning our world into the many bands of consciousness attached to our spirit level carrier wave. This seems to be where the universe ultimately stores its potential-in individuals!

Looking at the whole overall pattern, the entire human species seems to be a part of <u>one vast organism</u> wherein we seem to be individuated and separated from each other at the physical level only because our physical sensory systems work on the basis of contrast; that is, on a difference or derivative effect. During the course of evolution, we put forth effort to organize our individuated and collective being at successively more subtle and profound levels, storing more and more potential in the form of the negentropy of our being. As we become more collectively coherent, the entire earth develops into one harmonious cell that learns to function in a larger cosmic energy construct that is ever organizing itself closer and closer to the divine ideal.

In closing this chapter, it is perhaps important to delineate the evolutionary biological imperative that seems to be in place now. As background, from the Theosophical and other literature (see Chapter 3), it is indicated that, when, the chakras are all balanced and functioning well, they create a spinning action at the inlet location. This, in turn, leads to an energy vortex at the mouth of each center. As the individual develops, the frequency of spin increases and a greater energy flux flows through the individual (is processed by the individual). He/she begins to manifest greater and greater psychoenergetic capacities. At these higher energy fluxes, there is a very great need for balance to occur between the different centers, otherwise energy surges can occur which will damage the weaker links of the system and great imbalances in human behavior patterns can be expected to ensue.

At the other end of the spectrum, low spin frequency and low energy flux where most of humanity has been functioning, the different energy stations may not be spinning at comparable rates and some may even be spinning erratically (stop and start, etc.). As an analogy, we can visualize a wheel rotating a shaft that is mounted in bearings. If the wheel is eccentrically loaded (unbalanced) then, at small rotational velocities, it produces a slight thumping and most of the off-balance energy is dissipated in the bearings with no real structural problem occurring. However, as the wheel is driven faster and faster, the energy dissipation to the bearing mounts begins to become unmanageable, the vibrational modes become wildly erratic and the shaft is eventually torn out of its bearing mounts so that chaos ensues.

If one is in such an unbalanced energy function condition and one shocks open a particular energy center of the body either by the agency of an accident, the taking of drugs, a severe emotional experience, etc., then one may anticipate a type of personal havoc to follow. If one can develop slowly, by personal choice, then one can bring these key centers into a smooth and balanced system functioning, albeit they are still only processing a small energy flux. However, they do manifest a balanced and reliable behavior pattern.

Let us suppose, however, that via some energy condition at the spiritual or mental level of the cosmos, a pattern develops which <u>forces</u> the chakras of all members of the human ensemble to spin faster and faster. Now, we no longer have any choice about personal development--we must change our internal energy balance in order to survive! If such a cosmic condition did develop, people would have their chakras spinning faster and faster, energy imbalances in their body would increase and reveal itself first as enhanced tension and then as neural discharges and other pathway discharges in the body (much like a voltage breakdown phenomenon). This could be expected to damage certain insulating and functioning layers of such neural systems leading, perhaps, to "cross-talk" between different circuits. The consequence of this is that the body would perform actions out of registry with brain commands. We can also anticipate that individuals would begin to erratically manifest some psychoenergetic phenomena and, being unaware of what is really happening, begin to fear for their sanity because of the conflict between their normal mindset and these phenomena.

Being fearful, such individuals can be expected to try and force their body systems into either a condition of tense control or a drugged state. However, it is of no avail, because a tiger has been unleashed within and they don't know how to deal with it. Unless they do learn the inner self management and energy balancing techniques, one can expect them to slip inexorably towards the condition of schizophrenia. On the way, they can be expected to do irrational things seeking in a random empirical fashion to release this terrible internal pressure.

It is perhaps useful to realise that manifested problems at the chemical level require adjustments at the EM energy level for restoration of homeostasis; manifested problems at the EM level require adjustments at the etheric level for restoration of homeostasis; imbalances at the etheric level require movement to the emotional level to restore balance, imbalances at the emotional level require movement to the mental level to restore balance, imbalances at the mental level require movement to the spiritual level to restore homeostasis and imbalances, if they should exist at the spiritual level require divine intervention to restore balance.

I wish to suggest that the cycle has indeed been "kicked up" and that a biological imperative for the organization of our psychic awareness is now in operation in the human ensemble. Cognition of information patterns present in the inverse space-time frame as well as in the direct space-time frame can be expected to be natural capacities of homosapiens in the future. We can anticipate both great benefits and great problems to arise out of the manifestations of these new capacities in humans. We know that humans have been deeply attached to the material world of the direct space-time frame and suspect that humans could become even more strongly attached to the psychic world of the inverse space-time frame. Such an attachment could continue for a very long time if humans think of that world as reality. It behooves us to be aware that we are entering the phychic forest (as our chakras spin faster) and that we must travel through it in order to evolve. If we center our consciousness in our spiritual selves and focus our intentionality through our hearts, we will diminish any possible attachments to the psychic domain and quickly reach the other side of the forest where our real conscious evolution can begin!

# References

1. L. Childre, private communication, summer 1995

2. R. Rivlin and K. Gravelle, "Deciphering The Senses: The Expanding World of Human Perception" (Simon and Schuster, New York, 1984).

3. E. Knudsen, <u>Supervised Learning In The Brain</u>, J. Neuroscience <u>14</u> (1994) 3985.

4. S. LaBerge, "Lucid Dreaming", (Tarcher, New York, 1985).

5. I. Rock, "The Nature of Perceptual Adaptation," (Basic Books, New York, 1967).

6. K. Pribram, "Brain and Perception, Holonomy and Structure in Figural Processing" (Lawrence Erlbaum Associates, Hillsdale, New Jersey, 1991

7. L. Brillouin, "Scientific Uncertainty and Information" (Academic Press, New York, 1964).

8. I.C. Maby, <u>Radiesthesia and Wave Theory</u>, American Dowser, <u>14</u> (1974) 69.

9. W.A. Tiller and Wayne Cook, <u>Psychoenergetic Field Studies Using A Biomechanical Transducer</u>, Proceeding of "New Horizons in Healing" Symposium (A.R.E. Clinic, Phoenix, AZ, 1974).

10. B. McNamara and K. Wiesenfeld, <u>Theory of Stochastic Resonance</u>, Phys. Rev. A, <u>39</u> (1989) 4854.

11. Abbe Mermet, "Principles and Practice of Radiesthesia" (Stuart and Watkins, London, 1967).

12. A.T. Westlake, "The Pattern of Health" (Shambhala, London, 1974).

13. C. Hills, "Supersensonics" (University of the Trees Press, Boulder Creek, CA, 1975).

14. J.C. Maby, "Physical Principles of Radiesthesia" (Rank Xerox Ltd., Birmingham, 1968).

15. J.H. Reyner, "Psionic Medicine" (Routledge & Kegan Paul, London, 1975).

16. P.F. Nogier, "Auriculo-Therapy To Auriculo-Medicine" (Maissonneuve, Saint-Ruffine, France, 1983).

17. J.N. Kenyon, <u>Auricular Medicine: The Auricular Cardiac Reflex</u> in "Modern Techniques of Acupuncture, Vol II" (Thorsons, New York, NY, 1983) p. 82 and 191.

18. J.H. Navach, <u>The Vascular Autonomic System, Physics and Physiology</u> (The VIII Germano-Latino Congress on Auricular Medicine, Lyon, France, 1981).

19. J.M. Ackerman, <u>The Biophysics of the VAS</u> in "Energy Fields in Medicine" (The John E. Fetzer Foundation, Kalamazoo, MI, 1989) p. 124.

20. G.A. Ulett, "Principles and Practice of Physiologic Acupuncture" (Warren H. Green, Inc., St. Louis, MO, 1982).

21. L.E. Badgley, "Energy Medicine" (Human Energy Press, San Bruno, CA, 1985) p. 10.

22. J.H. Navach, <u>The Vascular Autonomic System Pulse Recording Techniques</u>, (First International Congress of Acupuncture and Auricular Medicine, Majorca, Spain, 1980).

23. L.E. Eeman, "Co-Operative Healing" (Frederick Muller, Ltd., London, 1947).

24. L. Patten, "Biocircuits", (H.J. Kramer, San Francisco, 1988).

25. BioCircuit, <u>Tools For Exploration</u> (4286 Redwood Hwy., Ste. C, San Rafael, CA, 94903).

26. J.R. Pierce, "Electrons, Waves and Messages", (Hanover House, New York, 1956).

# APPENDIX 4.1

## INFORMATION TRANSFORMATION IN THE BRAIN

Pribram[6] has written extensively on the brain processes involved in imaging and has a holonomic theory to explain them. It is based solely on a slight modification of the Fourier Transform duality between 4-D spacetime information patterns and spectral domain information patterns. An overly simplistic picture would be that a spacetime information pattern enters the body via the circular lens of the eye. Eventually, it activates the input and operator neurons of the brain's cortical columns. This leads to overlapping receptive fields of interneurons which are tunable by adaptation and habituation. Each interneuron thus acts like a bin in a computer that stores the averages of the part of the patterns of input to which it is exposed[6]. The ensemble of receptive fields (bins) stores the average pattern. When one plots these receptive field patterns, they bear a marked correlation to the Fourier transform of the spacetime pattern impinging on the iris of the eye. However, instead of working with the F.T., which is the integral over an infinite domain (see chapter 2), Pribram works with the Gabor function which is the same integral over a specific finite domain. Correlation between a 2D receptive field and a 2D Gabor function is shown in Fig 4.A1.1.

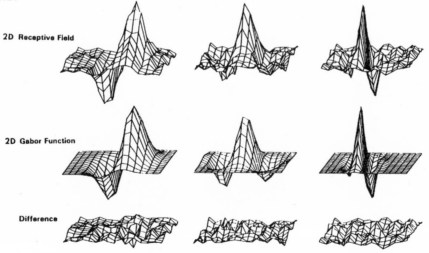

Fig. 4.A1.1  Top Row: illustrations of cat simple 2-D receptive field profiles.  Middle row: best -fitting 2-D Gabor wavelet for each neuron.  Bottom row: residual error of the fit, which for 97% of the cells studied was indistinguishable from random error in the Chi-squared sense.

The general view, then, is that cortical neurons act like individual receiving antennas in a large array converting the spacetime information into a diffraction pattern (see chapter 3) whose mathematical representation is very close to the particular Fourier Transform. This information conversion to the frequency domain appears to be ideal for subsequent brain processing and brain perception. The spacetime information map readily becomes a frequency domain information map and, although we are used to thinking of this as a physical level information map within the frequency range $v_1$ to $v_2$, the identical information map is postulated to be imprinted at the etheric level at a much higher octave of ME energy (see chapter 2) with the range $v'_1$ to $v'_2$ where $v'_1 - v'_2 = (c^*/c)(v_1 - v_2)$ and $c^*/c$ is the ratio of ME light velocity to EM light velocity ($c^*/c \gg 1$). It is also relatively easy for a minus sign to appear for the intensity profile of this "higher octave" information map in accordance with the etheric energy postulate of chapter 2 (see p100).

# APPENDIX 4.2

## POLARIZED WAVE CHARACTERISTICS

Let us suppose that we have an electromagnetic (EM) wave of angular frequency $\omega$ propagating in the z-direction of a particular medium with propagation decay constant $\beta$. Further, let us focus only on the electric field amplitude, E (the magnetic amplitude, H, is in the perpendicular direction) with $\overline{x}$ and $\overline{y}$ component given by

$$\overline{E} = \overline{x}E_x \sin(\omega t - \beta z) + \overline{y}E_y \sin(\omega t - \beta z + \delta) \qquad \textbf{(A1)}$$

where $\delta$ is a phase angle difference and t is time. Using the standard expansion, $\sin(A+B)=\sin A \cos B + \cos A \sin B$, equation A1 becomes

$$\overline{E} = (\overline{x}E_x + \overline{y}E_y \cos\delta)\sin(\omega t - \beta z) + \overline{y}E_y \sin\delta \cos(\omega t - \beta z)$$
$$\textbf{(A2)}$$

When we choose a zero phase angle difference ($\delta$=0), equation A2 becomes

$$\overline{E} = (\overline{x}E_x + \overline{y}E_y)\sin(\omega t - \beta z) \qquad \textbf{(A3)}$$

which is a linearly polarized wave whose angle of polarization depends on the ratio of $E_y/E_x$. When we choose $\delta$=90$^o$ ,

$$\overline{E} = \overline{x}E_x \sin(\omega t - \beta z) + \overline{y}E_y \cos(\omega t - \beta z) \qquad \textbf{(A4)}$$

which is a right-hand circular polarized wave if $E_y=E_x$.
When we choose $\delta$=-90$^o$ ,

$$\overline{E} = \overline{x}E_x \sin(\omega t - \beta z) - \overline{y}E_y \cos(\omega t - \beta z) \qquad \textbf{(A5)}$$

which is a left-hand circularly polarized wave when $E_y=E_x$. We thus see that a linearly polarized wave, equation A3, is constructed from a RT-hand plus a LT-hand circularly polarized wave with $E_y=E_x$ (equation A4 plus A5). For the general case when we choose $\delta$ not equal to zero or to $\pm$90$^o$, we obtain an elliptically polarized wave such as given by equation A2.

With respect to substances and dowsing responses, let us suppose that the basic EM or ME radiation emitted by a substance is linearly polarized (two oppositely circular polarized wave components of equal amplitude which are in phase with each other). Let us further suppose that, if the substance <u>is</u> harmonious to an individual, the velocities of the two circularly polarized waves through the body of the individual are identical. Then the dowsing wand response would exhibit the typical bipolar response. If the substance is <u>not</u> harmonious, let us suppose that the velocities of the two circular polarized waves through the body are not identical. Then a phase difference develops and an oscillating polarity, such as illustrated in Fig 4.A2.1, would develop for the material. These two circularly polarized waves appear to play a significant role in the positive VAS and negative VAS response as well.

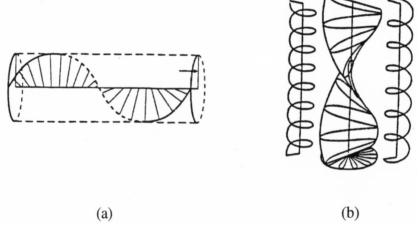

(a)                                                            (b)

Fig. 4.A.2.1   (a) A helical wave appearing in projection as a sine wave and (b) right and left circularly polarized waves on the sides while the wave form in the center is a composite of two out-of-phase helices. Two in-phase helices leads to a plane polarized wave.

# CHAPTER
# 5

## GROWING INTO COHERENCE

*Whether inner or outer self, wave superposition forms all*
*And, collectively, although appearing separate, we are not.*
*Our wave constituents flow and ebb, join, flicker, disperse and reunite.*
*Patches of order form, radiant power densities escalate and incandescence flowers.*
*First in one and next in all--then we are one!*

In the last chapter, we focussed our attention on intentional development of unique states of organization in our bodies, both at physical and at subtle levels. We learned that this is the location wherein the potential of the universe is ultimately stored and we saw how we can consciously participate in our evolutionary process. In this chapter, we want to carry these concepts forward to gain some measure of the enormous consequences involved when we reach our ultimate goal of becoming coherent--and not just at the physical level but at the subtle levels as well. Let us begin by considering some important features of waves.

## Aspects of Waves

Any geometrical form, static or time-varying, can be decomposed into a set of waves that, when faithfully superposed, reconstructs that shape. This is called Fourier decomposition and superposition after the 19th century French scientist. Thus, a complex-shaped potential like gravity, electrical voltage, temperature, etc., can be decomposed into a set of appropriate waves that fully describe the total potential in space and time. For some applications, the waves have spherical symmetry; for others they have cylindrical symmetry or planar symmetry; for still others the wave basis sets can have very special symmetries. The unique material aspects of a particular geometrical object are embodied in a complex wave function that represents the atomic nucleus and various electrons bound to that nucleus plus a set of similar but displaced wave functions to represent the locations of all the other atoms in the object plus another set of wave functions to account for the unbound electrons that wander freely in the object. So we see that waves on very different size scales and time scales are needed to completely describe the physical object.

For our purposes in this chapter, let us presume that we are a fixed observer at some point in space and we are monitoring the amplitude of a wavetrain that passes in front of us. We are thus monitoring the time variation of the wave amplitude. Let us presume that it is initially a perfectly harmonic wave of frequency $\omega$, amplitude A, and period $2\pi/\omega$ as represented by Fig 5.1a. Next, let us suppose that a second wave of the same frequency and amplitude, but shifted in phase has been added to the first. The superposition of the two will be as shown in Fig. 5.1b. Next, if the phase difference of the two waves is adjusted to produce almost complete <u>constructive</u> interference between them, we obtain the result shown in Fig. 5.1c. Fig. 5.1d shows the case where the phase difference of the two waves has been adjusted to produce almost complete <u>destructive</u> interference between them. In all cases of Fig. 5.1, the dashed line plots the square of the superposed wave amplitude (or signal amplitude) and this is proportional to the energy density inherent in the wave. We can thus see how strongly the energy density of the total wave can vary as we shift the phase difference between its components. The maximum energy density for the two combined waves can shift between $4\varepsilon A^2$, and zero (where, the proportionality constant, $\varepsilon$, is set equal to 1 for convenience) as the phase difference is shifted from zero to $\pi$ ($\pi$=3.14 radians). In the general case where the second wave component has amplitude $A_2$, the maximum and minimum energy densities for $\varepsilon$=1 are given by $(A_1 + A_2)^2$ and $(A_1 - A_2)^2$, respectively.

For our second example, suppose we change the second wave component to have a frequency $2\omega$ (which is the first harmonic of the fundamental wave of frequency $\omega$) and amplitude $A_2$ plus some phase shift relative to the first wave. By mathematical analysis, it can be shown that the average energy density over the period $2\pi/\omega$ of the fundamental wave is given by $(A_1^2 + A_2^2)/\omega$ <u>regardless</u> of the phase difference between the two waves. This would be the average energy density over this period if each wave component were considered on its own without superposition. Thus, the wave amplitudes definitely superpose but the average wave energy density does not yield the benefits (factor of two) seen in Fig. 5.1c. When we add additional higher harmonics to the total wave, its overall superposed shape can change as illustrated in Fig. 5.2 for those harmonics that lead to a square wave. However, the average energy density over the period $2\pi/\omega$ is just $(A_1^2 + A_2^2 + A_3^2 + A_4^2 + A_5^2 \ldots)/\omega$ and no additional energy benefits arise from the wave being in-phase as in the Fig. 5.1 example. In order to gain the great energy benefit that comes from coherence of these multiple wave components, the frequency of each harmonic <u>must</u> be reduced to $\omega$ and all phase differences <u>must</u> be eliminated. Then, the average energy density over the fundamental wave period of $2\pi/\omega$ will be given by $(A_1 + A_2 + A_3 + A_4 + A_5 + \ldots)^2/\omega$. Of course, in such a case, the wave shape will change from that of Fig. 5.2 to that of Fig. 5.1a.

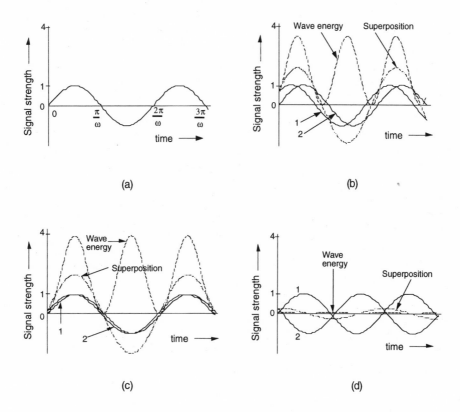

**Fig. 5.1** Illustration of constructive and destructive interference by wave superposition; (a) single simple harmonic wave, (b) two out-of-phase waves superposed (dot-dashed line) with the effective superposed wave energy (dashed line), (c) almost complete constructive interference and (d) almost complete destructive interference.

Let us now switch for the moment to the human domain and let us assume that a human can be approximated for present purposes by a nested set of multimode oscillators with each having a time-dependent amplitude spectrum, $A(\omega,t)$. One member of the set represents the physical body, another the etheric body, another the emotional body, etc. To simplify things further for discussion purposes, let us assume that all of these oscillators can be represented by a single frequency, $\omega_1$, and a single amplitude, $A_1$, for a single individual. By doing this, we can begin to appreciate the relevance of the previous discussion to specific human interactions. For example, if our individual is a healer and is working with a healee characterized by a "frequency" $\omega_2$, amplitude $A_2$ and phase difference $\phi$, the healer must obviously attune to the healee in order to produce an effective healing. Such attunement not only requires that the healer shift his/her frequency from $\omega_1$ to $\omega_2$ but also to shift phase so that the phase difference $\phi$ shrinks to zero. Then the two individuals are coherently coupled and manifest an average energy density of $(A_1 + A_2)^2 = A_1^2 + A_2^2 + 2A_1A_2$. This increased energy density, $2A_1A_2$, is readily available for the healing process.

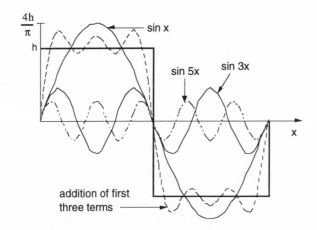

**Fig. 5.2**  Addition of the first three terms of the Fourier series for the square wave illustrating that the still higher frequencies are responsible for sharpening the edges of the pulse. Here, $x = \omega t$.

This same analogy applies to two individuals working on a joint project. If they work totally independently, their collective output could be maximally $A_1^2 + A_2^2$. If they work together in a coupled mode but at cross-purposes, their collective output could be minimally $(A_1 - A_2)^2 = A_1^2 + A_2^2 - 2A_1A_2$. However, if they work together in a coupled mode, but in total coherence, their collective output could be as large as $(A_1 + A_2)^2 = A_1^2 + A_2^2 + 2A_1A_2$. Thus, one can directly see the benefits of attunement and coherent coupling.

To extend the analogy one step further, if we had N individuals of different effective frequencies, $\omega_1, \omega_2, \ldots \omega_i, \ldots \omega_N$ and effective amplitudes, $A_1, A_2, \ldots A_i, \ldots A_N$ with phase differences $\phi_1, \phi_2, , , , \phi_i, \ldots \phi_{N-1}$, we can begin to see both the difficulties associated with trying to produce attuned coherence in the entire group and the tremendous payoff for achieving that goal. The collective output of the group would be the square of the sum rather than much less than the sum of the squares. To simplify this calculation, assume that each individual has some average amplitude of effectiveness, A. If so, the collective output of this group is maximally $(NA)^2 = N^2A^2 = N(NA^2)$, where the bracketed term is the maximum value for independent minimally-overlapping work. Thus, if $N = 10$, $100$ or $1000$, the gain from attuned group coherence is at least a factor of $10$, $100$ or $1000$, respectively. To see the value of adding just one additional individual coherently to an attuned coherent group of N individuals, the calculation is $(NA + A)^2 = N^2A^2 + A^2 + 2NA^2$. Thus, the effect of adding one more is the same as adding 2N uncoupled non-overlapping individuals. This is a tremendous effect for large N.

Applying this kind of reasoning to the corporate world is instructive. We can readily see why small companies can make rapid progress if the personnel are all strongly focussed on the success of their joint venture. Because the numbers are small, it is not too difficult to be coupled in an attuned coherent state so that the effective work output ratio to the number of personnel is very high and very competitive with the industry average. This is why a small company can grow rapidly. Likewise, one can see the possible benefits that will accrue to a large company if they can maintain attuned group coherence. However, this becomes increasingly difficult as the group size, N, increases, especially in a society like the American society that prizes individuality and is so confrontational and litigious. These qualities in themselves are extremely valuable to our society but in cooperative group action they need to be tempered by patience, care, consideration, appreciation of others, etc.

There are several possibilities for organized group action that lead to effective outputs. One is to accept the position that attuned coherent action is not possible. In that case the role of management is to subdivide the total project into non-overlapping pieces and assign one piece to each individual of the group taking care to try and match the type of work with the natural frequency, $\omega_i$, of the individual and taking care to try and motivate each individual to produce a maximum amplitude, $A_i$, of effort. Management must also assign "integrators" to the group so that all the individual efforts can be effectively combined to yield close to the maximum allowable output of $(A_1^2 + A_2^2 + \ldots + A_i^2 + \ldots + A_N^2)$ for this mode of operation. This is somewhat of an oversimplification but it surely illustrates the best possible output for the "non-coupled mode" of group action. In the more effective, but more difficult to achieve, "attuned coherence mode" of group action (frequency-locked and phase-locked oscillators) one role of management is to select the frequency, $\omega^*$, to which <u>all</u> members of the group will attune. Another role is to teach the members how to attune to another's frequency (like dancing together in perfect rhythm). Still another is to monitor and correct any phase differences between individual members and the attunement focus individual. If this can be achieved, the group output effort will be at least a factor N larger than the maximum output for the non-coupled mode, where N is the number of members in the group. There are also additional significant creativity benefits which will be discussed later after we discuss how we might achieve this goal.

In many instances, the group activity cannot be cast in the non-coupled mode and one <u>must</u> deal with frequency attunement and phase difference elimination. The prime example here is a team sport like football, hockey, basketball, etc. Here, a major component of the training is cooperative coherent action over an extended time period with other team members. Here, the $\omega^*$ focus frequency individual will generally be the one who has earned the greatest respect from his/her teammates.

The attuned coherence mode of human interaction has aspects much like molecule formation between atoms. The individual atoms maintain their core identity but share one or more of their outermost electrons with other members of the group. By such cooperative action, they gain a large set of new properties, become capable of new roles in nature and store more potential of the universe. The molecules' stability is ultimately determined by the strength of the bonding between atoms via the shared electrons. Laboratories all around the world spend many billions of dollars per year to convert groupings of atoms into unique molecules of very great utility. We can begin to do likewise at the human level as we learn to understand the processes involved!

## Aspects of Coherence

Perhaps the best example of coherence in nature comes from the laser. To illustrate, a solid state laser consists of a rod of a solid material in which some concentration of specific dopant atoms are embedded (they are in solution in the host material). In most cases, thin mirrors are fixed to the ends of the rod. Each specific dopant atom may be optically excited by shining a band of radiation that includes the "right" frequency of light into the rod from the outside (see Fig. 5.3b). This atom then acts as a microscopic radiating antenna and emits a photon (a light-pulse)[1]. This emission process lasts typically $\sim 10^{-8}$ seconds (10 billionths of a second) and the photon wavetrack has a length of $\sim 3$ meters. The pumping light raises most of the dopant atoms to their excited state. A special cascade begins when an excited atom spontaneously emits a photon parallel to the axis of the crystal as in Fig. 5.3d (photons emitted in other directions pass out of the rod)[2]. The end-mirrors serve as a concentrator of these axial tracks. Those travelling in the axial direction are reflected several times between the mirrors and stay longer in the rod. These back and forth travelling waves tend to "attune" or somewhat entrain the excited state dopant atoms to emit their photons along the axial direction and closer in-phase with all the others. When the amplification is great enough, some of the beam passes out of the rod through the partially silvered end of the rod as illustrated in Fig. 5.3f. Again we see a non-linear process occurring where a relatively broad frequency range of external pump-light produces very narrow frequency band dopant-emitted light that the rod geometry and the mirrors cause to shift in both direction and phase until coherence results.

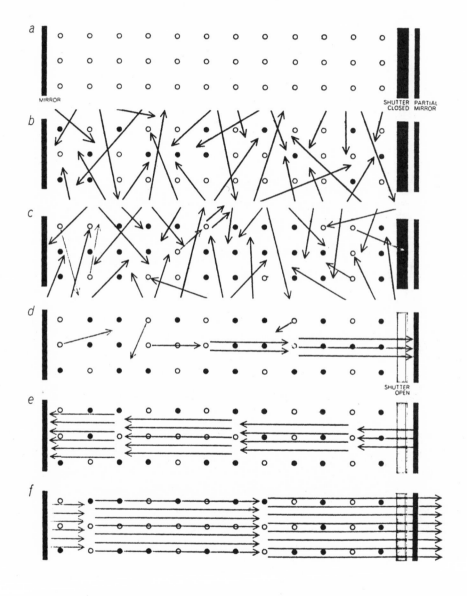

**Fig. 5.3** Photon cascade in a solid rod amplifies a light wave by stimulated emission.

When we begin pumping external photons into the rod at small pump power, the rod acts much like a typical lamp where the atomic antennas of the dopant atoms emit independently of each other (randomly or incoherently). Because this is essentially a non-linear process, at a certain pump power, called the lasing threshold, a completely new phenomenon occurs. At that point, the back and forth waves are sufficiently in-phase with each other and thus the average emitted light intensity, I, has grown to such a magnitude that massive entrainment of the individual dopant antennas occurs and they all begin to oscillate in phase. They now, collectively, emit a single giant wavetrack whose length may be ~300,000 kilometers! This phenomenon is illustrated in Fig. 5.4[1]. The emitted light intensity, or output power, increases drastically for further increase in pump power.

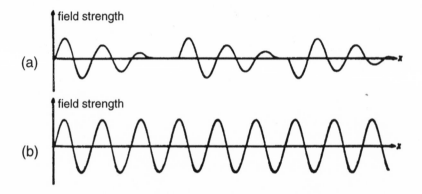

**Fig. 5.4**    Wave tracks emitted from (a) a lamp and (b) a laser.

To illustrate the energy changes involved in this example of incoherent light emission to coherent light emission, let us consider the case of a typical home-use 60 watt light bulb. It gives some light but not a lot of light. This is mostly because the emitted photons destructively interfere with each other and most of the bulb's potential effectiveness is destroyed. Such a light bulb emits ~1 watt per $cm^2$. In comparison, our sun emits ~6000 watts per $cm^2$ of its surface[3]. If we could somehow take the same number of photons emitted by the light bulb per second and orchestrate their emission to be in phase with each other, then we would have constructive interference of these same photons and now the energy density at the surface of the light bulb would be thousands to millions of times higher than the present photon energy density at the surface of the sun. This is a measure of the power transformation inherent in going from an incoherent device to a coherent device. That illustrates the unutilized potential in the typical light bulb.

In the previous example, what we are dealing with are states of <u>organization</u> of light. In nature, there are analogous discrete levels of organization of substance under certain sets of environmental conditions and these are all discrete shifts away from randomness or disorder toward complete order or maximum possible coherence for the system. One example from the area of hydrodynamics occurs when a density inversion exists in a fluid or gas, such as occurs when one heats a shallow layer of water in a saucepan. Here, in a completely homogeneous fluid, dynamic, well-ordered, spatial and temporal cylinders of circulating fluid develop in the saucepan. This mode of fluid convection has been called Bénard convection and it is often seen by airline travellers looking out of their windows and down onto a large cloud structure below the plane. In that particular example, the Bénard rolls can extend for miles. In the area of relatively simple chemical reactions, when special reactants are mixed and stirred and poured into a test tube, immediately spatio-temporal patterns begin to occur with the solution colours changing periodically from red to blue. This particular example has been called the Belousov-Zhabotinsky Reaction[1]. In the domain of simple living systems, it has been long known that a set of equal cells may self-organize into structures with well-distinguished regions. During the growth phase of dictyostelium, a type of cellular slime mold, it exists in the state of single ameboid cells. Several hours after the end of growth, these cells aggregate to form a polar body along which they differentiate into stalk cells or spores. The single cells are capable of spontaneously emitting into their surroundings a certain kind of molecule called $c_{AMP}$ (cyclic adenosin 3'5' monophosphate) in the form of pulses. Furthermore, the cells are capable of amplifying $c_{AMP}$ pulses. Thus, they produce spontaneous and stimulated emission of specific chemicals just as the laser produces stimulated emission of specific photons[1].

If we now make a large step up the biological scale to the human, we realise how far we have come with respect to unique states of cellular organization in our bodies and we may also begin to realise how far we have yet to go to reach coherence. Let us begin to look at this issue initially by how the various disciplines of daily life are related to the development of higher levels of organization in us.

The main thing we need to realize is that, just like the light bulb example, vast unutilized potential exists within us, the basic ingredients are already there but they are relatively incoherent with respect to each other. Our task is to transform the largely incoherent ingredients into a completely coherent system--and not just at the physical level but at all the subtle levels as well. In our homes and schools we learn and practice many forms of athletics which discipline us to develop coordination, motor function skills and organized muscle systems as well as exercising our ability to focus intentionality on the "game". We begin to learn about relationships, about sharing, caring and appreciating and, as well, about loving. Thus, we develop levels of organization and order at the emotional domain level as well as at the physical domain level. This becomes further developed by our growing appreciation for music and art. Of course, our intellectual development as a component of our mind domain properties is not neglected and organized states of order develop here as well. Thus, we have already been moving down the path towards coherence without realizing it. At present, little teaching time is devoted to consciously practicing intentionality in a disciplined way or to understanding the subtle dimensions of ourselves. However, that will come to pass in the not-too-distant future, so we need not be overly concerned about this present "lack" in our teaching institutions.

Perhaps the best example of the development of coherence and laser-like emissions in humans comes from the studies on Qigong masters mentioned in Chapter 2. They appear to generate EM emissions of IR radiation in the ~1 to 4.5 micron range that have healing benefits. These emissions and others are probably generated in the cells surrounding the Dan Tien (second chakra) area of the body at both physical and subtle levels. The physical IR portion of the cellular coherence signature would be generated via one or more of the various organelles in these cells since these wavelengths are smaller than the typical cell size. These radiations are expected to find their way out through the hands and other surfaces of the body via a variety of possible routes.

From my own teaching experience, students generally have had insufficient experience of the world to properly see the relationships between different areas of intellectual, social, political or spiritual, etc., endeavors. They tend to look outside of themselves for all the answers instead of looking inside themselves to perceive the unfolding "map" of their lives. Many are focussing far down the road towards some intended goal and having difficulty trying to figure out the most efficient path to get there and whether, in fact, it will still be there when they arrive at that particular point in space-time. They have not yet learned (1) that the "universe" has a plan for their development and "tilts" the statistics so that events and opportunities are caused to appear in their paths, (2) that it is better to do what is immediately at one's hand to do and to do it with all one's might, and to do it joyfully and then, without lingering attachment, to move on, confident that the unfolding prospects will lead to their greater growth and (3) that it is all right to stumble because such events show us what we have still to learn. My wife sometimes gets tired of hearing me say, "If we don't see the traps, we have to go through the crap until we can clearly see the traps." Such a stumbling process often appears to be the only real path to our future growth so <u>that</u> is our "teacher" and it awakens us to the need to expand our perspective. In this category of "stumbling" there is often a large degree of emotional pain involved and that is generally due to our not clearly understanding and accepting all aspects of the situation. We often cloud our perspective with unfulfillable expectations. However, all of these events are potentially growth events and, if we clearly see the lesson involved, we can move on; if we don't, the universe finds a way to put the same lesson in our path (but wrapped in a different appearing package) again and again until we finally "get" it. This is because <u>we are the product of the process</u> and <u>we are built by the process</u>.

We need to learn a key characteristic of our simulator--that which appears to us on the <u>outer</u> is just a materialized reflection of that which is on the <u>inner</u>. We need to realize that what we dislike in our society cannot be effectively changed from the outside because it is only symptomatic of that which is inside us. The only real change takes place within <u>us</u>. We must change there first and then the outer consistent materializations will naturally occur. We need to learn that what we are building outside of ourselves is indeed important and demands the full force of our attention; however, we also need to learn that <u>this</u> activity is largely a vehicle for building us inside (organizing us inside). That which is outside is just a great <u>exercise machine</u> for our internal development--just another part of our simulator. On one level, this internal organization is only part of our own vehicle development. On another, it is a service to future generations to provide them with a more suitable body simulator for <u>their</u> development. Thus, attitudes in work, as in play, profoundly influence our development. If we perform work of high quality, our transformation will be to a vehicle of high quality.

We need to become more aware of the real nature of our simulators. The body is a learning device of the <u>mind</u>. Learning devices are not lessons in themselves, their purpose is merely to facilitate learning. The body is merely part of our experience in the physical world. We can utilize our bodies best to help us enlarge our perception so that we can achieve <u>real</u> vision, of which the physical eye is incapable. Learning to do this is the simulator's real usefulness.

We need to also learn that we are <u>one</u> at the level of self that pushes the switches in our simulators--and that we are together for a good and valid reason. Evolution for all is ultimately necessary for evolution of the one. It is a family task as well as an individual task and it must ultimately be solved at the family level (group coherence level). And, as all families know, the only effective working fluid is <u>love</u>. Love seems strange in that the more one gives of it, the more one has of it (see Chapter 7); however, this may be just the reprogramming characteristic of the simulator in operation.

We may wish for the masses of humanity to show more altruistic and more highly motivated ideals than they presently do. Present humanity is clearly not as "enlightened" as we might like. However, it will become enlightened only if we believe it is possible for it to do so and if we act as if it were already well on the path to doing so.

All greatness springs from a state of mind! So let us visualize that personal expression and that societal character that is our highest ideal and then let us radiate its manifested perfection by every thought, attitude and action of our lives. Every action of our lives, no matter how small or commonplace, influences those around us and contains the potential for enhancing the level of benevolent radiation in our environment. The quiet radiation of inner joy is as nurturing to human life as the food on the table. As we become more and more our own person, we will find that we can profoundly perceive and enjoy all the beauty of the world and even uplift our environment wherever we go. Then, all those lives we touch are enriched by our having been there, and vise versa.

All of the things we do in life are individual acts of creation. If we would do this well, there are four important steps to consider with each meaningful act:

  1. We must clearly <u>visualize</u> our intention,
  2. We must build a strong <u>desire</u> to achieve that intention,
  3. We must develop the <u>faith</u> that the visualization can be achieved, and
  4. We must exercise the <u>will</u> to make it manifest; i.e., work at it.

And we must remember that <u>if the medium in which we wish to create offers us no resistance, then we can make no durable impression</u>! Once again, as we close this section, let us clearly remember that <u>we</u> are the product of the process!

## So, What Is The Process?

I have come to feel that human evolution is characterized by, and limited by, the penetration of <u>spirit</u> into dense matter[3]. And the more spirit there is present, the higher is the consciousness of the entity. On the one hand, some structural organization, neural and otherwise, is needed as a skeletal template for the spirit substance. On the other hand, the entity applies that in-dwelling consciousness, through its focussed intentionality in the various acts of daily life which is it's personal exercise machine. By the entity's thoughts, attitudes and actions, transformational changes occur in the dense and subtle matter which can produce a refined structure in the matter. This, in turn, allows a greater in-flow of spirit (or the specific exercise can produce a degraded structure which does the opposite). My experience has been that, when applied intentionality is focussed through the human heart into the daily life process, a greater rate of structural refinement occurs and, thus, the more rapidly does one's consciousness expand.

For most people, there is not a well-defined and accepted definition of consciousness; however, most would agree that one facet of consciousness has some association with the awake brain. Other facets of consciousness deal with (1) the awareness of perceiving information from the universe at large, (2) sleeping and dreaming, (3) hallucinations, (4) subliminal and what can be called unconscious information processing, etc. In addition, I tend to think that consciousness will eventually be discovered to be a quality of the universe that has the capability of generating radiations that eventually beget matter[3]. In this respect, the properties of matter will eventually be found to depend on the local consciousness[3] (see Chapter 6). Just as an infant seems to have a vast neural network capability, of which only a portion becomes "hard wired" because of specific sets of stimulations in early life (see Chapter 4), so too do we presently probe the topic of consciousness through only a few of its many facets.

The most common association of the awareness aspect of consciousness is with the brain/mind interface. However, that is probably a limited view. It is much more likely that the evolving human develops an ever-expanding set of information carrying/transforming/interpreting structures both physically neural and subtle, of which the brain/mind interface is only one. In particular, I tend to think that an even more important member of the set is the heart/mind interface of which more will be said later. My present working hypothesis is that, unlike the simple matter/energy relationship (characterized by $E = mc^2$), the energy/consciousness relationship is neither so simple nor so precise because <u>consciousness is a system property</u>. Thus, an atom, a molecule, a cell, an organ, an individual and a group all have consciousness (and they all have energy). The parameter that I currently use to minimally characterize the consciousness of a system is it's <u>channel capacity</u>, (discussed in Chapter 4) which depends on (1) it's bandwidth, $\Delta v$, (2) it's signal power, P and (3) it's noise power, N. In equation form, this is expressed by

$$\text{Consciousness} = A\, \Delta v_{sys}\, \ln_2(1 + P_{sys}/N_{sys})$$

where A is a constant. We shall see in the next section how continued practice of inner self-management techniques greatly diminishes emotional and mental noise within the individual so that $N_{sys}$ decreases. We shall also see how inner coherence is increased leading to an increase in individual signal power, $P_{sys}$. Finally, the development of one's intuition through repeated practice leads to an expansion of an individual's bandwidth, $\Delta v_{sys}$. A natural extension of this formula to the group system is obvious from all the foregoing.

To expand the picture, let us take a small diversion to see some differences, besides the obvious ones, between energy and consciousness. We shall first focus our attention on a particular aspect of the physical world that is well understood by present day science and use it as an analogy for trying to understand some aspects of consciousness.

# The Energy/Consciousness Differentiation

First, we begin by considering a box at a fixed temperature, $T_1$, which contains a large number, N, of gas molecules. For our present purposes, these molecules can be thought of as being like marbles (of extremely small size) that are constantly moving about in straight lines until they interact with and bounce off another molecule or the walls of the box (see Fig. 5.5). Thus, these molecules are in ceaseless motion, continually exchanging energy with each other. One might think that after some time these molecules would all have the same energy, but not so; the energy distribution among these molecules, after a long time, is as illustrated qualitatively in Fig. 5.6a. We see that the number of molecules, n, having a particular energy, E, varies strongly with the energy. We see that the molecules exhibit a wide range of energies, a few molecules having a very small energy and a few having a very high energy, with most having an energy slightly smaller than the mean energy, $kT_1$ (k is called Boltzmann's constant).

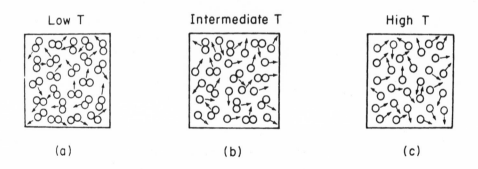

| Low T | Intermediate T | High T |
|-------|----------------|--------|
| (a) | (b) | (c) |

**Fig. 5.5** Pictoral representation of molecules moving about in a box, (a) undissociated state, (b) partially dissociated state and (c) completely dissociated state.

If, for example, we open a small window in the box and inject a quantity of heat, $\Delta Q$, into the box via a beam of light, the temperature of the box will be increased from $T_1$ to $T_2$ ($T_2 > T_1$). The new energy distribution for the molecules in the box is caused to shift up the energy scale compared to the old one since $kT_2 > kT_1$; however, it exhibits the same general shape and we still have N molecules in the box. This is illustrated in Fig. 5.6b where we note that the mean energy, kT, has moved up scale. In a real situation, the box cannot be completely isolated from its surroundings relative to heat losses so we can expect a general heat loss rate, q, from the box to its surroundings. Thus, if we do not inject heat into the box at the same rate q, we will be unable to maintain a constant box temperature, $T_1$.

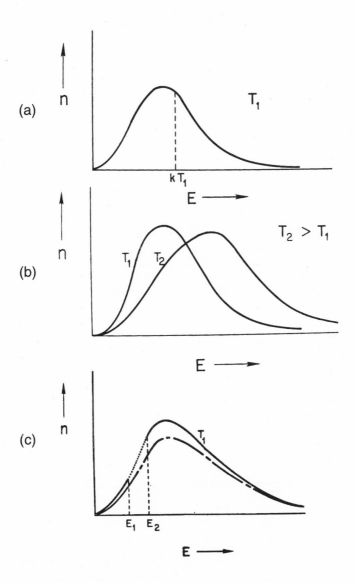

**Fig. 5.6** (a) Distribution of energies for molecules in a box at temperature $T_1$, (b) shift in energy distribution for molecules due to change in temperature from $T_1$ to $T_2$ and (c) illustration of distribution changes associated with the extraction of the group of energy states between $E_1$ and $E_2$ at temperature $T_1$.

If we were able to take the equilibrium distribution of molecules at temperature $T_1$, and remove all of the atoms having energies between $E_1$ and $E_2$, as illustrated in Fig. 5.6c (call this number, $\Delta N$), we would find that this gap in the distribution would not exist for long, but that the molecular collisions would allow the distribution to relax and give the dashed curve which is an exact replica of Fig. 5.6a but with fewer total molecules ($N - \Delta N$ molecules). Thus, no matter what arbitrary change we make in the distribution of molecules, when the system is allowed to relax, it quickly recovers its equilibrium distribution of energies.

This does not mean that things are static--far from it. Any particular molecule exchanges energy in each collision it makes with the other molecules and moves up or down the scale of energy so that, over a long period of time, any such molecule experiences <u>every energy state</u> in the system. In this example, we have invoked <u>conservation</u> of energy in each collision. Thus, if one molecule gains energy by the interaction, the other loses an equal amount of energy. From this example, it should be clear that it is not particularly meaningful to talk about the characteristics of a single molecule (because they change energy so quickly with time); it is only meaningful to talk about the characteristics of <u>the total ensemble</u> because that may not change with time.

If the temperature in our box is quite high, the molecules will probably have dissociated into atoms whereas, if it is low, we will find most of the species bouncing around in the box to be in the associated or molecular state. In this state, the electromagnetic nature of the individual atoms, leading to an attractive force between them, is on average sufficient to overcome the collision force of other molecules so that they remain strongly bound together. Thus, if we think of the marbles in the box as being covered with a coat of glue, they will stick to each other if they collide at a small velocity (low temperature), but will bounce off each other if they collide at a large velocity (high temperature). Further, a combined molecule colliding with a wandering, high velocity atom or molecule will generally be split up into its atomic constituents. At any particular temperature of the box, those molecules having kinetic energy greater than $E_B$, the electromagnetic binding energy, will be dissociated. As the temperature is raised, the fraction of marbles having energy greater than $E_B$ is increased.

Let us now turn to humans and consider the above discussion as an analogue. In this case, the important measure is not energy but <u>consciousness</u>. For our present purposes, we will lump all aspects of consciousness, denoted by the symbol C, together on one scale instead of discriminating physical, etheric, emotional, mental and spiritual scales. In this case, if we take a society of N people (N is large) and we plot the number of people, n, having the level of consciousness, C, at time $t_1$, we obtain a curve similar to Fig. 5.6. We find that we have a few individuals with a very low degree of consciousness but most have a level of consciousness near the mean consciousness, $C^*$ (see Fig. 5.7a). However, several important differences between the molecular and the human ensembles must be noted. First, a human entity has free will and can move either up or down the scale of consciousness as he/she chooses (of course, because we humans tend to polarize our attitudes around some focal point, it would take many lifetimes to span the entire distribution--which is probably a supportive factor in the need for reincarnation if one accepts the postulate that all states of consciousness must be sampled by each member of the ensemble). Next, for gas molecules, energy had to be conserved during an interaction, but for humans <u>consciousness is not conserved</u>. When one human entity meaningfully interacts and communicates with another, new information is exchanged and consciousness may be created.

Perhaps it is best to think of this in terms of a receptivity influence. As one meaningfully interacts with another, one's receptivity opens and radiation seems to pour in from some other dimension of the cosmos. This seems quite analogous to adding a quantity of heat, $\Delta Q$, to the box of molecules. Thus, as time passes, with meaningful interactions, the total amount of consciousness shared in the system (the human ensemble) grows so that, at time $t_2$ greater than $t_1$ ($t_2 > t_1$), the average consciousness of the collective ensemble is greater than it was at time $t_1$ (see Fig. 5.7b). Of course, various physical, emotional and mental practices on the part of the entities can lead to a type of forgetfulness and an overall loss of consciousness. Thus, we can expect that some positive rate of creation of consciousness is needed to maintain the ensemble at a constant $C^*$ level.

The correspondence between Figs. 5.6b and 5.7b is made more complete by recalling that, when we took our box of gas atoms at temperature $T_1$ and injected energy into the box, the molecules absorbed the energy and attained an average heat content characteristic of temperature $T_2$. Likewise, in Fig. 5.7b, time grows from $t_1$ to $t_2$ as this newly created consciousness content is absorbed by the people.

Once again, each part of the distribution is dependent on all the other parts. This is because, at the physical level, we sense only by contrast, and if entities are removed from the segment of states between $C_1$ and $C_2$ in Fig. 5.7a, other entities would soon develop those levels of consciousness because there is no awareness, or sensing ability, to keep them from occupying those states. Thus, it is with a broad spectrum of the distribution that an entity needs to

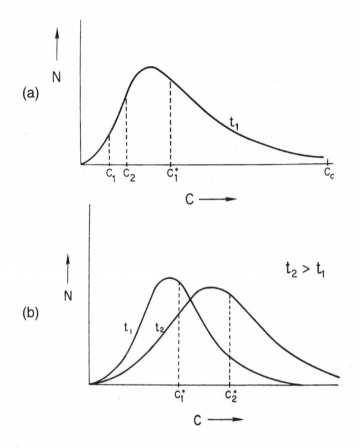

**Fig. 5.7** (a) Distribution of consciousness, C, for a human ensemble at time $t_1$ and (b) a shift in consciousness distribution to a higher mean value, $C_1^*$ to $C_2^*$, as time grows from $t_1$ to $t_2$.

meaningfully interact in order to enhance his/her consciousness. Again, one part of the system is dependent upon the others and <u>collectively we form a species</u>. The important thing to remember is that all members of the ensemble are part of the one--the whole system is ourselves. In part, I am you and you are me. That which I do reflects your growth and that which you do reflects mine. When we see something in our individual entity (our personal selves) that we do not esteem, we cannot disown it--we must work on it until we have mastered and perfected it. Likewise, if we see something in another human entity that we do not esteem, we cannot disown it and must find a suitable way to work on it until it is in harmony--for we are perfecting ourselves. And this we do by increasing the average consciousness, $C^*$, of our ensemble.

Perhaps a useful analogy here would be a laser system comprised minimally of (1) a suitably doped host crystal, (2) a suitable pump source and (3) suitable mirrors. It is the cooperative action of these three elements that leads to the lasing action and the resulting high intensity beam of coherent light. One cannot endow ownership of this new quality to any one of the three elements because <u>all</u> are necessary to achieve this result. Often it is the same with humans, someone occupies the role of coherent host, someone else acts as a broad band pump source while still someone else acts as a kind of mirror to produce a resonant system. In such a case, abundant new creative expression is often manifest and, even though it issues forth from the coherent host, the ownership belongs to the group because all three elements were necessary for the manifestation.

Returning to Fig. 5.7b, at the very high end of the consciousness scale $(C > C_c)$, there have been a few entities like Buddha, Krishna, Mohammed, Jesus, etc., who all became the Christ, whose enlightenment enriches all the rest of us and who communicate so meaningfully that we are shown a more effective way to grow in consciousness. As time passes, the average consciousness, $C^*$, generally increases so that the number of entities endowed with the level of consciousness $C > C_c$ increases. If we knew the exact shape of the distribution curve in Fig. 5.7a and knew the ratio of $C_c$ to $C^*$, we could calculate the probability of such an entity being born at any time or the length of time humankind would have to wait for such a birth event to occur by chance. Certainly, one point seems clear from this model, the rate of growth of consciousness depends upon how meaningfully each of us communicates in each human interaction with another entity. If, through fear or insecurity, we shield (or screen) ourselves with an idealized image, then image communicates with image, receptivity is absent and very little consciousness is created in the interaction events, so collective humanity's consciousness does not increase and, indeed, may even decrease with time. Thus, we must learn to communicate fully and honestly.

We must also learn to abandon judgement of others because they are constraints that reduce the degrees of freedom and thus the possible creative expression available in an interaction. To illustrate the relative, rather than absolute, scale of our judgements concerning good versus bad (or good versus evil) behavior, consider Fig. 5.7b. At time $t_1$, the average (at level $C_1^*$) look "up" the consciousness scale to $C > C_1^*$ and proclaim that in that direction lie "good" states of consciousness. They then look "down" the consciousness scale to $C < C_1^*$ and proclaim that in that direction lie "bad" states of consciousness. At a later time, $t_2$, the average consciousness (now at level $C_2^*$) again look up and down scale and make similar pronouncements. However, there are now a set of states between $C_1^*$ and $C_2^*$ that were pronounced "good" at time $t_1$ but "bad" at time $t_2$. So much for the absolute nature of our judgements!

From the modelling of this section, we see that there is a natural inequality between humans taken as individuals. However, our states of consciousness are generally interdependent and it is much more meaningful to consider the average of the total ensemble when one wants to assess the growth (meaningful communication) or the decay (forgetfulness) of humanity.

Recalling the association-dissociation reaction in the molecular ensemble, let us now consider the analogy in the human ensemble. Here, the counterpart to molecule formation would be the dimer unit (man-woman, etc., pair), the family unit and other major cooperative human institutions. Treating the dimer unit as our simplest example, the major attractive force binding them together is "love" (although very strong forces can come from other chakra-chakra interactions as well). It is the love force, in all its various manifestations, that creates this important bond. The stronger is the love force between the pair, the greater will be their binding consciousness and the more will they be able to resist the dissociation forces of their environment. In the molecule ensemble case, it was the kinetic energy of the impinging molecules at high temperature that created dissociation. In the human ensemble, it is the frequency of, and degree of, consciousness impacts between the pair and their surroundings (other people, situations, stresses, etc.) that determines the probability of dissociation. If life is allowed to become so hectic and stressful, with little attention being applied to vitalizing the love bond, then, after a period of time even a trivial impact can precipitate a chain of sequences that ends in dissociation of the pair.

## Transpersonal Interactions and Increased Channel Capacity

In the atomic/molecular ensemble, the interaction potential, $\Phi$, and the interaction force, $F$, vary with separation distance, $R$, between two atoms as illustrated in Fig. 5.8a. When the atoms are far apart, $\Phi$ is constant and a very small attractive force exists between them. As they move closer together, the attractive force increases and $F$ decreases until, at a separation distance $R^*$, the force is zero and $\Phi$ has a minimum value (maximum energy, $E$, is being stored in this bond). At even smaller separation distances, $R < R^*$, the force becomes repulsive and $\Phi$ begins to increase.

Two very common types of atomic interaction forces are (1) the Van der Waal's dispersion force (due to instantaneous dipole-dipole interactions) and (2) the static dipole-dipole interaction force. In Fig. 5.8b, we deal with two symmetrical atoms separated by distance R.

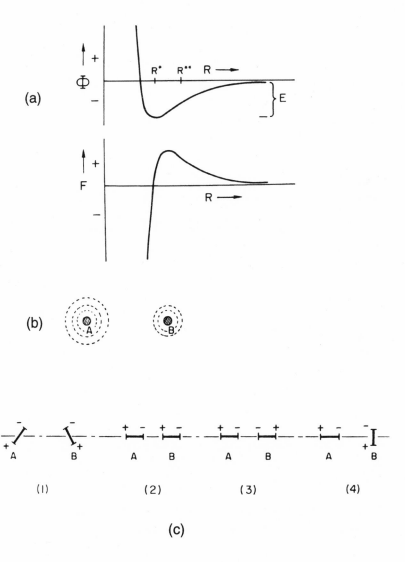

**Fig. 5.8** (a) Interaction potention, $\Phi$, and interatomic force, F, as a function of separation distance, R, between two atoms, (b) schematic representation of interatomic dispersion forces and (c) static dipole-dipole interaction geometries.

In both atoms, although on a time-average basis there is no electric charge asymmetry, moment to moment the electrons are moving in their orbits and constitute a net instantaneous electric dipole moment that moves rapidly over the electrons with time and ultimately averages out to zero for each atom over sufficient time. However, this means that, instantaneously, the atoms must be emitting electromagnetic, (EM) waves because moving charge always requires EM wave emission. Thus, think of atom A as a broadcasting station operating on a band of frequencies determined by the orbital electron characteristics of A. After a short time, this wave, having decayed a little in intensity because of the distance travelled, reaches atom B and acts as an exciting field on atom B, which was initially performing its own random oscillations (its own dance pattern). This driving EM field of A at B acts as a force tending to polarize B so that its orbital electrons begin to move more into synchronization with those of atom A. If atom B is very polarizable in the frequency band of atom A (very responsive in this frequency range), a sympathetic resonance is set up between A and B so that atom B oscillates in phase with atom A (now they are both dancing in the same rhythm) and sends out its EM wave in phase with that from A. When this wave reaches atom A, it acts as a driving force for atom A and, since it is nearly in phase with A, it is like an additional in-phase push on a swing, and the energy builds higher. Quantitatively, the force of attraction between the two atoms is given by the product of the instantaneous electric dipole moment of A and the amplitude of the EM field from atom B at the location of atom A. If atom B is not very polarizable in this frequency range, it does not respond to the EM stimulation from atom A so that its own broadcast EM field will generally be strongly out of phase with that from A so that the two EM waves <u>destructively interfere</u> and the interaction energy is small; they are not responsive to each other. If atoms A and B are both very polarizable in the broadcast frequency range, a sympathetic resonance of electron motion in the two atoms will be set up, their broadcast EM fields will <u>constructively interfere</u> and they will strongly attract one another. This is one of the few examples in physics where <u>like attracts like</u>!

Turning, now, to the static dipole-dipole interaction of Fig. 5.8c, the force of interaction is just due to the sum of the charge-charge interactions. Here, opposite sign charges attract and same sign charges repel. Thus, the net force of attraction or repulsion depends upon the relative orientation between the two dipoles and upon their separation distance. The geometry of Fig. $5.8c_2$ yields the maximum force of attraction, Fig. $5.8c_3$ yields the maximum repulsive force and Fig. $5.8c_4$ gives a zero force of interaction. In most real cases of two molecules interacting with each other, we must consider <u>both</u> the dispersion force and the fixed dipole force interactions. If there is a large fixed dipole moment on the molecule, there is unlikely to be a strong dispersive force interaction and the molecules will not be sensitively responsive to each other.

Now we are ready to apply this model to the interaction between two human entities. General interactions occur via the auric sheaths discussed in Chapter 3. More specific interactions occur via the endocrine/chakra pairs and, since the heart is by far the strongest EM oscillator of the physical body, most specifically by the entire heart antenna system at physical and subtle levels. This set of radiations is broadcast by the sender and is received by the similar center in another entity's body. The absorption of this radiation generates a biological activity in the receiver's body. If the receiver is polarizable (responsive) in the particular frequency range of the broadcast radiation, the biological activity will be high and the receiver will respond by broadcasting its own "heart" signals and a heart-bond can form between them.

If one transmits only small power and in a very narrow frequency band from this center, then only a few certain individuals will receive and sense this love. If one builds his/her self to transmit large signal power over a broad band of frequencies, many entities will be able to absorb this radiation and be aware of this love. Since most of the audiences of the truly great teachers like Krishna, Buddha, Mohammed or Jesus, who all manifested the Christ consciousness, did not understand them intellectually, their strong response to these teachers was probably due to the high power, broad band, love radiation signal that they broadcast.

The more constantly polarized (judgemental) is an individual in his/her attitudes, the less <u>awake</u> or <u>responsive</u> is he/she to such broadcast radiations. They are too rigidly aligned in a certain attitude direction (mindset) to sense the projection from a sender not similarly aligned. The response of two human entities via a fixed dipole-dipole type of interaction is in complete accord with Fig. 5.8c for molecules; that is, maximum positive interaction if like fixed-polarization occurs and negligible interaction for indifferently-coupled fixed-polarization.

The Soviets purportedly[4] performed a sympathetic resonance experiment on two animal hearts that had been removed from their respective bodies and maintained separately in a stable functioning condition via fluid and electrical connections. Each had its own separate support system and they were not linked in any obvious way. The hearts were then placed at the two foci of an elliptical mirror so that any physical radiation leaving one heart would be reflected from the mirror to focus on the other heart, and vice versa. Initially, the two hearts were beating with very different rhythms. However, after a few minutes, the rhythms and phasing began to shift and, after about ten to fifteen minutes, the two hearts were beating in perfect synchronization (identical rhythm and phase). Of course, this same phenomenon often occurs when a mother holds her child to her breast and they both quietly go off to sleep.

From the foregoing, we have seen that humans can indeed attune to the frequency transmissions of others and develop a positive interaction force between them, especially for heart-heart interaction. In Chapter 3, we found that allowing atomic orbitals to strongly interact led to a broadening of "bandwidth" for the group of atoms. Likewise, it can be shown mathematically that, for a linear system, the addition of two harmonic waves of frequency $\omega_1$ and $\omega_2$ leads to a combined waveform of frequencies $(\omega_1 + \omega_2)$ and $(\omega_1 - \omega_2)$. Thus, a concommitent of the attuned coherence state is not only a major increase of average energy density but also a <u>major increase in bandwidth</u> for the state. According to our discussion in Chapter 4, a major increase in bandwidth means a major increase in channel capacity. This, in turn means a major increase in information capability of the system--for both <u>processing</u> and <u>accessing</u>. Such a system has a greatly enhanced ability to serve as a channel for universe expression because it is a system of expanded consciousness.

Following the thread of this chapter, we have discussed the great benefits that accrue to the development of group coherence with respect to both energy effectiveness and creativity effectiveness. For each member of the group to be able to frequency-lock and phase-lock with other members of the group, they must first have learned how to be inner self-managed at mental and emotional levels and then they must learn how to do it with others. The procedures are somewhat similar and we will devote the next section to their discussion.

It has often been said that the essence of a human is to be found in his/her state of consciousness and that the larger purpose of human life is the successive evolution through ever higher states of consciousness and awareness. As Aurobindo has said[5], "A change of consciousness is a major fact of the next evolutionary transformation, and the consciousness itself, by its own mutation, will impose and affect any necessary mutation of the body." As we proceed along the path of inner self-management, structural changes occur within us that allow a significant increase in the level of in-dwelling spirit and this, in turn, appears as a significant increase in one's level of consciousness.

## Choosing The Path Of
## Individual Inner Self-Management

Over the last few decades, the event density flowing into our daily lives has increased exponentially and there is no indication of a deceleration in this world-wide process. Just the individual process of attention switching from event to event to decide which to neglect and which not to neglect creates a large fatigue stress in our neural systems. Thus, today, almost everyone is over-stressed. And signs are that it will only get worse! Accordingly, there is a great need for individuals to learn how to move themselves to new levels of effectiveness which do not overstress the biological system. The available techniques for this fall under the heading "inner self-management at mental and emotional levels" and three of them were briefly mentioned in Chapter 2. Yoga is the most well known and via its methodology one focusses on the mind in order to <u>still</u> the mind and thus find inner peace and relaxation of internal stresses[6]. Qigong is less well known and here one focusses on the "Dan Tien" point in order to still the mind [7]. HeartMath is even less well known (at the moment) and here one focusses on the heart in order to still the mind[8]. In all cases, experienced practitioners gain great inner stability at mental and emotional levels and manifest very special human capabilities related to developed levels of organization at both physical and subtle levels. In this section, we will limit our focus to the HeartMath approach[8-10].

One of the key tools in the kit of HeartMath techniques is called "Freeze Frame"[10]. This consists of consciously disengaging the mental and emotional reactions to either external or internal events and then shifting the center of attention from the brain and the emotions to the physical area of the heart while intentionally focussing on someone or something to love and/or sincerely appreciate. This allows the individual to access a wider and more objective perception in the moment.

Some higher band qualities of the heart are love, care, appreciation, forgiveness, humor, compassion, patience, tolerance and kindness. Love, in this context, is defined as benevolent heart focus towards the well-being of others and it is found that the heart-focussed feeling for any of these mentioned qualities produces profound electrophysiological changes in heart rate variability (HRV) as contrasted with the mental focus on the concept of these heart qualities, which does <u>not</u> produce such HRV changes.

It is well known that the heart is autorhythmic; that is, the source of the heartbeat is within the heart itself rather than coming from some other portion of the body. The heart appears to be a self-controlled organ although its beat rhythm can be modulated by other segments of the body. Both sympathetic and parasympathetic nerve links connect the brain to the heart allowing one-way signal communication. Reverse direction signals also flow along nerves of the baroreceptor system to the brain making it a two-way communication system. The sympathetic nerve link of the ANS (autonomic nervous system) causes the heart rate to increase while the parasympathetic causes the heart rate to decrease. The degree of change depends on the activity of the nerve channel. It is the interaction between these two signal links that produces what is technically called heart rate variability (HRV), the periodic time variation in number of heart beats per minute found in an individual's electrocardiogram (ECG). Of course, the reverse direction signals are well known to profoundly influence brain function (the cardiovascular system is the only known nerve input to the brain that will <u>inhibit</u> the activity of the brain's cortex which is usually regarded as the seat of higher brain function including perception and learning). Thus, although the heart has its own basic rhythm, this rhythm appears to be modified by how we mentally or emotionally perceive events in the moment.

Here, I wish to show that repeated practice of the HeartMath inner self-management techniques produces a balanced mental and emotional nature that, in turn, manifests a set of uniquely defined physiological states as seen via analysis of HRV and ECG data.

Fig. 5.9a has been constructed to illustrate how the sympathetic (LF) and parasympathetic (HF) branches of the autonomic nervous system (ANS) influence the sinus node (SN) of the heart and influence its HRV as seen in the HRV power spectrum (Fig. 5.9b). Using the real-time ECG signals of Fig. 5.10a, from the intervals between the R-waves, the variability in heart rate can be determined and plotted as the real time HRV signals of Fig. 5.10b. This latter time domain signal can be analyzed into its primary wave components to give the amplitude of each wave component as a function of wave frequency (called Fourier decomposition). Since the energy or power in a wave is proportional to the amplitude squared ($A^2$), the power spectrum of a real-time signal is thus a plot of $A^2$ for each wave component. Examples are given in Fig. 5.9b and Figs. 5.10c. In the power spectrum of Fig. 5.9b, the very low frequency signals, largely associated with thermoregulation of the body are often ignored. Although it is not a perfectly clean measure of ANS balance, many investigators use the ratio of total HF power (0.15 Hz to 0.40 Hz) to total LF power (0.05 Hz to 0.15 Hz) as an approximate measure of ANS balance.

Fig. 5.10 illustrates some qualitative and quantitative differences between the real time heart rhythm signals for an individual feeling frustration versus appreciation versus a deeper internal state of inner self-management where one can reduce the HRV to near zero. This deeper state has been called the internal coherence state. As one practices the Freeze Frame technique, a conscious awareness of one's own electrical body and it's minute currents is reached. The ability to focus in the heart area and balance these electrical energies leads one to a state of order which is called amplified peace and this leads to the internal coherence mode of heart function represented in the extreme right boxes of Fig. 5.10. In Fig. 5.10, frustration and appreciation are words that characterize the mental and emotional state that the individual is in while the graphs are the HRV and ECG electrophysiological correlates that correspond with these states. Although we don't see much difference in the real-time ECG data for these three states, clear differences are seen in the real-time HRV data. Spectrum analysis of these heart rhythm signals (both HRV and ECG) allow us to detect the difference in internal order associated with the three states. Fig. 5.10c allows us to measure the degree of signal balance between the two branches of the ANS (for the normal state, e.g., frustration).

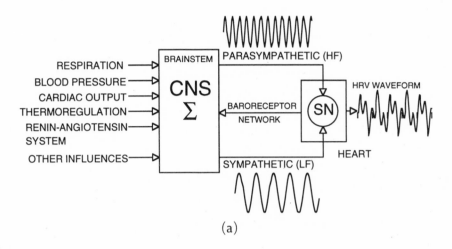

(a)

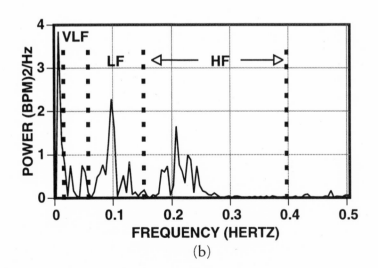

(b)

**Fig. 5.9** (a) Schematic illustration of sympathetic (LF) and parasympathetic (HF) nerve signal superposition at the sinus node (SN) of the heart to influence the ECG and HRV and (b) the low frequency band (LF) is mostly sympathetic influence with some parasympathetic influence on HRV, while the high frequency band (HF) is only parasympathetic influence on HRV.

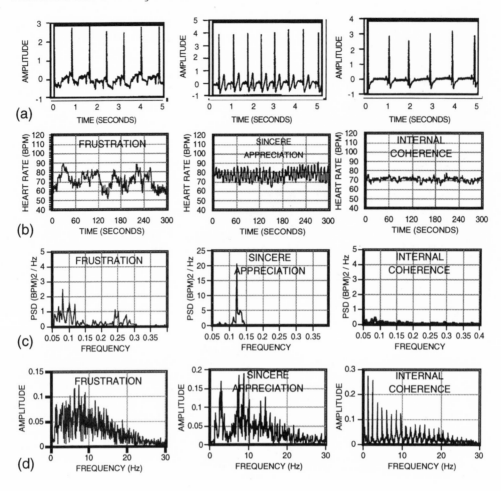

**Fig. 5.10** Different modes of electrophysiological data presentation for three different mental and emotional states: frustration, sincere appreciation and internal coherence; (a) real-time representation of ECG data for these three states, (b) real-time HRV data for these three states, (c) simultaneous HRV power spectra and (d) simultaneous ECG amplitude spectra in the frequency domain.

An even more significant level of order occurs when the two branches of the ANS are "in sync" or integrated. Such an entrainment mode of heart function, associated with the sincere appreciation heart focus, represents optimum coupling efficiency between the two branches of the ANS. Whenever one sees such a narrow band signal in the power spectrum of the HRV (as in the middle box of Fig. 5.10c), or a relatively harmonic signal in the time domain representation of the HRV data (as in the middle box of fig. 5.10b), it is called "entrainment"[11]. Likewise, whenever one sees an <u>intentionally</u> produced very low amplitude signal in the HRV power spectrum (as in the right hand box of Fig. 5.10c), or the "very clean" display of both the heart fundamental mode and its higher harmonics in the ECG amplitude spectrum (as in the right hand box of Fig. 5.10d), we define this as "internal coherence". In this state, differences in amplitude of the higher harmonics reveal changes in the detailed shape of the R-wave in the real-time ECG data (analogous to Fig. 5.2 data) for the heart.

Normal individuals (without much inner self-management) generally exhibit imbalance in their sympathetic versus their parasympathetic innervation and this is a good datum from which to measure progress in the development of inner self-management via steady use of the HeartMath techniques. Fig. 5.11 illustrates possible achievement plateaus relative to this datum for Freeze Frame practitioners. With training, individuals first learn to balance the two branches of the ANS. Next, the entrainment state is achieved at the natural baroreceptor frequency ( ~0.1 Hz). This appears to be followed by entrainment state shifts to alternate specific frequencies depending on the specific heart intentionality focus used. Then, one reaches the internal coherence state of heart function in which the real-time HRV signal is held at an approximately zero amplitude level which means that the ECG signal is exhibiting almost perfectly periodic behavior (in normal individuals, small to near zero HRV is thought to be a potentially dangerous condition as it connotes a loss of flexibility in the system. However, for these trained subjects, it is an indication of exceptional self-management because their resting HRV is quite large).

Continued practice of the Freeze Frame and heart focus techniques appears (subjectively) to produce structural changes in the general heart area of the chest--certainly at subtle levels and perhaps also at physical levels.

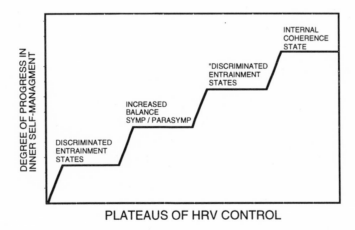

**PLATEAUS OF HRV CONTROL**

**Fig. 5.11** Schematic illustration of relative attainment plateaus in a progress map for subjects trained in the Freeze Frame technique as a function of their statistical capacity to actualize their applied intentionality capabilities.

This subtle level structure appears to be a type of antenna array system for both receiving and transmitting the various qualities of love both over an increasingly broad frequency band and with increasing gain. As a consequence of such changes, an individual's intuitive skills greatly increase.

Although a few other individuals have shown exceptional conscious heart rate control, particularly Swami Rama[12], it is not a presently normal human capacity. It is thus all the more significant to underscore the point that a set of relatively simple techniques[8-10] exist whereby otherwise normal individuals can, in a reasonably short period, gain a sufficiently high level of inner self-management at mental and emotional levels to automatically manifest conscious ordering of their ECG and HRV. In Fig. 5.12, we see that twenty individuals readily achieve either the entrainment or the internal coherence plateau on demand[11]. No biofeedback of any type was involved in this data collection and these 20 individuals had been practicing the Freeze Frame and heart focus techniques for periods of only 6 to 36 months.

During the course of these studies, it was observed that other major biological oscillators of the body frequency-locked and phase-locked to the heart during the entrainment state. This is shown in Fig. 5.13a for HRV, pulse transit time (PTT) and respiration. In Fig. 5.13b, it is shown for the HRV and the brain waves (electroencephalogram). Thus, we see that the entire body is functioning more in phase and thus more efficiently when these inner self-management procedures are utilized.

These electrophysiological changes appear to have beneficial correlates at the chemical and hormonal level of the body as well as at the energy field level of the body. At the biochemical level, salivary IgA was measured on a group of 20 HeartMath practitioners both before and after experiencing the emotional states of care and compassion (C+C) as a heart focus versus anger and frustration (A+F). These emotional states were aroused in two ways; (1) by using the inner self-management techniques (internal) or (2) by showing participants video tapes (external). The heart focus feelings of C+C were enhanced by simultaneously listening to music[13] specially designed to facilitate mental and emotional balance.

Secretory immunoglobulin A (S-IgA) is frequently used as a measure of immunity in psychoneuroimmunological studies. S-IgA is the predominant antibody class in body secretions. S-IgA antibodies in mucosal secretions provide a first line of defense against pathogens producing infections in the upper respiratory tract, the gastrointestinal system and the urinary tract. Higher levels of S-IgA in saliva are associated with decreased incidence of disease, particularly upper respiratory infections, and have been correlated with decreased susceptibility to infection.

218

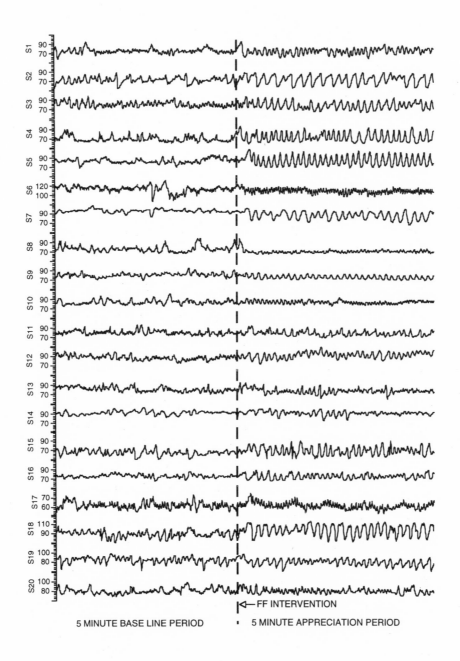

**Fig. 5.12** Real-time HRV rhythm patterns for 20 individuals in the laboratory during a 5-minute baseline period, the Freeze Frame and heart focus intervention point and a 5-minute period focussing on appreciation. This data collection was preceeded by a 10-minute rest period.

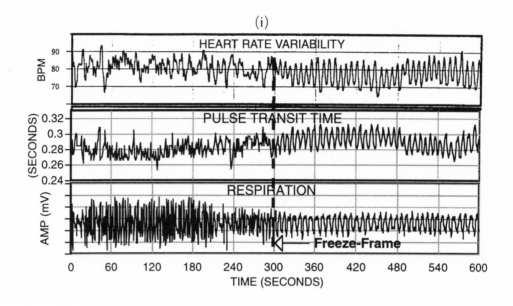

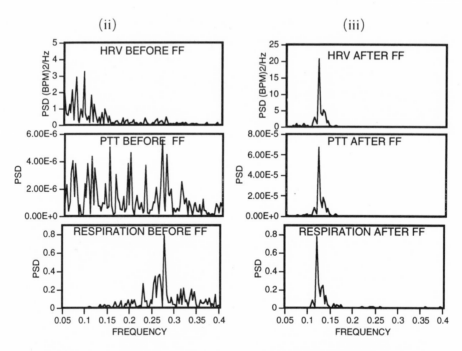

**Fig. 5.13a** Three simultaneously recorded body information channel responses to the freeze frame (FF) and sincere appreciation heart focus intervention at ~300 sec; (i) real-time data for HRV, PTT and respiration, (ii) power spectrum for the before-FF condition and (iii) power spectra for the after-FF condition

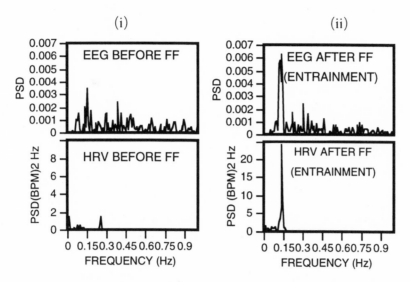

**Fig. 5.13b** EEG and HRV power spectra in the normal state (i) and in the entrained state (ii). Note the large peak at the entrainment frequency of ~0.12 Hz in the EEG for (ii).

A+F-induced changes in S-IgA were only seen by using the internal self-generation technique of recalling situations in one's own life which aroused feelings of anger and frustration. The external induction of emotions by watching a specially edited video of war scenes was not effective in changing the S-IgA level. With the internal technique, there was an immediate increase in S-IgA level after a five minute period of anger. As seen in Fig. 5.14a, this was followed by a large decrease which was sustained below baseline levels over the following 5-6 hours[14].

For the C+C test, self-generated feelings produced significantly larger increases in S-IgA than the video induction method using a tape of Mother Teresa caring for the diseased and dying in the slums of Calcutta. For the internal method, the immediate increase in S-IgA following the C+C intervention was not itself followed by a net decrease in S-IgA as in the A+F test. Instead, as shown in Fig. 5.14b, a steady rise from baseline levels occurred over the next 5-6 hours. If one looks at the average change in S-IgA over the 5 hour period following the stimulation, then one clearly sees an increase beyond baseline for the C+C test but a decrease below baseline for the A+F test. Such results[14] confirm and extend previous studies that have investigated the immunoenhancing effects of positive emotional states and indicate the need for effective management of the long term immunosuppressive effects of negative emotions.

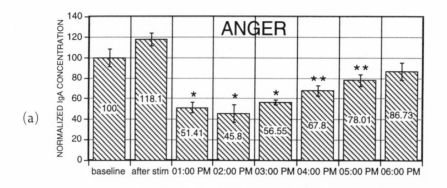

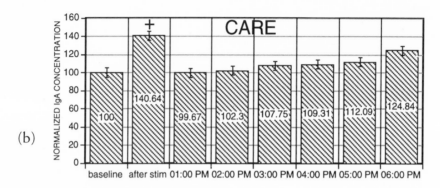

**Fig. 5.14** Short and long-term changes in S-IgA concentration after experiencing the emotional states of (a) anger/frustration or (b) compassion/care. There were 20 individuals tested (10 in each group). These results represent averages of the 10 subjects.

The foregoing has indicated internal changes in HeartMath practitioners. Let us now look at some data that illustrates changes in their auric fields, associated with the inner self-management techniques, that impact both the structure of water held near the body and the structure of human DNA in aqueous solution held near the body. Suppose we take a trained practitioner and an untrained practitioner seated in the same room and two jars of aqueous solution containing human DNA. We first obtain the ultraviolet (UV) absorption spectra of this DNA solution and place a jar in the left hand of each individual while asking them to focus on their heart and feel sincere appreciation for someone or something for a period of 5 minutes. After this time period, we again measure the UV spectrum of the DNA solution and find (a) no change in the jar from the untrained practitioner and (b) a significant change in the jar for the trained practitioner (see Fig. 5.15). If such a change can occur to DNA held <u>outside</u> the body, imagine what is happening to the DNA of the practitioner's cells <u>inside</u> the body!

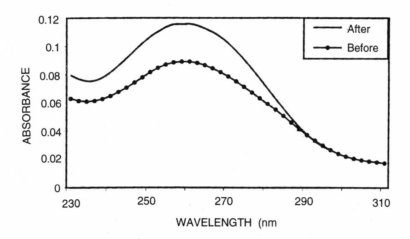

**Fig. 5.15** Subject's intentional unwinding of human DNA in aqueous solution held 12" from the body while in the "internal coherence" state.

To illustrate the foregoing more concretely, using 5 trained practitioners, for a total of 10 trials on different days, ECG monitoring was used to tell when a subject was in the entrained state and a sample of UV absorbance-tested distilled water in a test tube was placed in the left hand of the subject. While holding the sample, the subject was asked to focus on the water and intentionally alter its molecular structure for a period of five minutes. The experimental result revealed a statistically significant difference in the entrained state-intentionally treated water compared to the controls ( $p < 0.01$ )[15]. The results indicate that treated water shows higher absorbance values at 200 nanometers than the controls and lower absorbance values at 204 nanometers. It is interesting to note that (a) if the individuals are in the entrained mode or the internal coherence mode but <u>not</u> intentionally focussing on the water, no statistically significant effect is found and (b) if the individuals are not in the entrained mode or the internal coherence mode but <u>are</u> focussing intention on the water, no statistically significant effect is found. Thus, it seems as if <u>both</u> the entrained heart mode (or the internal coherence heart mode) <u>and</u> directed intention are required to produce a statistically significant effect. The internal coherence heart mode produces larger effects than the entrainment mode in general.

Individuals trained in the heart focus techniques who had achieved the internal coherence plateau of attainment, with a high level of coherence indicated in their ECG power spectrum, were all able to intentionally produce a change in the DNA conformation of vials of human DNA in aqueous solution placed ~12" from the body. Ultraviolet spectroscopy provides information concerning the chemical interactions between the two strands of the DNA helix, the resonant energy transfer along individual strands plus the interaction between the strands and their environment (water). In these studies, all three types of interaction were present. The observed changes in Fig. 5.15 reflected the subject's intention to denature the DNA (unwind and separate the strands). The observed changes were three times larger than the maximum thermal or mechanical perturbation imposeable on the system (well known to denature DNA) and well beyond those observed for complete denaturation of DNA. In Fig. 5.16, both the ECG power spectrum of the individual <u>and</u> the UV absorbance of the test sample in the before and after state are provided[16].

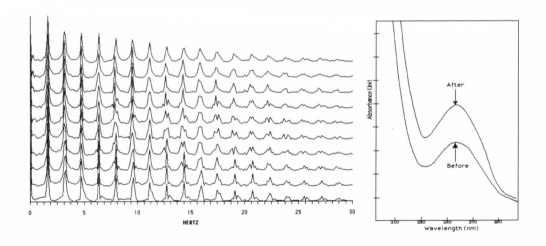

**Fig. 5.16** In the subject's ECG power spectrum on the left, all the 10 sec epics are coherent. The correlated change in DNA denaturation on the right was much larger than maximum normal, physico-chemical processes suggesting some basic alteration in the DNA bases.

Generally, when the ECG spectral data is viewed in 10 second epics, not all epics show coherence. Rather, what is seen is some ratio of coherent to incoherent patterns. Thus, the time average degree of coherence can be defined as a percentage of totally coherent to incoherent epics. Fig. 5.17 illustrates four different ECG power spectra associated with the four emotional states of planetary love, care, worry and anxiety. Feelings of anger, frustration and worry create higher percentages of incoherence in the ECG spectra while feelings of love, care or appreciation create higher percentages of coherence[16].

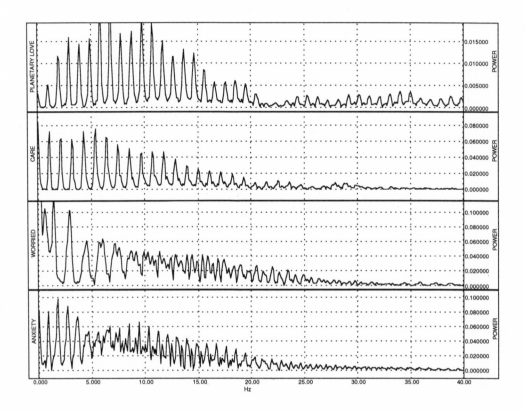

**Fig. 5.17** Four ECG power spectra illustrating various levels of coherence.

In Fig. 5.18a, we note a somewhat coherent ECG power spectrum for an individual in state #2 and the corresponding test sample effects when the intention to <u>rewind</u> the DNA strands was held for two different tests labelled state #1 and state #2. In Fig. 5.18b, for a relatively incoherent ECG spectrum, the corresponding test sample shows a negligible change in the conformational state of the DNA even though the <u>intention</u> to rewind the strands was held. Again, we see that <u>both</u> the maintenance of the internal coherence state via heart focus <u>and</u> a specific held intention are necessary to create the desired effect in the test sample.

225

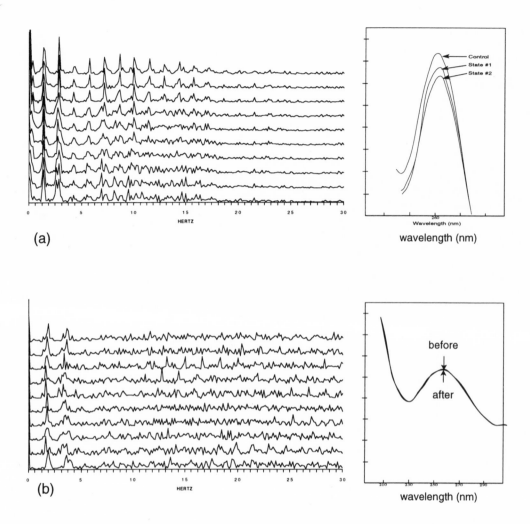

**Fig. 5.18** (a) An individual's ECG power spectrum epics (10 sec) correlated with the test sample changes in UV absorbance (held intention was to rewind the DNA). (b) A less coherent individual's intention to do the same as in (a).

Fig. 5.19 provides an experimental result to illustrate that coherent heart energy can influence DNA at a distance. Here, the subject was approximately 0.5 miles from the DNA sample and held the intention to increase DNA winding. In contrast to many of the experiments, in which DNA conformation was measured immediately after being exposed to heart energy, this result was part of a study to understand the time evolution of the UV absorbance changes. The overall results are complex and depend on the level of the energies involved; different individuals and different intentions produce characteristic time-course changes. Thus, in some experiments, effects are seen immediately after sending energy, but in others they manifest only after a given period of time. This time period varied from ~10 minutes to ~60 minutes, depending upon the type of subtle energy being transmitted. Furthermore, once the effect on the DNA solution was initially manifested, it either continued to increase or reach a plateau (depending on the experiment)[18]. More will be said about this time-course phenomenon in Chapter 6.

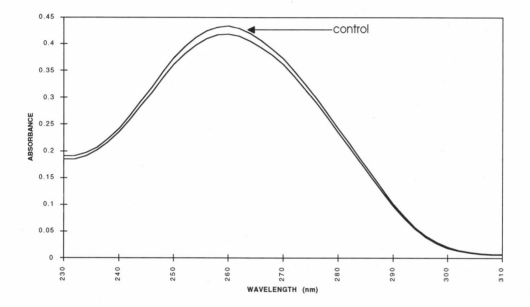

**Fig. 5.19** The long distance effect (0.5 mi) of coherent heart energy plus the intention to increase DNA winding. This measurement was taken 90 minutes after initial exposure to heart energy.

From the foregoing, we have seen how inner self-management of the heart focus variety leads to higher degrees of mental and emotional order in our multidimensional bodies with correlates appearing at electrophysiological, biochemical and energy field levels. Such heart focus practices clearly enhance our progress towards personal coherence. This work tends to suggest that the heart is the "mainframe" of the body and that humans function best and most effectively when all the biological oscillators of the body take their lead from the heart.

For a very long time, humans have looked at each other from the brain/mind level and have easily seen the differences in gender, in color, in race, in language, in religion and in the abstract symbols we use to describe our culture. This has led to hatred, violence, wars, etc., and it has often seemed to be a hopeless path for human development. However, when humans look at each other from the heart with a focus on one of the many qualities of love, one does not see these differences. Rather, one tends to see another human heart wherein mutual resonance can produce a cooperative state whose resultant is greater than the sum of the individual parts. This is a much more fruitful pathway for human evolution--the development of heart/mind consciousness!

## Towards Group-Attuned Coherence

Very little is known scientifically about this topic but we can use the techniques of the previous section as a guide. One could take two trained individuals in the same room being simultaneously monitored for ECG, PTT, respiration, etc., and in a normal state. Then ask them to Freeze Frame, appreciate each other through their heart focus and <u>intend</u> to come into close attunement with each other. One might expect to see an entrainment state in each real-time HRV signal followed by frequency and phase-locking of their other biological oscillators followed by frequency <u>and</u> phase-locking of the two individuals' entrainment states. When readily successful, a third trained individual can be added to the group and practice continued until three-fold entrainment frequency and phase-locking is easily achieved. Then, a fourth, fifth, etc., trained individual can be added to the group experiment. In this way, one might expect to attain attuned coherence of a fairly large group of individuals who have personally achieved a fairly high level of inner self-management.

Eemans[19] developed a group harmonizing technique many years ago using an extension of his individual circuit technique. Fig. 5.20a shows how one can hook up two people in a series arrangement so that there is etheric energy flowing through both individuals. One can use either series or parallel connections for energetically joining people. Fig. 5.20b shows such a possibility with four people. From his studies, Eemans found that one can have a variety of energy-types in one's group; that is, energy emitters, energy resistors, energy conductors, energy relayers, etc. He found that the order in which one arranges people in the circuit became important in terms of the magnitude of energy flow around the circuit. It seemed that the basic energy flow in the circuit is sometimes large enough (when the emitter strength is high) to break down the energy barriers (resistances) to flow in certain individuals so that, eventually, this energy loop operates like an amplifier to increase the energy of everyone in the circuit. The energy loop closes on itself and the energy just keeps circulating around the loop bringing reduced resistance to its flow and bringing about balance and equalization of everyone's primary body energies (much as discussed in Chapter 4 for the trunk circuit). Here, the copper wire connections aid the flow from individual to individual to produce aura to aura coupling. With training and focussed intentionality such wires are no longer needed.

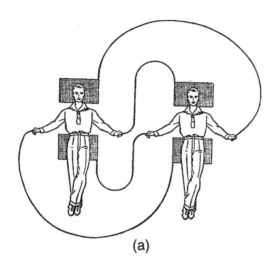

(a)

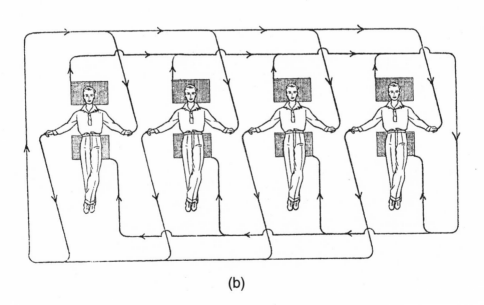

(b)

**Fig. 5.20** (a) Two subjects in closed series-type Eeman's relaxation circuit and (b) four subjects in a closed parallel-type Eeman's circuit (all H to all S and all R to all L)

# References

1. H. Haken, "Synergetics: An Introduction" (Springer-Verlag, Berlin, 1977).
2. A.L. Schawlow, in "Lasers and Light" (W.H. Freeman and Company, San Francisco, 1958-1969) p. 232.
3. Private discussions with Doc Lew Childre (1994).
4. E. Naumov, Private communication (1970).
5. Sri Aurobindo, "The Adventure of Consciousness," (Satprem, Pondicherry, India, 1968).
6. W.B. Gibson, "The Key To Yoga" (Ottenheimer Publishers, Inc., New York, 1958).
7. C.T. McGee and E.P.Y. Chow, "Qigong: Miracle Healing From China," (Medipress, Coeur d'Alene, Idaho, 1994).
8. D.L. Childre, "Self Empowerment" (Planetary Publications, Boulder Creek, CA, 1992).
9. S. Paddison, "The Hidden Power of the Heart" (Planetary Publications, Boulder Creek, CA 1992).
10. D.L. Childre, "Freeze Frame" (Planetary Publications, Boulder Creek, CA 1994).
11. R. McCraty, M. Atkinson and W.A. Tiller, <u>New Electrophysiological Correlates Associated With Intentional Heart Focus</u>, ISSSEEM Journal,<u>4</u> (1993) 251; Cardiac Coherence: <u>A new, Noninvasive Measure of Autonomic Nervous System Order</u>, Alternative Therapies, <u>2</u> (1996)52; <u>The Effects of Emotions on Short-Term Power Spectrum Analysis of Heart Rate Variability</u>, Am. J. Cardiology, <u>76</u> (1995) 1089.
12. E. Green and A. Green, "Beyond Biofeedback" (Delacorte Press/Seymour Lawrence, New York, 1977) p. 201.
13. D.L. Childre, "Heart Zones" (Planetary Publications, Boulder Creek, CA, 1991).
14. G. Rein, M.Atkinson and R. McCraty, <u>The Physiological and Psychological Effects of Compassion and Anger</u>, To Be Published, 1996.
15. G. Rein and R. McCraty, <u>Structural Changes In Water and DNA Associated With New Physiologically Measurable States</u>, Proc. Society For Scientific Exploration Conf., Austin, TX, June 1994.
16. G. Rein and R. McCraty, <u>Modulation of DNA By Coherent Heart Frequencies</u>, Proc. 3rd Ann. Conf. ISSSEEM, 1993.
17. R. McCraty, M.A. Atkinson and G. Rein, <u>ECG Spectra: The Measurement of Coherent and Incoherent Frequencies and Their Relationship to Mental and Emotional States</u>, Proc. 3rd Ann. Conf. ISSSEEM, 1993.
18. G. Rein and R. McCraty, <u>Local and Non-Local Effects of Coherent Heart Frequencies On Conformational Changes of DNA</u>, Proc. Joint USPA/IAPR Psychotronics Conf., Milwaukee, 1993.
19. L.E. Eemans, "Co-Operative Healing" (Frederick Muller Ltd., London, 1947).

# CHAPTER
# 6

## TRAINING WHEELS FOR HUMANITY

*As toddlers transiting between tricycles and bicycles,*
*Some needed training wheels to gain the confidence and find the sense of*
*balance. To glide freely and joyously -- without aids of any kind.*
*Teacher/student, guru/chela, pendulum/dowsing wand,*
*All serve to enrich and build those inner circuits allowing us to be free --*
*And be -- as we were meant to be.*


In the last chapter, one of the points I tried to emphasize is that <u>we are the product of the process and we are built by the process</u>. By this I meant that, by continued interaction with the simulator around us, we eventually develop all the necessary circuitry at physical and subtle levels that are required to both fulfill our evolutionary needs and our intentionality exercises. However, on this path towards total integration and complete coherence, we encounter "seeming" barriers to our forward progress and, at such times it is beneficial to have some <u>aids</u> to help us pass these particular barriers. These material, mechanical, electrical, etc., devices which serve as aids, I categorize under the label "training wheels". Thus, the dowsing wands used to locate water or as an aid to energy transfer discussed in Chapter 4 are examples of "training wheels". When our own body's structural organization at physical and subtle levels has reached the point where it has attained a high level of geometrical, radiation type, radiation frequency and radiation amplitude discrimination for both receiving and sending, then these particular training wheels are no longer needed and they can be dispensed with. Until that graduation day, they are useful in that they enhance our present capabilities. Of course, it is also important to remember that one can become chained to a crutch by failing to exercise without it.

In this chapter, I wish to discuss a number of such training wheel-type devices so that we can understand their utility, how they work and what possibilities are open to us to invent a future technology based upon these concepts.

In particular, I wish to emphasize that energy medicine, as distinct from chemical medicine, can utilize such devices for subtle levels of diagnosis and therapeutic treatment.

## Some Components of The Talisman Effect

My Oxford Dictionary gives the following definition for talisman: "A stone, ring or other object, engraved with figures or characters, to which are attributed the occult powers of the planetary influences and celestial configuration under which they were made; worn as an amulet to avert evil from or bring fortune to the wearer; also used medicinally to impart healing virtue. Anything that acts as a charm or by which extraordinary results are achieved." This implies some magical connotation to the word which is a reasonable implication based upon the conventional paradigm of present-day science. However, this is <u>not</u> a reasonable implication based upon the foundation of the higher dimensional paradigm that I have tried to lay with this book. The talisman effects are just a consequence of natural phenomena that involve more than our physical 4-space. In this section, we will briefly discuss some of them.

**Geometrical Patterns and Shapes:** In Chapter 2 we learned that the two companion 4-spaces wherein physical and etheric substances function are duals or conjugates of each other. In this case, the complementary material forms or geometrical shapes hold a type of inverse relationship, one to the other. In particular, for a fixed physical shape in the 3-D part of positive space-time, its complementary etheric shape is just the Fourier Transform in its 3-D part of inverse space-time with the frequencies kicked up to a higher octave. Thus, shape is an important quality of any object! Since planar geometrical physical patterns are essentially 2-D shapes, they have complementary or conjugate etheric shapes which are just the 2-D Fourier Transforms (see chapter 2 appendix). In certain cases, the shapes and patterns seem to form a relatively efficient resonant system for energy transfer between domains.

Using a dowsing wand of the type illustrated in Fig. 4.1c, one can detect unique energy patterns associated with different shapes. Using the snowflake-type pattern of Fig. 6.1 etched on a standard drinking glass, water held within it was found to alter its structure leading to a change in its UV absorbance compared to a similar amount of water held in the same type of glass with no surface pattern for the same length of time. One series of experiments involved placing a test tube of DNA solution on top of this pattern for 30 minutes. Depending on the experiment, UV absorption ratios (after/ before) for DNA near the geometrical pattern ranged from ~5-10 times that for control samples with no pattern nearby.

**Fig. 6.1** Pattern etched into the outer surface of a water glass so that water held therein alters its ultraviolet absorbance.

To illustrate another aspect of the shape-effect, like many individuals in the early 1970's, I was intrigued by the claims concerning the use of particular pyramids for the preservation of food, for altering the taste of wine, for sharpening razor blades, etc[1]. I decided to carry out the razor blade sharpening test myself so I took a Gilette razor blade and made it dull by cutting thin cardboard with it. I even looked at it under a microscope and saw that it had been made dull by my actions. I then placed it on a plexiglass pedestal (on an upper shelf in my home office) at the correct height of the queen's chamber and carefully placed a plexiglass pyramid over it. I aligned everything correctly and then I left it alone in that position for 1 month because, if anything was to happen, I wanted to provide sufficient time for it to take place. At the end of the month, I took it down and looked at it under my microscope and it definitely appeared to be sharper. Then I tried to cut the thin cardboard I had used before and it seemed to cut much more easily than just prior to the experiment.

I was elated that this preliminary experiment seemed to yield a positive result and thought that now I would do a more careful experiment and show the results to my Stanford colleagues because the purely physical forces on this razor blade are all in the direction to increase the blunting of its edge. This time, I made a scratch on the blade edge and took scanning electron micrographs of the region of the edge near the scratch so that I had a good measurement of its local curvature. Then I proceeded exactly as before with the blade lying in exactly the same environment for a month. At the end of the month, I carefully took the blade back to the scanning microscope and took another set of photographs near the scratch and I was very surprised to find <u>no change at all</u>!

This result puzzled me; it could be attributed to carelessness on my part the first time or that I mistakenly saw what I wanted to see the first time or that it was all associated with statistical fluctuations. I was doubtful that this was the correct line of reasoning to take and eventually thought of another possibility. In the first experiment, there were no observer constraints placed on the ultimate result and my qualitative recollections of sharpness/bluntness was the final measurement gauge. I had allowed the universe maximum freedom to express itself in novel as well as in ordinary ways. In the second experiment, I interjected an observer constraint of a quantitative nature and asked for a result that violated physical experience. I didn't get such a result! I did not proceed with other experiments of this nature because I was becoming aware of the possibility that if one wishes to observe subtle energy effects manifesting in our physical 4-space then one should not constrain the experimental protocol too tightly. It began to seem as if a type of Heisenberg Uncertainty Principle could be operating here on a global scale and that one should minimize physical observer effects in order to maximize possible subtle domain effects.

**Experimental Constraints and Consciousness:** Very recently, I was reminded of this old supposition of mine by reading a short article by W.B. Jonas[2]. Quoting him:

"Therapies delivered under optimal clinical conditions in which a person is trying to resolve an identified problem in another, and in which all the attached expectations, personal selection processes, ritualistic and social context, driving efforts, etc., are present, will usually result in about an 80% success rate. This is called the absolute effect size of the treatment. Of course this varies with the problem. More "solid" problems change at a slow pace or to a small degree, but this may reflect more duration of the observation period than their inability to change. Rapidly changing objective problems such as skin lesions, certain infections, GI ulcers, ECG changes, etc., will follow this 80% rule even in short term studies under normal conditions.

However, the relative effectiveness of these same therapies, when they are compared to similar interventions without the assumed treatment effect are usually dramatically reduced, even with drug and surgical methods and when based on objective parameters. Simply putting a control group of any type (without the assumed therapy) into a study will often produce relative effectiveness of 40% less than are found in before and after treatment studies. Adding randomization as an additional control measure will often reduce effectiveness by 20% more, and adding a sham or placebo treatment that is similar to the real treatment reduces the effect size still more. If the sham treatment is similar enough to the treatment being studied, the effects attributable to the treatment are often eliminated entirely, indicating that the absolute effects are due to other non-specific or non-identified factors."

This is essentially how one would expect a global expression of the uncertainty principle to operate.

We usually apply the principle to two conjugate physical variables of a system wherein, if we want to specify very tightly the value of one of them, we must accept a great range of uncertainty concerning the value of the other. Here the physical body/etheric body are conjugate systems so that, there is some rationale if we constrain the physical parameters of a therapy or process too tightly, we produce great uncertainty with respect to the etheric parameters of the same therapy or process. It is too early to say whether or not this speculation will hold up to careful scrutiny but, at least, it adds a useful perspective for future considerations of the interplay of physical/subtle materials and consciousness. This, too, can be considered to be an intriguing part of the talisman effect.

To illustrate yet another aspect of the talisman effect, consider a very recent experiment with a special type of inanimate object[3]. In this case, test tubes containing human DNA solution were placed over two color photographs. One was of a Russian healer and one was of an American highly skilled in generating coherent heart frequencies. Each test tube was exposed to the photograph for up to three hours with UV absorbance measurements at 260nm being taken at 30 minute intervals. Both photographs produced a decrease in absorbance (DNA winding) relative to the control and both slowly increased their magnitude of change with time but with a different time courses. The control DNA absorption values varied between 0.5 and 1.0%; the photograph of the Russian produced a maximum change of 3.8% in DNA absorption and the photograph of the American produced a maximum change of 10% in DNA absorption. In this case, a property of our simulator is such that an aspect of the consciousness of the individual photographed is somehow transferred to the photograph which then acts as a talisman to alter the DNA solution.

## Some Consequences of Subtle Substance Titration Into Physical Host Materials

As was pointed out earlier with regard to Fig. 2.2, when a particle appears in physical reality because of a fluctuation in the vacuum, its ground state energy is determined by the interaction between this particle and the chaotic virtual particle sea of the vacuum. Thus, if our state of consciousness produces a high level of inner self-management at subtle levels and, since these levels constitute the substructure of the vacuum, the wave functions of this chaotic Dirac Sea can be altered. This, in turn, would bring about a change in the ground state energy level of the particle mentioned above because the interaction is now changed. Further, if this can be done with one particle, it can be done with any particle. What this means to us is that a real possibility exists wherein one's consciousness allows one to alter the ground state energy levels of molecules A, B and C or fundamental particles d', e' and f' such that, under a standard set of conditions where one obtains

$$A + B \rightarrow C \quad \text{and} \quad d' + e' \rightarrow f',$$

with the introduction of a sufficiently strong consciousness field, one can obtain the reverse reactions. Potentially, this allows one to influence any chemical or nuclear reaction in the universe and thus to alter our present-day technologies in significant ways. Let us proceed to try and understand this possibility a little better from a theoretical modeling viewpoint before we consider some devices designed to manifest this possibility in a small way.

**A Thermodynamic Perspective:** In purely physical reality, we can mix two or more different chemicals, called components, under specific conditions of temperature, T, and pressure, P, (both thermodynamic variables) and produce alloys of solid, liquid or gaseous constitution at some specific mole fractions of the components (another thermodynamic variable). Gibb's Phase Rule[4] tells us, for equilibrium conditions, the number of degrees of freedom, f, available to a system of c components when there are p coexisting phases present. The main extrinsic thermodynamic variables are T and P (although the electrical potential, $\phi$, could be added for electrochemical systems). For only two extrinsic variables, the phase rule statement is

$$f = c - p + 2$$

Thus, if we have only one component (c=1) and one phase present (p=1), T and P can be varied independently ( f=2) without changing the phase (called a bivariant domain in Fig. 6.2a). When there are two coexisting phases (p=2), it is a univariant condition (f=1) with some fixed relation between T and P (see the curved lines in Fig. 6.2a). When there are three phases present (p=3), it is an invariant condition ( f=0) and it can occur only at a single point in Fig. 6.2a (designated $T^*$, $P^*$). Addition or subtraction of heat from the system will merely change the proportions of the three phases. The pressure and temperature remain stable against all heat losses or gains until one of the phases disappears. As a practical example, the system $SiO_2$ - $H_2O$ in Fig. 6.2b is a classic one and is relevant to the hydrothermal growth of quartz crystals[5]. A logarithmic scale has been used for pressure (largely proportional to $H_2O$ content) with the result that the solid-solid equilibria appear distorted. The horizontal dashed line shows the isobar at 1 bar ( ~1 atmosphere pressure) with the traditional phase transition temperatures of the solid $SiO_2$ polymorphs.

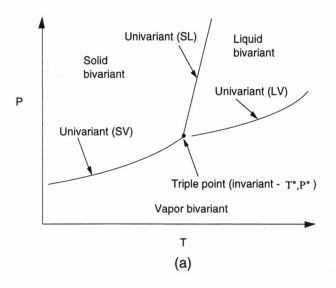

(a)

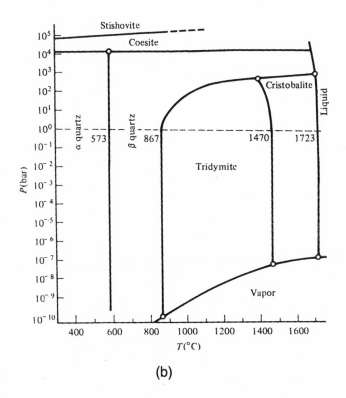

(b)

**Fig. 6.2** (a) A typical pressure (P) - temperature (T) phase diagram for a one-component system and (b) the P-T phase diagram for silica ($SiO_2$) showing the stability regions for the various equilibrium phases.

Just as we have unique chemical phases forming when we mix two or more different physical chemicals under specific conditions of T and P to form a multicomponent physical phase, we can expect unique material phases to form when we mix one or more physical elements or compounds with a combination of subtle materials at a certain concentration and under specific thermodynamic constraints of T, P, intentionality, I, and consciousness, C. In this case, we must increase our number of independent thermodynamic variables by two (I and C) so that the phase rule statement now becomes

$$f = c - p + 4$$

and many more degrees of freedom are available for equilibria between these <u>multicomponent/multidimensional phases</u> (this means that the location of the lines and intersection points in Fig. 6.2a can be shifted by variations in I and C). Following standard thinking concerning phase equilibria, wherein a particular subtle material is treated as an additional component, one can have a region of solid solubility of the component in the host physical phase up to some solid solubility limit. The fact that the free energy of the subtle component is negative and the entropy of mixing is favorable suggests that large solubilities are possible before phase instabilities develop and a new physical/subtle hybrid phase appears.

As is well known, composite physical materials (multiple physical phases in an aggregate) exhibit unique physical properties (mechanical, electrical, optical, etc.) depending upon the proportions and geometrical arrangements of the different phases. Likewise, we can expect to create composite physical/subtle materials with unique physical/subtle properties. For example, the embedding of certain subtle energies into electronic devices will imbue the electrons with some aspects of consciousness so that they will respond to intentionality forces as well as to the standard electrical forces. This can lead to a large family of new electronic devices. We can expect similar effects relative to sound and photon properties of materials so that interesting new audio and video devices should naturally appear.

**A Kinetic Perspective:** Let us suppose that, at time t = o, we place a physical object at a fixed position in space (the object could be a test tube filled with DNA solution). The thermodynamic desire for equilibrium requires that etheric substance begins to collect both within and around the physical object to build its etheric conjugate (its Fourier Transform). The dynamic movement of the atoms and molecules of the physical object requires active oscillators in the (1/t) domain of inverse space-time; some of low frequency, some of mid-frequency and some of high frequency. It will be the cooperative modes of atomic/molecular motion at the physical level that produce the low frequency spectrum and one expects these to take a relatively long time to stabilize. It is the instantaneous electric dipole moments on the individual physical atoms that produce the high frequency spectrum and these should stabilize very quickly. At normal temperatures, one expects the binding energy between the electric (physical) and magnetic (etheric) counterparts to be small but non-zero because some deltrons will always be present (see Chapter 2).

As mentioned in Chapter 2, if one has a rod-shape in physical space (direct space or positive S-T), then the complementary shape in etheric space (inverse space or negative S-T) is a disc perpendicular to the rod with its center located at the rod center. Thus, if our physical object mentioned above is indeed a test tube filled with DNA solution, then its etheric conjugate will be of disc shape. If, for the moment, we approximate the test tube and DNA solution as a completely homogeneous material down to atomic dimensions and the tube is short and fat in shape, the etheric disc will also be homogeneous but thick and of small radius as illustrated in Fig. 6.3a. However, if the tube is long and thin, the etheric counterpart disc will be thin and of large radius as illustrated in Fig. 6.3b. At variance with the above assumption concerning the DNA solution homogeneity, the DNA solution is actually a <u>composite</u> of aqueous electrolyte, containing no DNA molecules, and a series of sphere-like DNA particles forming a dispersion in the water. Thus, the consititution of the physical/etheric counterparts is expected to be inhomogeneous much as illustrated in Fig. 6.3c. The Fourier Transforms of this dispersion of DNA spheres is expected to be much like that illustrated in Fig. 2.17 depending on sphere radius and sphere density. Since some details of the physical chemistry of this dispersion process are important for overall understanding, I need to briefly go into a little more detail on that process before moving on to describe what happens when one abruptly removes the physical object from its fixed point in space.

Each sphere-like DNA particle is a single chain of DNA (of some fixed chain length) that contorts itself into a ball-like shape with a size that minimizes its free energy (a very important thermodynamic quantity). The size of the ball is determined by the energy of interaction between the water and the DNA strands. For a given DNA chain length, if this interaction energy is weakly attractive, then parts of the chain prefer to interact with other parts of the DNA chain rather than with water so the ball becomes tightly wound up and has a small radius. If this DNA/water interaction is strongly attractive, then the ball opens up to allow more of this interaction and the radius becomes appreciably larger. Because of the natural surface electrical potential at the water/DNA strand interface, the outside of each ball has a higher electrical potential, $\phi_s$, than the bulk liquid. This causes many of the ions of the electrolyte to move from the bulk solution to the "ball" surface region creating a diffuse electrical double layer of ionic charges around each DNA particle as illustrated in Fig. 6.4. When the number of DNA particles per cm³ is low, we have a dilute solution with a large amount of space existing between DNA particles so they move around slowly via what is called "Brownian" motion. Depending on the rate of sphere movement (temperature dependent) in physical space, dynamic etheric conjugate changes are required in inverse space leading to a different time-average picture in Fig. 6.3c. As one increases the number of DNA particles per unit volume, they become closer together and can only diffuse about in a small restricted space.

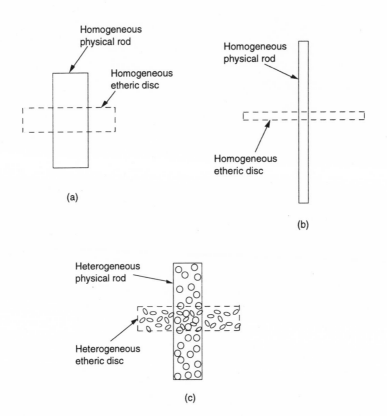

**Fig. 6.3** The geometrical relationships expected between some physical/etheric conjugates, (a) a short, large diameter, homogeneous physical cylinder, (b) a long, small diameter, homogeneous physical cylinder and (c) a heterogeneous (particles in a matrix) physical cylinder.

The electrical double layers of any two particles repel each other because they are of similar sign of charge while the electrodynamic force between the DNA particles produces a force of attraction. When the latter force is the weaker one, the particles bounce off each other and maintain a stable dispersion even though they are close together[6]. When the latter force is the stronger one, the particles stick together in a clump and gravitationally settle to the bottom of the solution. One can alter the relative size of these two forces by changing (1) the bulk electrolyte content of the water, (2) the pH (hydrogen ion content) of the water, (3) the DNA chain length, (4) the DNA particle density per unit volume and (5) the addition of a chemical surfactant to the solution. Maintaining DNA particle dispersion at high particle density is a technical challenge but it is possible and the physical dispersion can be made to become fairly close-packed with little macroscopic motion of the particles. In this case, its etheric counterpart is well defined and also relatively unchanging. Therefore, this etheric counterpart can form reasonably quickly and the constituent etheric molecules can bind together in a relatively stable configuration.

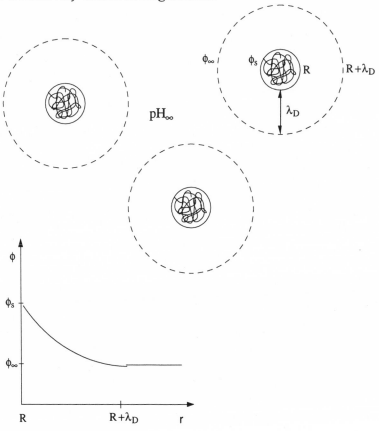

**Fig. 6.4** Schematic illustration of "balled-up" DNA molecules of net radius, R, in a solvent surrounded by an electrical double layer sheath of thickness, $\lambda_D$, whose potential $\phi$, falls off from the ball surface value of $\phi_S$ to the bulk solvent value of $\phi_\infty$.

241

Abrupt removal of the solid physical object from its fixed point in space to a far-removed location, leaves a portion of its former etheric conjugate behind. Since this etheric substance now has no thermodynamic force to sustain it in that configuration, it will begin to dissolve, unravel and, like smoke, diffuse away. Some of this is expected to occur fairly quickly and not be observable by conventional techniques. However, the low frequency etheric correlates of the cooperative physical modes are expected to be present at long times because of the inverse relationship between etheric frequency and physical time (recall Fig. 2.15). This is quite similar to some of the water UV absorbance results discussed at the end of Chapter 5. If the etheric signals that ultimately produce the absorption change are of a high frequency nature, then the physical effect will be manifest very quickly; however, if they are of a low frequency nature, then it will take a substantial time passage before the effect will appear in the physical data. This is just the "Mirror Principle" in operation.

One should be able to detect "phantom" signals associated with the presence of this etheric substance via the use of either very sensitive magnetic field detectors or specially correlated light beams[7]. Although this phenomenon should be a general one, the effect is expected to be larger for organic physical matter than for inorganic physical matter because the former is more organized with more adhesiveness between its several subtle components and it has more consciousness.

Another correlate of the Mirror Principle relates to the temperature effect and this has an important consequence here. At the physical level, increasing the temperature reduces the chain length of physical long chain molecules because thermal dissociation of the chain (bond breaking) occurs more readily at high temperatures. Via the Mirror Principle, this requires that long chain etheric molecules dissociate more readily as the temperature is <u>decreased</u>. Thus, in the foregoing experiment, if we want to change the kinetics of the phantom effect in reproducible ways, we need to adjust the temperature of the environment. For example, if we want to erase the phantom effect very quickly, we could lower a test tube filled with liquid nitrogen into the location of the original physical DNA solution.

Such experiments herald a new era in physics because reproducible phenomena of the cause/effect variety can be gained from a region of physical space that is not supposed to generate such phenomena based upon the current paradigm!


# Water As A Host For Subtle Energies

In both Chapter 1 and Chapter 5, many examples have been presented of subtle energy effects taking place in water. In this section, let us gain some additional insight into the structure and properties of water so that we might begin to understand why it is such an excellent host for subtle energies.

**Water's Physical Structure:** The $H_2O$ molecule shape forms an isoceles triangle with the oxygen at the apex and the hydrogens at the base as shown in Figure 6.5. Because of the electric charge transfer between the H and the O species, the molecule exhibits an electric dipole moment of 1.85 Debyes so that dipole-dipole interactions should form a strong binding force between $H_2O$ molecules in water and one might expect a fixed dipole alignment of these $H_2O$ molecules. However, such a fixed dipole alignment provides very little configurational entropy for the water and an alternate possibility exists when the dipole interaction energy between two $H_2O$ molecules in the head-to-tail configuration (lowest possible energy arrangement) is close to the average thermal energy, kT (where T is temperature and k is Boltzmann's constant). In this case, the mutual orientation of any two dipoles may be destroyed in the thermal collisions occurring between molecules. At room temperature (T~25oC), the energy doesn't change much but now the system has abundant configurational entropy due to the random orientation of the dipoles, so the <u>free energy</u> of the bulk water is lowered by going from a fixed dipole alignment to a continuously varying dipole alignment at room temperature. At a free surface (or any surface for that matter), other forces come into play and one expects water to exhibit a surface with aligned dipoles (the H are found to be immersed in the liquid while the $H_2O$ molecules are somewhat randomly oriented in a rotational sense in the surface plane. Calculations show this oriented dipole layer to be ~6 to 8 molecules thick) because this lowers the surface free energy for the water. As one reduces the temperature, the bulk entropy contribution to the free energy decreases so one should expect more ordering of the $H_2O$ dipoles to occur and, when one reaches 0oC, a transition to the fully ordered structure of ice is expected (see Fig. 6.6). Via studying the chemical bonding in ice, we have learned a great deal about the detailed chemical interactions in water.

Perhaps the major key to understanding liquid water and its various solutions lies in the concept of the "hydrogen bond". Hydrogen bonds are strongly directional with a strength of only ~5 kilocalories per mole. Because of this bond, the $H_2O$ molecule can act as both an acceptor and a donor of hydrogens. This dual ability is most readily seen by considering the fragment of ice shown in Fig 6.5[8]. We see that each $H_2O$ molecule in the crystal has four nearest neighbours to which it is hydrogen-bonded; it acts as a hydrogen (H) donor to two of the four and as an H-acceptor to the other two. These four H-bonds are spatially arranged with local tetrahedral symmetry (like silicon in a silicon crystal or $SiO_2$ in one of its crystal forms) and they form a space-filling three dimensional network.

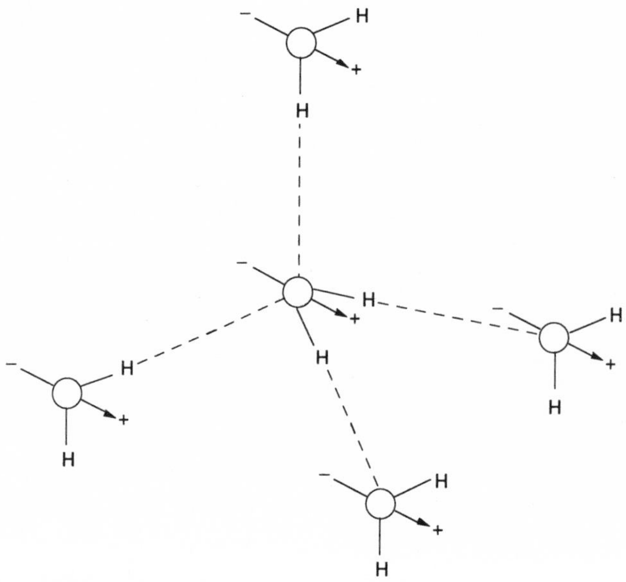

**Fig. 6.5** Here, an arbitrary central $H_2O$ molecule in ice is shown with its four nearest neighbours. The electrostatic field, $F$, arising from the fixed neighbours induces an addition, $aF$, to the dipole moment of an isolated water molecule, $m$, ($a$ is the molecular polarizability).

The view of liquid water that emerges from this line of thinking is that of a random, three-dimensional network of H-bonds. This network has a local preference for tetrahedral geometry, but it contains a large proportion of strained and broken bonds that play a large role in the kinetic properties of water. Molecules can switch allegiances by readily trading a strained bond here for one there so that the network topology is easily altered. In supercooled water, some kind of structural order-disorder phenomenon appears to be at work in the H-bond network to produce some spatial distribution of relatively unstrained (and hence bulky) H-bonded polyhedra, which are embedded within and linked to the random network.

The behavior of water towards nonpolar solutes (and nonpolar side-groups attached to biopolymers) leads to what has been called a "hydrophobic" interaction. Because nonpolar solutes fill space, the random H-bond network must reorganize around it in such a way that not too much damage occurs to the already defective network[7]. Network rearrangement occurs towards formation of a local clathrate-like cage that is far from perfect. The decrease in solution entropy associated with the presence of nonpolar molecules comes partially from the bond strengthening in the imperfect solvation cage and partially because the

$H_2O$ molecules in that cage layer around the solute have markedly reduced orientational options. Because of the energetic advantage associated with having H-bonds, each solvation sheath $H_2O$ molecule prefers to "straddle" the nonpolar molecule with its OH covalent bonds so that they can bond to other solvation layer water molecules and not waste any H-bonds[7] (see Fig 6.7)

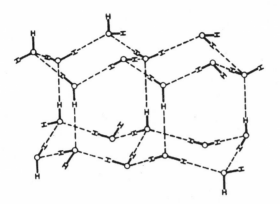

**Fig. 6.6** The structure of hexagonal ice, solid lines are covalent chemical bonds while dashed lines are hydrogen bonds.

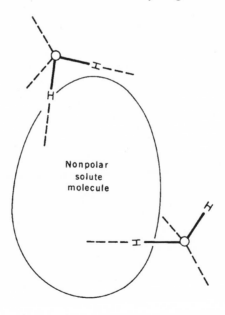

**Fig. 6.7** Orientational arrangement for water molecules surrounding a nonpolar solute. They tend to straddle the inert solute and create a cage with the maximum number of hydrogen bonds.

Pairs of nonpolar solutes in water experience an entropy-driven net attraction for one another via this so called "hydrophobic bond". This is thought to be an important factor for the native conformation of biopolymers containing both hydrophobic and hydrophyllic side groups. Insertion of nonpolar solute molecules into water biases the configurational probabilities for water molecules in the immediate vicinity towards formation of a convex H-bond polyhedron of sufficient size to contain that solute[7].

What we think of as pure water contains a minimum of five chemical species. Besides $H_2O$, $O_2$ and $N_2$ are present because air dissolves readily in water with a solubility that is a function of temperature. Unless one evacuates the water and keeps it in a vacuum bottle, air components will always be present in the water. The other two constituents that are always present are H+ and OH- which form via the thermal dissociation/ionization reaction

$$H_2O \rightleftarrows H+ + OH- \quad ; \quad K_i(T) = a_{H+} \, a_{OH-}$$

where a represents the chemical activity of the species and the equilibrium constant $K_i$ is an increasing function of temperature. Fig. 6.8 shows a plot of the equilibrium H+ concentration as a function of temperature. In this case the solution pH, which is a measure of the H+ concentration, is 7.0. Addition of acids to the water increase the H+ concentration leading to a pH less than 7 while addition of bases to the water decrease the H+ concentration leading to a pH greater than 7.

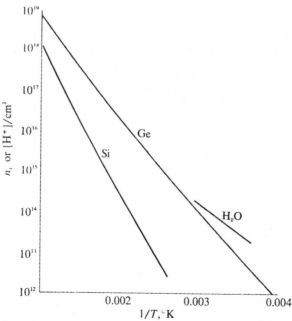

**Fig. 6.8** Intrinsic electrical ion concentration in water compared to the intrinsic carrier concentration in the elemental semiconductors silicon (Si) and germanium (Ge) as a function of inverse temperature.

As stated in the beginning, at any surface, the water molecules tend to line up for several layers. This molecular alignment produces an electrostatic potential difference, $\Delta\phi$, across the interface that also leads to a redistribution of all the ionic species present in the solution. This is most readily illustrated by using the ice/water system shown in Fig. 6.9a[5]. In this case, the measured $\Delta\phi_{max} \sim -250$ millivolts with the ice being positive relative to the water. The $H^+$ species adjust their local concentrations near the interface in response to the initial electric dipole field associated with these aligned $H_2O$ species (see Fig. 6.9b) leading to the net potential distribution shown in Fig. 6.9c. When electrolytes are added to the solution, the potential difference between the ice and the water changes and is given by Fig. 6.9e as a function of electrolyte concentration. In general, at any such interface, there are specific sites where positive or negative ions like to adsorb and this changes slightly both the bulk concentration of the charged species and the bulk solution pH.

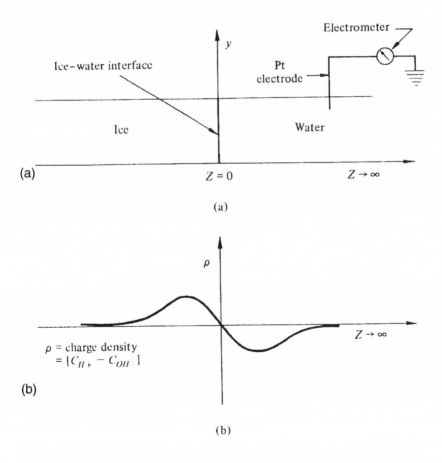

**Fig. 6.9** Relevant figures for evaluating the electrostatic potential, $\phi$, of water, (a) one experimental geometry relative to ice, (b) spatial redistribution of charge at the ice/water interface.

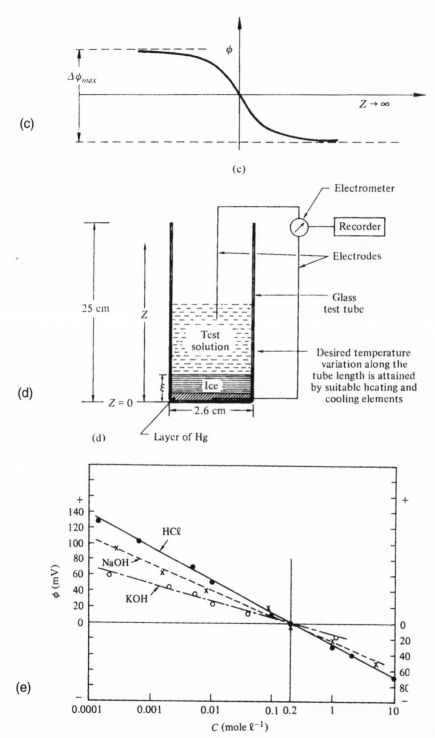

(c)

(d)

(e)

**Fig. 6.9** (c) spatial distribution of $\phi$ due to the charge distribution in (b), (d) an actual experimental set-up for determining $\phi$ as a function of ice thickness, z, and (e) near equilibrium values of $\phi$ as a function of molar electrolyte content in the water.

248

**Some Physical Field-Effects on Water:** Some of the simple tools we have in most laboratories with which we can measure property changes in water structure are: (1) pH, (2) surface tension, (3) electrical conductivity and (4) optical absorption spectra in the ultraviolet (UV) and infared (IR). It has been stated[9] that (a) all light is capable of structuring water with the blue to UV end of the spectrum leading to an alkaline pH change while the yellow to red end of the spectrum leads to an acid pH change, (b) North Pole DC magnetic fields are purported to produce an alkaline pH change and an increased surface tension while South Pole DC magnetic fields produce an acid pH change (see Table 1.7) and a reduced surface tension and (c) light and magnetic fields alter the ionic solubility of water. Fig. 1.19 reveals a 15% reduction in water surface tension due to a DC magnetic field and, on removal of the magnet, a relaxation occurs back to its normal value in ~24 hours. Further, other studies[10,11] show that electromagnetic fields alter the UV spectrum of water and that AC magnetic fields can be used to "write" a marker in water that later can be "read" by special instrumentation.

Some preliminary work[10], that still needs substantial replication to evaluate its statistical significance, indicates that the UV absorbance of pure water is influenced by the EM field from a solenoid-type coil at 29 KHz and even more substantially by a caduceus-wound coil fed by a scan signal (from 37 Hz to 37 KHz). In this experiment, square wave signals were used with either a single repetition rate of 29 KHz or by scanning all frequencies between 37 Hz and 37 KHz (one second per frequency). The input signals to the coils were all in the 9-12 volt range. The coils were used to charge water for 24-36 hours by placing pure distilled water in a sealed glass container directly on top of or adjacent to the coils. Water taken from the same stock bottle was placed in an identical sealed glass container as a control sample and was placed at least 50 feet from the sample being charged. The experiments were done at room temperature in the absence of EM shielding.

Smith[11] has demonstrated that electromagnetically sensitive individuals, known to respond to specific EM frequencies, respond to the same frequencies when they are transferred to a sealed vial of water that has been exposed to the EMF field from a solenoid coil for less than 1 minute. Later studies showed it was the magnetic vector potential that caused the changes in the water[11]. It was shown that a specific frequency could be imprinted (or potentized) into the water when an alternating current of this frequency was passed through the solenoid. The threshold strength for the AC magnetic field at an extremely low frequency (ELF) was found to be 7.6 $\mu T$ (microteslas) if the axis of the solenoid was north-south and half this value if it was east-west. Succussing the vial of water against a wooden surface, near but external to the solenoid, imprints the water at a thousandth of this field strength[11]. Initially, a pendulum held over the water was used to indicate when the water had been imprinted.

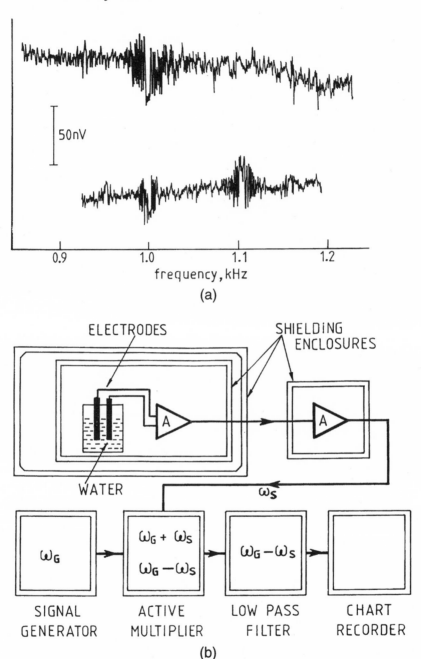

**Fig. 6.10** Resonances imprinted by an alternating magnetic field into a sample of bottled mineral water that originally exhibited only noise between 0.9 KHz and 1.1 KHz, (a) upper trace is the chart recorder output of a frequency scan after the water had been exposed to a 1.0 KHz magnetic signal. Subsequently, the same treated water was exposed to a 1.1 KHz magnetic signal and the lower trace shows the output of a later frequency scan revealing both resonances and (b) diagram of the water measuring system showing electrodes, shielding and active filter placements.

250

More recently[12], a known frequency of 1.0 KHz has been imprinted into the water and correctly read out again a short time later. After that, a slightly different frequency (1.1 KHz) was superimposed in the same water and then both frequencies were read out correctly. These chart recorder traces are given in Fig. 6.10a. A block diagram of the apparatus used for making these traces is given in Fig. 6.10b. In this case, the water was contained in a 75 ml carefully cleaned beaker into which two gold wires were dipped and arranged parallel to the beaker axis with 5 mm spacing. They were directly connected to a low-noise preamplifier and then to a high gain amplifier. Both systems were inside custom built mu-metal shielding boxes (see Fig. 6.10b). The frequency imprint "resonances" were detected in the output of the amplifiers via use of an "active" multiplier circuit whose output frequency contains the sum and difference frequencies between the signal generator output and the water imprint frequencies. The low-pass filter allows only the difference frequency component to pass through to the chart recorder.

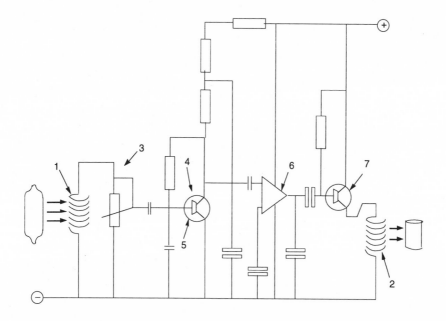

**Fig. 6.11** Amplifier circuit diagram, (1) input EM coil, (2) output EM coil, (3) high frequency filter, (4) preamplifier, (5) transistor, (6) amplifier and (7) common transistor

They found that some water was intrinsically more "noisy" than others for this type of experiment so they used a special mineral water (Volvic) for their tests. The appearance of the beat frequencies in Fig. 6.10a as the tuning oscillator approaches a resonance is an indication that actively oscillating resonances are a permanent feature in the water[10].

   In France, Benveniste[13] has been studying the effect of very dilute solutions on both invitro cells and whole organs. In one typical experiment, he
would innoculate guinea pigs with hen egg albumin before removing the hearts
and suspending them in glass cylinders to keep them alive. He then dripped
highly dilute solutions of egg albumin into the disembodied hearts. A typical
immune reaction, wherein the coronary arteries dilated and the blood flowed
faster, indicated that the disembodied hearts recognized the egg albumin. Even
when a homeopathic dilution of egg albumin below the Avogadro limit (see
later section) was used, the blood vessels of the disembodied hearts responded
by dilating a measureable amount. He then went on to build an electronic amplifier circuit (see Fig. 6.11) fitted with one input and one output EM coil. In
blind and open experiments, vials of ovalbumin were placed in the input coil
while pure water vials were placed on the output coil for 15 minutes. Water
from the output coil vials was then tested via the disembodied hearts and coronary flow variations were observed as if the water contained egg albumin [14].
Thus, the physical carrier of this specific molecular signal can be an EM field
somehow imprinted into the water in ways we do not yet fully understand.

   **Some Non-Physical Field Effects On Water:** Miller[15] developed
the following simple procedure for transferring energy from human test subjects into water. Exactly 100 ml of distilled water was placed in a glass beaker
and allowed to reach room temperature. The initial surface tension and temperature were recorded. The test subject then holds two stainless steel rods, 1/
16 inch in diameter and 7 inches long, one in each hand, by an end and im-
merses the other end in the water for exactly 3.0 minutes. Care must be taken
to keep the rods and hands from touching each other during this transfer period. At the end of 3 minutes, the rods are withdrawn and the surface tension
and temperature are again measured. The difference in surface tension readings is a measure of the energy transferred from the test subject to the water
(no change occurs if the subject is not holding the ends of the rods). Table
6.1 provides some data for a group of men and women, ages 18 to 60. We see
that, in all cases, some energy transfer occurred and, in some cases, substantial
changes occurred.

   Control samples of this water and water which has been energized as
mentioned above (subject D') were then analyzed by infrared (IR) absorption.
These results are shown in Figs. 1.20a and 1.20b Fig. 1.20a shows the control
to have a single peak in the hydrogen bonding range of 2.8 to 3.2 microns indicating that 100% of the water is hydrogen-bonded. Fig. 1.20b shows the
treated water exhibiting a non-hydrogen-bonded peak at 2.6 to 2.8 microns
with the hydrogen-bonded peak reduced to 97.04% of its normal value. These
IR traces support the conclusion that energy from the hands of selected individuals produces changes in the bonding and structure of water.

   With respect to these studies of Miller[15], it is interesting to note that the $H_2O$ molecule possesses a zero-point vibrational energy of 0.575 eV. Under a variety of conditions, this molecule can undergo a transition to higher vibrational levels with energy differences of 0.20, 0.39, 0.45 and 0.47 eV for the first four levels above the ground state[16]. Water excited to this fourth level has an energy content ~80% higher than water in the ground state. Such vibrational level changes are detectable via Raman Spectroscopy (~1600 cm⁻¹ to ~800 cm⁻¹).

**Table 6.1** EFFECT OF BIOLOGICAL ENERGY ON THE SURFACE TENSION OF WATER

| TEST SUBJECT | SURFACE TENSION (dynes/cm) | | |
|:---:|:---:|:---:|:---:|
| | BEFORE | AFTER | DIFFERENCE |
| H | 68.0 | 58.7 | 9.3 |
| I | 68.5 | 63.5 | 5.0 |
| J | 71.8 | 63.7 | 8.1 |
| K | 67.7 | 65.5 | 2.2 |
| L | 71.5 | 66.2 | 5.3 |
| M | 71.2 | 66.8 | 4.4 |
| N | 69.0 | 66.0 | 3.0 |
| O | 65.0 | 65.2 | 2.8 |
| P | 70.5 | 68.0 | 2.5 |
| Q | 77.2 | 70.0 | 7.2 |
| R | 74.9 | 68.4 | 6.5 |
| S | 74.0 | 71.9 | 2.1 |
| T | 74.9 | 69.5 | 5.4 |
| U | 77.2 | 74.2 | 3.0 |
| V | 77.2 | 74.6 | 2.6 |
| W | 79.0 | 78.0 | 1.0 |
| X | 77.2 | 74.4 | 2.8 |
| Y | 77.2 | 75.0 | 2.2 |
| Z | 79.0 | 77.3 | 1.7 |
| A' | 79.0 | 78.0 | 1.0 |
| B' | 79.0 | 78.0 | 1.0 |
| C' | 79.0 | 76.8 | 2.2 |
| D' * | 78.1 | 64.4 | 13.7 |
| E' * | 78.2 | 67.2 | 11.0 |

\* These individuals, one a minister, were also noted for their healing abilities.

253

In closing this section, the area of homeopathic medicine is a prime example of water being used as a host for subtle energies. The majority of the effects found in homeopathy occur at the subtle levels, particularly at the etheric, rather than at the physical level.

**Pertinent Facts Concerning Homeopathy:** Hahnemann[17,18] was the first to come upon the idea that a substance which can produce symptoms in a healthy person has the potential of curing them in a sick person. This has since been called <u>The Law of Similars</u> and was discussed somewhat in Chapter 1.

In the conventional method of potentizing a homeopathic remedy, the physical ingredient is placed in a suitable vial of water or alcohol, or a solution of the two, suitably stoppered and vigorously shaken or succussed. A small portion (one part in a hundred) is extracted and diluted into a similar vial of pure water or alcohol or solution and the succussion process repeated. Again a small portion of this second vial is diluted into a third, and so forth, until the stage is reached when a small portion of the n - 1th vial is added to the nth vial. The homeopathic potency of the nth vial increases with n, provided both the succussion and addition steps are used. This method has persisted for about 200 years. Table 6.2 illustrates the increase of potency and decrease of concentration of the physical substance at each step of succussion and dilution.

**Table 6.2** POTENTIZING PROCEDURE

| Concentrate | + | Solvent | + | Succussion | → | Potency | : | Physical Concentration | Step |
|---|---|---|---|---|---|---|---|---|---|
| $^1C_0$ | + | $^{99}H_2O$ | = | 100 | → | 1X | | $C_1 = 10^{-2} C_0$ | (1) |
| $^1C_1$ | | $^{99}H_2O$ | | 100 | | 2X | | $C_2 = 10^{-4} C_0$ | (2) |
| $^1C_2$ | | $^{99}H_2O$ | | 100 | | 3X | | $C_3 = 10^{-6} C_0$ | (3) |
| . | | . | | . | | . | | . | . |
| . | | . | | . | | . | | . | . |
| . | | . | | . | | . | | . | . |
| $^1C_{11}$ | | $^{99}H_2O$ | | 100 | | 12X | | $C_{12} = 10^{-24} C_0$ | (12) |
| . | | . | | . | | . | | . | . |
| . | | . | | . | | . | | . | . |
| $^1C_{n-1}$ | | $^{99}H_2O$ | | 100 | | nX | | $C_n = 10^{-2n} C_0$ | (n) |

With this range of potency, provings are first done at the hypotoxic level (1X to 8X) for relatively non-toxic substances, such as edible plants, and from the 8X to 12X for more toxic substances, such as hydrocyanic acid[18]. Doses are given three times a day for one month to the healthy subjects, located in a healthy environment, and symptoms are carefully recorded. Later, after enough time has elapsed that no new symptoms appear, the more sensitive subjects of the initial sample are tested with a 30 X remedy once a day for two weeks. All new symptoms are carefully recorded. One year later, the sensitive subjects are tested with one dose of 10 M or 50 M and observations relative to new symptoms are made for a subsequent one to three months![18] At the present time there are hundreds of remedies, derived from minerals, plants and diseased tissues, whose characteristics have been fully delineated through carefully conducted provings and thousands more which have been at least partially proven[18].

It has been noted[18] that a loss of potency for a remedy occurs when (a) it has been exposed to heat above 110°F-120°F and (b) it has been exposed directly to the sun. It has also been noted that some remedies are inactivated by exposure to strong aromatic substances, especially camphor. No precise information seems to be available on how long an exposure is needed for deactivation. Likewise, no information on the effect of extreme cold on potency deactivation is available.

Recently, an alternate potentization procedure was developed by Malcolm Rae[19]. This is a "radionic" (see next section for radionics) potentization procedure during which a vial of pure alcohol, water, or solution of the two, is placed in a static device containing a potency selector dial and a charging symbol (code) for a short period of time. The same charging time is used for all potencies, only the selector switch is changed for the different potencies. In this case, no physical additives, no succussions and no dilutions are used. The charging symbol is a cardboard disc containing a series of concentric circles and radial lines at various angular orientations (see Fig. 6.12). The angular spacing of the lines represents a specific code identity for the particular homeopathic remedy desired. An altered spacing of any two lines indicated a different substance in the radionic coding system which uses angular referents.

These two very different procedures seem to give very similar results and, on the surface, it is difficult to detect any common features. Yet each has a strict protocol which must be followed to the letter to obtain reliable and reproducible results. How are we to understand this and the other homeopathic facts listed in Table 6.3?

**Table 6.3**   HOMEOPATHIC FACTS TO BE EXPLAINED

| | |
|---|---|
| 1. | Law of similars |
| 2. | Potentization beyond 12X |
| 3. | The Rae potentizer |
| 4. | The Voll remedy testing method |
| 5. | Loss of potency by heat, sunlight, etc. |

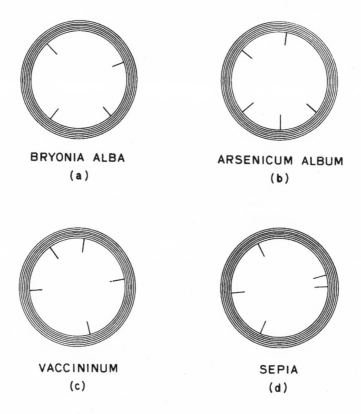

BRYONIA ALBA
(a)

ARSENICUM ALBUM
(b)

VACCININUM
(c)

SEPIA
(d)

**Fig. 6.12**  Examples of four Rae coding cards used for potentizing specific homeopathic remedies following his radionic procedure.

**Towards Understanding How Homeopathy Works**: A key postulate of this book is that the condition of health occurs when each type of physical chemical in the physical body (call it the j-species) has its chemical counterpart in the etheric body at the appropriate concentration ratio $C_E/C_P$, of the j-species. Disharmony leading to disease is thought to occur when this ratio is seriously out of balance. Some of this has already been discussed in Chapter 2.

It is the chemical potential of the j-species, $\mu_j$, that drives its chemical reactions. From thermodynamics, $\mu_j$, is given by the slope of the free energy curve, given in Fig. 2.8. Here, Fig. 6.13, which is a plot of $\mu_j$ versus the concentration of j, shows us that $\mu_j$ approaches $-\infty$ as $C_j$ goes to zero and has a large region of negative values ($0 < C_j < C^*_j$) followed by positive values as $C_j$ increases. Nature abhors large negative $\mu_j$ and will do everything possible to reduce it towards a zero value which produces a system of minimum free energy. Let us keep this in mind as we now consider the physical and etheric aspects of a biomolecule in aqueous solution.

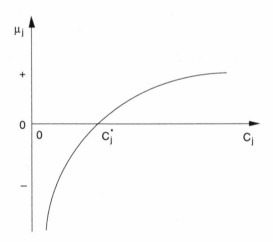

**Fig. 6.13** Plot of the chemical potential, $\mu_j$, for a j-species as a function of concentration, $C_j$, of this species in the solution.

When we put a specific physical biomolecule in water, two important things happen; (1) an H-bond cage of structured water forms around the biomolecule in all its conformations[7] so that, as far as entropy of mixing in the solution is concerned, the presence of that structured water cage indicates that the biomolecule is present and (2) the etheric counterpart of this biomolecule grows in the frequency domain of the solution and is identified via an assemblage of δ-function oscillators such as illustrated in Figs. 2.15 and 2.16. These are the etheric correlates to the spectrum of electrodynamic oscillations that characterize the molecule's van der Walls forces discussed earlier in this chapter with respect to Fig. 6.4.

The procedure of dilution/succussion with archetypal intention is particularly interesting when $\mu$ for this biomolecule falls into the negative region of Fig. 6.13. Here, three important things happen; (1) the etheric counterpart molecules are still at full strength and exert a small force, proportional to the deltron content, on the physical domain to resist the dilution process, (2) physical thermodynamics, because $\mu < 0$ for the physical biomolecule, also tries to resist the loss of entropy of mixing by the dilution process and (3) the succussion process is a chaotic process acting on a non-linear system (with archetypal intention acting on it) so that, via the process of sympathetic resonance discussed in Chapter 4, order is developed. This order is thought to take the form of enhancing the deltron content at each step of the succussion/dilution process so that the etheric/physical coupling strength increases. The consequence of this increased force transfer from the etheric counterpart molecules to the very dilute water is thought to be the creation of <u>empty</u> H-bond cages of close to the exact conformation of the physical biomolecule cage. This stabilizes the etheric counterpart and provides the needed physical entropy of mixing to lower the free energy of the system. Such an empty H-bond cage in the water acts as a "negative image" for the physical biomolecule that originally produced the same set of patient symptoms that are present in a particular illness. Thus, having the patient ingest a quantity of the "negative image" water effectively neutralizes the original symptoms present in the patient restoring balance at the physical level. The details of this process will be dealt with at the Level Two modelling; however, here, let us just note that the "negative image" cage will have some errors of geometry relative to the biomolecule (especially in its cyclical time evolution characteristics) and these will have important consequences with respect to the maintenance of homeopathic potency over time.

This discussion has focussed on the manufacture only of etheric molecules; however, it should be recognized that both the intention and the archetypal code deal with the formation of health restoring constituents which must also occur at the emotional and mental levels. The state of health must be written as

$$\text{HEALTH} \leftrightarrow (C_E/C_P)_j + (C_A/C_P)_j + (C_M/C_P)_j + ; j = 1,2,...$$

where A and M refer to the emotional level and the mind level respectively. The multi-state reaction equation is thus of the following symbolic form

$$P_j \rightleftarrows E_j \begin{array}{c} \overset{\delta}{\nearrow} A_j \\ \updownarrow \\ \underset{\delta}{\searrow} M_j \end{array} \qquad ; j = 1,2,....$$

258

such that substance at any proposed level can act as the template for formation of the remainder of this reaction chain to their equilibrium concentrations. In accordance with this hypothesis, the growth in $C_E$, $C_A$ and $C_M$ resulting from potentization can be expected to resemble Fig. 6.14. Depending upon relative magnitudes of activation barriers for the $A_j/E_j$, $M_j/E_j$ and $A_j/M_j$ reactions, the order of the curves in Fig. 6.14 may vary. Here, for a given potency X, $C_E > C_A > C_M$. It may be useful to note that one should be able to develop kinetic laws describing the growth of $C_E$, $C_A$ and $C_M$ as a function of X in terms of the essential parameters of the problem.

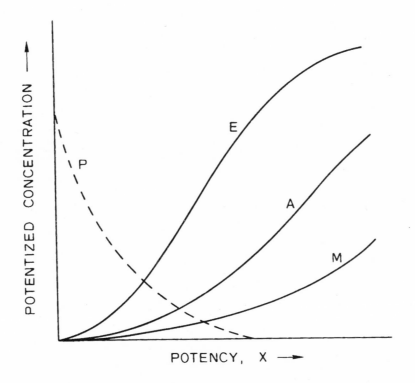

**Fig. 6.14** Schematic illustration of the increasing etheric (E), emotional (A) and mind (M) level substances in the homeopathic solution as a function of increasing potency, X (repeated dilution of physical substance following succussion).

In the Rae method, the intention of the individual is made coherent via the Rae coding symbol (see Fig. 6.12) plus the potency dial setting. This simple device serves as an amplifier to build the requisite molecules inherent in a pattern residing at the mind-lattice level of the universe. This pattern utilizes normally unavailable deltrons inherent in the solvent at the 9-D level and charges the solution, contained in a recessed wall of the device, with the requisite pattern to the requisite potency. It is a materialization event on the etheric and deeper levels of substance. It works via the archetypal pattern of properly-constructed radionic devices (see next section) and via processes inherent in the above equations.

To understand the loss of potency caused by heating to a high temperature or by strong sunlight, one needs only consider the effect of these forces on degrading the H-bond structure of the negative image cages in the water.

# Some Subtle Energy Devices

Biomechanical Transducers: This class of device was discussed at some length in Chapter 4 when we dealt with the "dowsing" response. The most familiar examples in this category are the pendulum and the dowsing wand[20].

Electrodermal Devices: This class of device is, more-often-than-not, unintentionally used as a bioelectrical transducer. One of the earliest and most popular examples of this type of device is the Voll dermatron, illustrated in Fig. 6.15[21]. In standard practice (without homeopathic remedy testing), the hand contact electrode is held in one of the patient's hands while the practitioner holds the A.P. contact electrode and applies it successively to acupuncture points (A.P.) on the other hand, the feet, etc. In each case, the meter on the front of the instrument gives a reading that is a measure of the low frequency skin conductance at that A.P.[22]. Either fortunately or unfortunately, depending on your point of view, changing the pressure or angle of the probe at the A.P. produces a change in the meter reading. Thus, it is possible for the practitioner to unconsciously produce a conductance measurement, by varying these experimental parameters of the measurement technique, that is in accord with some subtle information level within his/her self. In this mode of operation, the electrical device is acting like a very sophisticated pendulum. To most simply test this idea, one need only turn the instrument around so that the practitioner cannot see the face of the meters. When he/she operates the instrument in this mode, one obtains two important results: (1) repeated measurements give very inconsistent results compared to the normal mode where the practitioner can see the meter face and (2) the diagnostic success of the practitioner is appreciably reduced. A more complex test would be to use a spring-mounted measuring electrode so that a constant electrode pressure would be made to the A.P. regardless of the practitioner's pressure. In this case, repeated measurements yield fairly consistent results but such measurements appear to yield less diagnostic value. My conclusions are that this is a very good diagnostic instrument in the hands of a good practitioner who allows his unconscious level signal information to influence the probe measurements. Not all electrodermal instruments may be used in this bioelectric transducer mode and the best current example of that is the Motoyama AMI machine which measures aspects of the high frequency conductance properties of the skin[22].

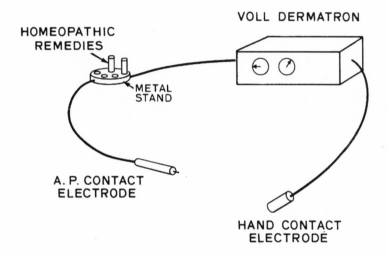

**Fig. 6.15** Schematic illustration of homeopathic remedy selection via use of the Voll dermatron.

Radionic-Type Devices: The word radiesthesia may be defined as sensitivity to radiations, both physical and subtle. Radionics is an instrumental form of radiesthesia and, as such, deals with the interaction between mind and matter. The notable names connected with the early development of this subject are Abrams, Drown, De La Warr, Heironymus, Rae, Farrelly and others[23-27]. Although it has other important uses, radionics is primarily used as both a method and a device for the diagnosis and healing of plants, animals and humans. One of its most striking features is that it seems to function effectively over separation distances between operator and patient of thousands of miles, using only a spot of the patient's blood or other suitable witness as a link between the two. The technique has been used to heal the general spectrum of ailments in humans, from the common cold to serious illness of the various body glands; in animals from distemper to hoof and mouth disease and in plants from stimulating nutrient uptake from the soil to inhibiting pests from destroying a crop. The method has also been used for prospecting for oil, water or minerals (using only a good map of the area); for finding lost articles or people; for designing industrial equipment or selecting staff; in education for lowering a student's resistance to a subject, school or teacher and in research for probing theoretical and experimental directions.

The minimum set of components needed for an operating device is four (as indicated in Fig. 6.16)--operator, device, patient and information source. As already stated above, the patient does not need to be physically present so long as a reliable link (drop of blood, sample of hair, picture, etc.) is present. The energy (or information) vehicle being used here (mind) is relatively non-spatial and non-temporal so that distance is not a factor. The information source is thought to be our "intelligent universe"[27] at the mind level which can be accessed via correct codes and procedures (much like a computer's data base).

An operational physical diagnostic device must contain at least the following in functional form, (a) a receptical to hold the link material of the patient, (b) a system (set of dials, etc.) for setting (displaying) the specific code for the body organ, body system, body tissue, etc., under test, (c) a system for identifying (specifying) the level of functioning (compared to normal) of that organ, system, tissue, etc., (d) some type of magnetic linkage or tuning between (a), (b) and (c) and (e) a detector capable of revealing to the operator when he/she has found the correct setting for (c). Some individuals who are fairly gifted psychically can control their minds sufficiently to pose and hold the question mentally (replace b) and also ask mentally for the level of functioning (replace c) by simply rubbing one thumbnail across the other to serve as the detector via a "dowsing" reaction (acts as d). In this case, the <u>individual is the instrument</u>! For the rest of us who may not be so gifted, so evolved or so confident, we need an intuition enhancement aid, our radionic device, to act as "training wheels" for us. Fig. 6.16b presents a schematic diagram of the De La Warr radionic diagnostic instrument while Fig. 6.16c presents a photograph of one of their standard instruments.

A radionic detector is thought to act something like a radio receiver which picks electrical waves out of the atmosphere, discriminates a certain frequency set by adjustment of the tuning dial and transduces this signal into an audible set of sound frequencies. We hear this sonic information. A radionic detector is thought to receive a subtle energy wave from the "information source" by a detection mode involving the unconscious level circuitry of the human operator discussed in Chapter 4. On the other hand, a radionic treatment device is thought to act as an analogue to a radio transmitter designed to send

EM signals out through its antenna into space. However, the radionic transmitter is also thought to be a type of "instrumented prayer" system with an amplification mechanism imbedded in it. It is designed to transmit the "corresponding" frequencies needed to balance the particular organ, body system, tissue, etc., much like the etheric domain imprinting of Fig. 6.10a or like the homeopathic chemical imprinting of the previous section. Since the dial settings hold this information precisely, it is thought that this narrow band signal can be very intense at subtle levels. Of course, specially designed antennas are usually built into the device to enhance signal strength output at subtle energy levels.

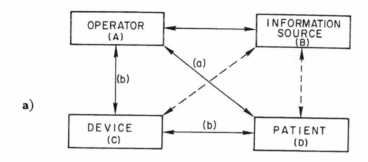

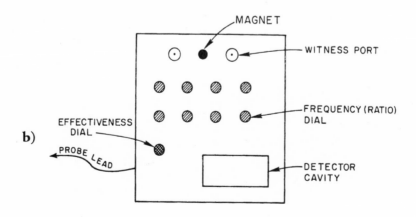

**Fig. 6.16** (a) Essential components of the general radionic diagnostic/treatment system for both three-body and four-body interaction methods, (b) schematic diagram of the Delawarr diagnostic instrument

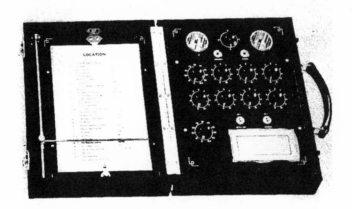

**Fig. 6.16** (c) photograph of the standard Delawarr radionic instrument for diagnosis.

**Hybrid Intention Imprinted Electronic Devices:** In an earlier section of this chapter, some consequences of subtle substance titration into physical host materials was discussed. Here, we shall mention some "Model T"-type devices wherein the design utilizes the consciousness of specially trained individuals to "imprint" specific electronic devices so that another dimension is added to the electron properties and thus the functioning of the <u>host device</u>. The higher the state of consciousness of the individual during the subtle energy imprinting stage of the process, the more definitive and with higher energy potential storage is the information imprinted on the subtle domain templates of our multidimensional universe. Even with this, there are natural leakage or dissipation mechanisms that degrade the quality of subtle energy storage in the physical host material so that special engineering at both subtle and physical levels is needed to minimize the degradation of the information storage.

An overly simplistic analogy to illustrate how an intention-imprinted electronic device (IIED) would differ from the standard host device without imprinting is the following. Let us presume that the standard host device generates a frequency spectrum of signals that are converted to a sound pattern which we call music. This sound pattern can be represented as a plot of sound intensity versus frequency over some time interval. Let us presume that the z-axis represents intensity while the x-axis represents frequency. Likewise, the imprinted device has this quality but it also has a designed subtle plane pattern imbedded in it which can also be represented as an intensity versus frequency plot and this spectrum could be plotted in the z-y plane much as if it constituted the mathematically imaginary part of a complex frequency. Then, the total $z(x,y)$ plot as a function of frequency for this imprinted device would reveal the linear and nonlinear interactions between the physical plane and the subtle plane phenomena. The unimprinted device would have a smaller inherent information content in that its intensity would be represented by only $z(x)$.

Along this same line of thinking, individuals attending a live concert or symphony hear not only the physical sound but "hear" or "feel" the subtle emotional, mental or spiritual quality of the performers. When that same performance is converted to a tape or a CD, the high fidelity audio equipment used does not "catch" the subtle level signals riding on the sound waves so much much less of the subtle quality comes through to the listener. What an IIED does for the recording system is to selectively amplify those weak subtle level signals so that live performance quality or potential live performance quality (depending upon the amplification spectrum) is imprinted on the recording or is broadcast from the sound system.

In this general category of devices, let us next suppose that we wish to create an electronic device that protects individuals from dileterious biological consequences associated with electromagnetic radiation (EMR) from TV's, electrical equipment, electrical power lines, etc. There are at least two ways to approach this question: (1) since the cells of the body are electrical in nature, they respond to electromagnetic fields. They respond by electron and ion displacement plus dipole alignment which generates mechanical fluctuations at the cellular level. Thus, if the body is being repeatedly driven by EM waves, especially if they are of the steady harmonic variety of the proper wavelength, the cells move into a kind of resonant state where they oscillate back and forth in phase with the driving EM signals. If the EM waves are of the chaotic variety and still of the proper wavelength, they try to drive the cells in all kinds of different directions so the cells can never develop an easy resonance and cellular fatigue is thought to develop. (2) A second main avenue of EM influence on the body is via the acupuncture points since A.P. responses have an influence on the associated body organs or systems (see Chapter 3). Thus, incoming EM fields may be inharmoniously driving the organs to move out of their normal stable functioning state.

Current discussions and experiments dealing with electric power lines and electrical equipment as potential health hazards do not mention any specific causative mechanism. Rather, the data gathering has been designed to test the hypothesis of a positive correlation existing between specific human pathology and the environmental strength of the electric field vector, E, and the magnetic field vector, H. Positive correlation, where it exists, is largely found with H which is very difficult to shield around the exciting electric current.

Let us now consider a novel and speculative mechanism, that is as yet untested, and see where it leads us. The basic territory to be considered is that, as electric current flows through wires in response to the driving voltage gradient, inelastic collisions occur between the conduction electrons and the relatively immobile atoms of the wire. The current picture of this process is that lattice phonons (vibrations) are completely involved to balance the energy exchange in these collisions because we know that considerable heat is released. However, a second process, the emission of a helical photon could also participate in the overall energy balance equation under certain conditions. The strong local magnetic field carried by the conduction electron creates magnetic energy level splitting for the electrons of the lattice atoms and it is these energy levels that are needed for the excitation and photoemission process. Most of these photons convert to phonons by internal absorption in the wire, but some can escape through the surface and these are the focus of our attention. For a photon of frequency ~10 MHz, this escape depth is ~10 microns. For 0.05 centimeter diameter copper wire at room temperature with a current of 10 amperes flowing through it, this is the calculated average photon frequency so one could expect these emitted photons to fall in the range ~1 to 100 MHz. If only 1 percent of the inelastic collision events results in an emitted photon, the emitted power is ~0.1 watts per meter of wire length. The other 99% of the energy exchange is released as heat in the wire which increases the wire temperature. The wire then dissipates this heat by conduction, convection and radiation of thermal photons of frequency ~1 million times higher than the 1 percent of 10 MHz helical photons. Thus, our helical photon flux is imbedded deeply in a much larger flux of optical photons and these two fluxes can be distinguished from each other only by frequency and helicity (spin character or polarization). This 10 MHz photon flux scales linearly with the current in the wire as does the magnetic field H; thus, if dileterious biological effects scale linearly with flux for some fixed time period then these would also correlate linearly with H as noted experimentally.

Photon interaction with the human body can occur directly as a field/ion coupling with the tissues or indirectly via piezoelectric coupling. The photons having wavelengths that resonate with various organs, muscles, membranes and cells via the direct coupling mode fall in the ~$10^9$-$10^{13}$ Hz range. Because the velocity of light is ~$10^4$-$10^6$ times the velocity of sound in human body materials, the indirect coupling mode leads to resonances when the EM frequencies are in the ~$10^5$-$10^9$ Hz range. The center of this latter range is almost exactly that of the helical photons (circularly polarized) generated from the inelastic scattering events in the copper wire example mentioned above. It is interesting to note that protein chains, made from monomer peptides, are generally helical in structure and of considerable length. While collagen, one of the basic constituents of proteins, has an amino-acid sequence forming a triple α-helix. Piezoelectricity has been observed in many polypeptides, where it arises from the α-helical backbone of these chains, and in some cases exhibits values as large as quartz. Thus, from all this, there appears to be little doubt that many of the important materials comprising the human body generate a significant stress wave when driven by an EM signal. This means that the proposed causative mechanism for EMR effects on humans seems to be, at least, theoretically viable. If it is actually the correct mechanism, then the chaotic (~10 MHz) photons emitted from electrical equipment generate a set of chaotic stress waves that excite and <u>eventually</u> fatigue the body's cells, synaptic responses, neurological function and the immune system.

As we look at this proposed EMR mechanism, there are at least two possible paths for diminishing the human cellular fatigue via intentional imprinting of an electrical device: (1) reduce the proportion of inelastic scattering events in the electrical wiring that result in photon emission and (2) reduce the absorption cross section of human cells for photons in the ~1 to 100 MHz range. Unfortunately, neither of these pathways significantly alter the local magnetic or electric fields around the electrical equipment at the driving frequency so they cannot be monitored in standard ways. If one was set up to monitor circularly polarized EM fields in the ~1-100 MHz range, one could test this idea. Using the human response as a measuring yardstick of the device efficacy, one would need to perform a double blind study on a group of people rather than just rely on the subjective statements of a few individuals who say that they feel better when such a hybrid device is plugged into the electrical power grid of their home or office. Such a hybrid device, using a simple digital clock as its host, has been developed and it is being sold commercially[29]. However, the needed electrical and double blind testing has not yet been carried out and only subjective testimonials are available on its behalf.

For the general hybrid IIED, the multidimensional process path appears to be very much like that illustrated in Fig. 6.17. It is thought that the imprinted intention marshalls the subtle energy particles in the "zero point vacuum" of the electronic device, especially at the etheric level, to modify normal electron function in accordance with the specific intention.

A few years ago, I worked with a hardware-modified version of the EMR-IIED mentioned above in order to carry out a pair of interesting experiments. The experiments were never carried to completion and I mention them here only because they illustrate what is possible in the future with upgraded versions of this type of hybrid device.

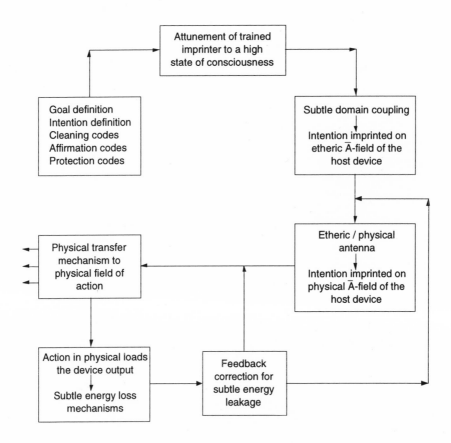

**Fig. 6.17** Block diagram process path defining the factors involved in developing an effective subtle energy potentized device for physical level action.

**Nuclear Decay Rate Experiment**: The ultimate experiment was designed to use identical electronic host devices. One was to be left unimprinted. One was to be imprinted to increase the radioactive decay rate of a material and one was to be imprinted to decrease the radioactive decay rate of the same material. The radioactive material selected for the test was Thorium because it was readily available in the form of a thoriated gas lamp mantle even though it was not the best material to choose for such a test. This is because there are 12 members in the decay series of which one is radon, a gas that can escape from the experimental environment. The IIED design was to either increase by a factor of 7 or decrease by a factor of 7, the decay rate of only the first member of the radioactive series, Thorium 232. Because there are seven $\alpha$-particle emitters in the series this could lead to an observable count ratio change in the $\alpha$-counter measuring procedure use of $\pm 2$. I never did reach the double blind testing stage with the three devices for a variety of reasons; however, during the "mucking about" stage with the two imprinted devices, a couple of the observations were encouraging. One of these is illustrated in Fig. 6.18b using the device set-up as in Fig. 6.18a with the IIED located a few inches from the Thorium mantle.

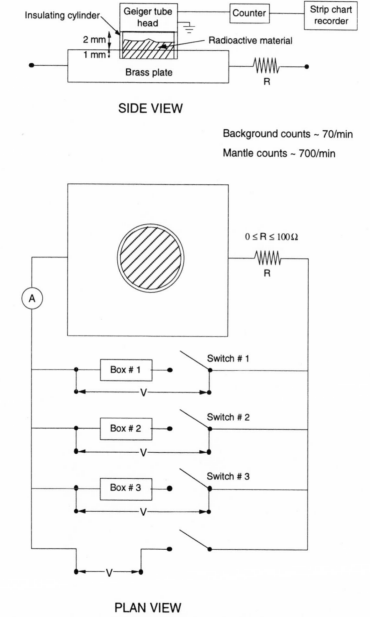

**Fig. 6.18** (a) Side view and plan view of schematic experimental set-up for the 3-device (neutral, increased rate and decreased rate) test of modified counting rate from a radioactive material.

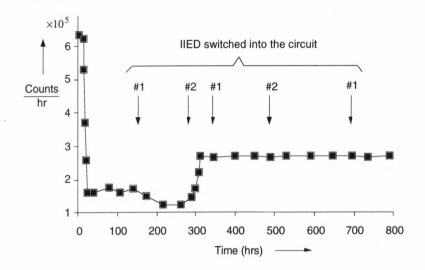

**Fig. 6.18** (b) actual α-particle counting rate as a function of time when different IIED's were switched into the circuit of (a) (here, IIED #3 is unmodified, #1 has a decreased rate imprinting while #2 has an increased rate imprinting).

In Fig. 6.18b, after ~20 hours with the unimprinted device in the circuit, the α-counts have decayed to a reasonably stable level of ~160,000 per hour, presumably the time needed to build up a constant radon concentration in the measuring enclosure. At ~160 hours, the unimprinted device is switched out and the first IIED is switched into the circuit, and an average drop in α-counts of ~30,000-40,000 occurs over the next 120 hrs until this device was switched out and the other IIED was switched into the circuit. At this point (280 hrs.), the α-counts increase by ~120,000 counts to a plateau at ~270,000 counts and thereafter remained flat even though three device changes occurred over the next 400 hours. After this test, the IIED devices were sent to the imprinter for checking and were found to have lost their subtle energy imprinting (subjective evaluation). For some presently unknown reason, allowing the devices to function in their design-mode, deactivated the subtle level processing. I decided that we didn't know enough to continue this type of nuclear experiment and that it was perhaps foolhardy to continue nuclear studies until more was known about the general process.

**Cell Multiplication Rate Experiment:** I originally designed this experiment for keratinocyte cells in the arrangement of Fig. 6.19. On the cell surfaces, there are specific structures called "gap junctions". When these line up between adjacent cells, transport of proteins and other chemicals can occur from one cell to the other and this intracellular communication is important to a large group of cells combined to form a tissue. If this communication cannot occur, then the cells go into the division mode and multiply. Thus, increasing the density of gap junction structures should decrease cell division rate while decreasing gap junction density should increase cell division rate. This then became the focal point of the intention imprinting for the electronic devices so that, in Fig. 6.19, devices A, B and C were either unimprinted or imprinted to increase gap junction density and decrease internal cell protein production by a factor of 10 or to decrease gap junction density and increase internal cell protein production by a factor of 10.

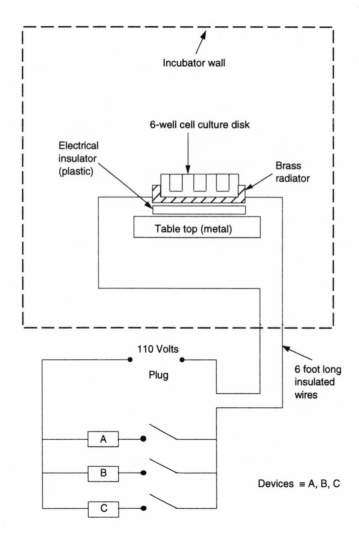

**Fig. 6.19** Side view of schematic experimental set-up for a 3-device test of modified karatinocyte cell multiplication rate.

When this experiment was finally due to be tested, the biologists involved felt that, whereas keratinocytes are specialized cell types used for assessing human effects, their differentiated functions would very likely restrict the expression of effects. They chose to first investigate trypanosoma cruzi which is a primative eukaryotic cell and, as such, should respond to agents that produce general effects on cells. The t. cruzi metacyclogenisis assay was chosen because it had been shown to be responsive to a number of external agents that induce or inhibit the physiological stress levels of the organism.

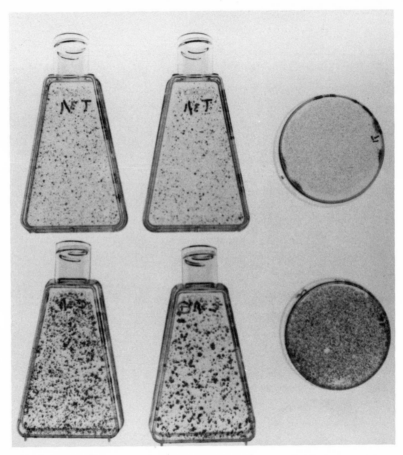

**Fig. 6.20** Actual results from a 2-device (neutral and decreased rate) test on the primative eukaryotic cell, trypanosoma cruzi metacyclogenesis assay. The top results with the imprinted unit shows a greatly reduced number of cells compared to the bottom results (control unit).

In preliminary studies with the imprinted unit, they noted significant changes in the t. cruzi metacyclogenisis assay. In this study, metacyclogenisis, or conversion to the infective stage of the human parasite, t. cruzi, was induced in cell culture. They found that the imprinted device inhibited metacyclogenisis (as it was designed to do)[30]. In Fig. 6.20, the upper vials demonstrate the imprinted device effect relative to the lower controls. This transformation inhibition also appeared to be affected by the test position within the incubator relative to the location of the IIED. Those cultures sitting directly on top of the unit were not inhibited (in fact, they were slightly enhanced) but those that were positioned on the shelf above the unit or on a shelf below the unit were greatly inhibited. Blind studies with both an unimprinted and an imprinted device were then performed and it was statistically confirmed that the imprinted device was inhibitory to metacyclogenisis of t. cruzi while the unimprinted device was inactive.

As stated several times in this book, these hybrid devices (IIED's) have very widespread applicability in industry with great potential cost savings for existing processes. We are only at the very beginning of this category of future technology and great benefits are possible for humanity as we expand our mindset to allow for such possibilities.


## Future Energy Medicine

Until humans grow further and develop the conscious capacity to reliably detect and discriminate subtle energies, these energies will not be directly observable and useful medical training wheel devices will need a transducer capability from non-observable subtle energies to physically observable energies. One side of this transducer will be the patient while the other side is the read-out mechanism based on (1) electric or magnetic field effects, (2) photon effects in a variety of frequency ranges, (3) acupuncture point response effects, (4) electrodermal effects, (5) homeopathic remedy effects, (6) kinesiological effects, (7) mental/spiritual level effects of the radionic type and (8) mental/spiritual level effects of the IIED type.

Since the practitioner is not a passive element in the human/device energy circuit, intuition enhancement training programs are expected to become commonplace in order to discipline the subconscious stimuli in the practitioner into becoming a reliable dowsing response. In this way, the subconscious capability of the practitioner can be integrated with the device to gain a conscious awareness of the patient's condition. Although one may not fully understand how the subtle energy information is being gathered, it is certainly possible to develop double blind testing procedures to prove statistically the efficacy of a device for diagnosing various health conditions in comparison with other conventional medical procedures. These same types of tests can be utilized to prove the statistical efficacy of one device compared with other devices and of particular device/practitioner units compared to other device/practitioner units. One will be able to <u>pragmatically</u> show what works and is effective. This type of proving can be done today so the energy medicine practitioner associations should begin to statistically design the double blind tests and gather the data. Then, they would have less difficulties with their conventional medicine counterparts.

# References

1. G.P. Flanagan, "Pyramid Power" (Pyramid Publishers, Glendale, CA, 1973).
2. W.B. Jonas, <u>Therapeutic Labelling and The 80% Rule</u>, Bridges, ISSSEEM Newsmagazine, <u>5</u> (2), 1 (1994).
3. G. Rein and R. McCraty, <u>DNA As A Detector of Subtle Energies</u>, Proc. 4th Ann. Conf. ISSSEEM, Boulder, CO, June 1994.
4. J.W. Gibbs, "The Collected Works, Vol 1" (Yale University Press, New Haven, 1957).
5. W.A. Tiller, "The Science of Crystallization: Microscopic Interfacial Phenomena" (Cambridge University Press, Cambridge, UK, 1991) Ch. 6.
6. W.A. Tiller, "The Science of Crystallization: Macroscopic Phenomena and Defect Generation" (Cambridge University Press, Cambridge, UK, 1991) p. 353.
7. V. Poponin, <u>A Phantom DNA Effect</u>, J. Nanobiology, 1995.
8. F.S. Stillinger, <u>Water Revisited</u>, Science, <u>209</u> (1980) 451.
9. N.D. Mikesell, <u>The Mikesell Water Papers</u> (1986, P.R.I.)
10. G. Rein, <u>Storage of Non-Hertzian Frequency Information In Water</u> Pro. Int. Testa Soc. (Ed) S. Ellswick (Tesla. Soc. Pub., Colorado Springs, 1994).
11. C.W. Smith, <u>Electromagnetic Bioinformation and Water</u> in "Ultra High Dilutions--Physiology and Physics", (Eds) Endler and Schulte (Kluwer Acad Pub., New York, 1994).
12. P. Tsouris and C.W. Smith, <u>The Detection of LF Resonances In Water</u>, Submitted to Physics Letters A, 1992.
13. J. Benveniste, B. Armoux and L. Hadji, <u>Highly Dilute Antigen Increases Coronary Flow of Isolated Heart From Immunized Guinea-Pigs</u>, Fased J. ,G. (1992) A 1610
14. J. Benveniste, J. Aissa, M. H. Litime, G. Th. Tsangarij and Y. Thomas, <u>Transfer of the Molecular Signal by Electronic Amplification</u>, Faseb, J., 8 (1994) A 398
15. R.N. Miller, <u>The Relationship Between the Energy State of Water and its Physical Properties</u>, in "Future Science", Eds, J. White and S. Krippner (Anchor-Doubleday, New York, 1977) p431.
16. D. Eisenberg and N. Kauzmann, "The Structure and Properties of Water", (Oxford University Press, Oxford, 1969) p. 20.
17. T.L. Bradford, "Life and Letters of Dr. Samuel Hahnemann" (Boericke and Tafel, Philadelphia, 1895).

18. G. Vithoulkas, "The Science of Homeopathy" (Grove Press Inc., New York, 1980).

19. M. Rae, <u>Potency Simulation By Magnetically Energised Patterns (An Alternate Method of Preparing Homeopathic Remedies)</u>, British Radionic Quarterly, March 1973.

20. C. Hills, "Supersensonics", (University of The Trees Press, P.O. Box 644, Boulder Creek, CA, 1975).

21. R. Voll, Special EAV Issue, American Journal of Acupuncture 1978.

22. W.A. Tiller, <u>On The Evolution and Future Development of Electro-dermal Diagnostic Instruments</u> in "Energy Fields In Medicine" (The John E. Fetzer Foundation, Kalamazoo, MI, 1989) p. 257.

23. L. Day and G. De La Warr, "New Worlds Beyond The Atom" (Vincent Stuart, London, 1956).

24. L. Day and G. De La Warr, "Matter In The Making" (Vincent Stuart Ltd., London, 1966).

25. D.V. Tansley, "Radionics and The Subtle Anatomy of Man" (Health Science Press, Rustington, Sussex, 1972).

26. H.S. Burr, "Blueprint For Immortality, The Electric Patterns of Life", (Neville Spearman, London, 1972).

27. E.W. Russell, "Report on Radionics, Science of The Future", (Neville Spearman, London, 1973).

28. D. Foster, "The Intelligent Universe" (Abelard, New York, 1975).

29. R.O. Williams, <u>Clarus CL-100 Device</u> (7720b El Camino Real #507, La Costa, CA   92009).

30. R.O. Williams, <u>Clarus Biovoyager Device</u> (NIAIS Report, April 21, 1994).

# CHAPTER
# 7

## TOWARDS STEWARDSHIP OF THE HOME PLANET

*Yearning to <u>be</u>, yearning to <u>know</u>, yearning to <u>do</u> —*
*Fulfillment of the eternal evolutionary adventure*
*Of transforming self towards ever-higher states of being.*
*And fit now to heal the Earth — at consciousness levels —*
*So that it might quicken in the flow of planet to planet spirit*
*And symbiotic humanity, in turn, is then actualized*
*And accelerated on its Homeward Path.*

Probably we would all agree that one simple prerequisite for being a good steward to a planet is to be good and conscious stewards of our own bodies. One prerequisite to this latter condition is the development of inner self-management at mental and emotional as well as at physical levels. In Chapter 5, data was presented to illustrate the heart focus path to this goal. There, we saw special electrophysiological and biochemical correlates <u>inside</u> the body associated with becoming adept at such practices. We also saw that, with the addition of specific directed intention when in these internal ordered states, one had the ability to alter the structure of water or DNA located <u>outside</u> the body. This appears to be a natural actualization of inherent human abilities once one has developed certain subtle level structures in the body via practicing these heart focus techniques for transmitting love, in its various forms, from the area of the heart. This heart structure development at subtle levels appears to allow significant levels of spirit to enter the body which raises the consciousness of the individual to such a level that the properties of the seemingly physical materials around that body are readily altered by directed intention. Certainly this is a useful human capability for a planetary steward.

In Chapter 3, considerable attention was given to the development of various biological antennae for humans in order to channel large flows of various types of energies into, through and out of the body envelope. In Chapters 4 and 5, we gained some appreciation for the huge energy density amplification involved in reorganizing ourselves from an incoherent system to a coherent system. Before proceeding to the main topic of this chapter, it is probably useful to (1) spend a little time discussing why special focus on the heart center in contrast to any of the other six main body centers is beneficial and (2) try and clear up any possible confusion between the energy band picture and its dimensionality (3D, 4D, 8D, 9D, 10D, etc.) and the consciousness band picture and its dimensionality (3D, 4D, 5D, etc.).

## What Makes The Heart Center So Special?

Although the heart chakra is the balance point with three chakras above and three chakras below so that they can all spin and be momentum-stabilized by the spinning heart center, this is probably not the main reason why the heart center should open first in the human transformation to a significantly higher level of both consciousness and energy flow. The main reason for the heart being the dominant center has to do with the fact that the increased coherence associated with our next <u>level of being</u> brings on-line huge increases in radiant flux through our multiple bodies. The question is, how can they handle the flow without burnout? The analogy worth considering here, comes from the area of electrical engineering and contrasts normal electrical equipment needs in the home versus the electrical equipment in a power station sending electrical power to millions of homes. In the latter case, major power transfers require rugged and robust switch-gear, handling-gear, trunk-lines, etc. In the human body to handle the projected power levels, a "beefed-up" system is needed, largely at the etheric level because that level processes a higher energy density, but somewhat at the physical level as well, and we now seem to be moving deeper into the domain of etheric level functioning.

We know that the heart is the organ that nourishes all the cells throughout the physical body (via the blood flow); thus, it must be the organ involved in building the more rugged system to handle the greater power densities. This process of change must occur first at the cellular level, but largely at the etheric level of the cell with some essential "conjugate" changes at the physical level of the cell. I would propose that, it is for this reason, primarily, that the heart is the vehicle for spirit entry into the body and why it is the key center on which to focus to initiate the coherence-making process. In this way, the body cells adjust in energy-handling ability as new levels of energy are tapped from the cosmos by the increased coherence. If one seriously opens another center before the heart center, either by accident or by directed intention, then the increased power density starts flowing through underrated conduits which may blow circuit fuses and seriously damage the subtle level circuitry. Only when the heart is able to provide the nutrients for strengthening the subtle level circuitry is it safe to bring the power stations of the other centers on-line and produce the operational system functioning at design levels. In this regard, it should be remembered that most solid state power laser systems fail via the presence of one or more microdefects in the laser rods. As the energy density increases, the scattering from the microdefect sets non-linear consequences in motion that increase the effective size of the defect and destructively quench the lasing action. This gives us some indication of the need for cellular perfection at both physical and etheric levels if we are to stably sustain large power flows through our system. It is also important to understand that we have a wide spectrum of defects in us, some large and some small. As we remove the large ones by directed intention and practice, our operating power level can now be safely increased. However, now we are limited by the smaller ones and our attention must be shifted to these because they become our limitation as a high power-handling conduit.

## Consciousness Band Versus Energy Band Considerations

Both the conventional physics model and the Level One model of this book deal primarily with energies of various different types. In the Level One model, different energies function in different dimensions of the universe in the form of subtle substances and subtle radiations. Even within a single dimensional frame, 9-space for example, multiple energies will be present expressing themselves in discrete bands of frequency (just like sound and light in physical crystals). Some of these will be predominantly associated with the solar plexus center and some with the heart center. We can expect all centers to be transducers for <u>all</u> higher dimensional energies but with the efficiencies of transduction peaking for different energy types in the different centers. All the inner self-management models, and the HeartMath model in particular, are consciousness-type models not energy-type models.

An additional problem for us in integrating these two kinds of models is that most of us don't really grasp what consciousness is and how it differs from energy. It is uniquely amusing that we haven't grown enough in <u>consciousness</u> to clearly articulate the difference between these two qualities. However, some have begun to grasp that, in the hierarchy of <u>things</u>, consciousness begets energy which begets matter[5]. Fig. 2.24 is an attempt to provide a visual perspective on this difference.

In earlier chapters, I have mentioned a correlate of consciousness, the channel capacity, C, given by

$$C = \Delta v \ln_2 (1 + P/N)$$

(see Chapter 5). The channel capacity, C, relates to the capacity of a particular communication channel to transfer information and, for the total human system, it should be written as

$$C = \sum_{ij} C_{ij} = \sum_{ij} \Delta v_{ij} \ln_2 (1 + P_{ij}/N_{ij})$$

where $\Sigma$ refers to summation, i refers to the different energy types in a particular domain and j refers to the different domains: physical, etheric, emotional, mental and spiritual.

This is one measure of consciousness, but it is merely a shadow or facet of consciousness and it would be very limiting if we accepted it as being the full measure of consciousness via simply relating it to consciousness with a proportionality constant. However, it is a system property like consciousness and it seems to be something that we can pinpoint at the moment that communicates with humanity's average level of consciousness. Thus, let us use it as a temporary vehicle to help us go forward, recognizing its limitations, and with the hope that we will grow sufficiently to eventually reach a clear understanding of what we are talking about.

One of the useful concepts that comes from correlating channel capacity, C, with consciousness is that the different qualities of consciousness can be defined as unique frequencies in the band $\Delta v_{ij}$. Thus, for example, the different qualities of love discussed in Chapter 5 would be represented as different consciousness frequencies in a particular consciousness band called "love" which would be quite different than the 9-D or 10-D <u>energies</u> of love discussed in Chapter 5. As discussed earlier, practice of the IHM heart focus techniques organizes structural circuits in our bodies at subtle levels and, the more effectively are these circuits built, the larger is the signal to noise ratio, $P_{ij}/N_{ij}$, in the channel capacity formula for various i and j.

An example that illustrates the incompleteness of the channel capacity concept as a stand-in for consciousness comes from modern microelectronic systems. An electronic device is made up of "active" circuit elements, such as diodes or transistors, in combination with "passive" elements such as resistors or capacitors that, together, produce the special function of the device. Combining such devices into systems led naturally to a digital system as compared to an analogue system such as a radio. In digital electronics, a given element is either switched on or off depending on the input so that a very large number of stages can be cascaded with the overall gain (voltage amplification) remaining at unity. Analogue circuits, on the other hand, typically require amplification of the input signal in order to fulfill the circuit function. Since the gain of a typical amplifier is ~10, only a few stages can be cascaded before practical voltage limits are exceeded. Thus, an analogue system cannot handle large numbers of microcircuits while a digital system requires them; e.g., a typical pocket calculator contains ~100 times as many transistors as a radio or television receiver.

Science, technology and society depend on the ability to measure an enormous variety of phenomena that the unaided human senses cannot detect or generally cannot measure with precision. These are control system instruments (thermostat, etc.) that all incorporate a feedback loop along with a microprocessor and some digital memory to fulfill their function. The essence of systems like the telephone, radio, television, etc., is signal processing where the large capacity, high reliability and low cost of the microelectronic devices make them ideal for such purposes. Both small and large modern computers could not exist without microelectronic components. Today, network-connected minicomputers compete quite effectively with large computers and massive parallel processing with small computers has recently doubled the world's record for the computational speed of any computer.

Present day microelectronic systems can interface with simultaneous inputs from thousands of sensors and can process, discriminate and integrate the signal data to provide a perception and an awareness of what is on the other side of the interface. In this sense, as the size and complexity of the integrated microelectronics system grows, its channel capacity grows so the information aspect of consciousness grows. We can properly call this robotic consciousness and, when we do, we realize how much further we must go to begin to really understand human consciousness. As we turn to the human body at the physical level, all of the roughly 180 different cell types function as integrated self-replicating, microchemical factories. They group together to form super systems called organs with unique functions and with feedback loops between the different organs. The whole constitutes our body but description at this level only leads us back to what we have called robotic consciousness. Something major must be added to expand our picture.

Paddison[1] provides a useful perspective on different dimensions of consciousnes taking the view that a dimension is actually a specific frequency range of perception and intelligence. In her model, each dimension embraces the intelligence of the dimension below it, and thus has much in common with the channel capacity viewpoint expressed above. Starting at the third dimension, it is defined as a range of frequency bands that are bound by many illusions of limits and with a picture of reality that is only what can be perceived by the physical senses. In such a dimensional consciousness, we are all separate, isolated but interacting, entities. To quote her[1],

"The problem is that third dimensional frequency perspectives see people, structures—everything—as separate from each other, with tremendous duality, antagonism and opposites. So, in this dimension people gain a little hope, then revert back to fear. There are still thick boundaries and strong limitations in the thinking of the world. Mind-sets are so rigid that, when amplified by unmanaged emotions, tremendous conflict results. Third dimensional awareness keeps hitting its head on the ceiling of its own limitations. Because it sees with separate eyes, there are many enemies. If you project into the future and can't see a way out of a dilemma, you can become fearful. When fear is present, the consistency of love cannot hold."

Paddison[1] indicates that fourth dimensional consciousness develops in an individual when the level of self integration and perception lift one beyond the illusion of limits and separateness. The lower fourth allows one to philosophize, ponder new possibilities and refine old inefficient patterns of human behavior. At this level, total inner self-management of these concepts and behaviors is not robust so that pain, guilt, hurts, etc., are still part of the baggage we carry around with us. At the upper fourth, the frequencies of love, care, compassion, forgiveness, inner peace, hope, etc., dominate one's behavior. She states, "As the global transition from the third to the higher fourth dimension continues, more people will become unwilling to participate in actions that do not promote real wholeness and well-being for themselves, their country and their world. Increasingly, people are waking up to the inefficiency of old patterns of thinking and acting. As our social frequency perspective shifts into the fourth dimension, we will establish proven paths to global well-being that do not depend on illusory short-lived attempts that always crumble. Ongoing racial and ethnic conflicts will accelerate mass realization that we need to finally build a foundation of real care and love in our interactions. As a result of global TV and satellite communications, millions are recognizing that antagonism and separation only result in greater despair, stress and planetary distortion. Real peace will come as people decide there is no choice but to make peace within themselves. Following the heart is the key."

Paddison[1] states that, by operating from the heart, one builds a bridge of awareness from 3D to 4D consciousness. Practicing the heart focus techniques develops inner circuitry changes that produce individual consciousness changes to a state of inner knowingness and one becomes aware of intuitive directives within self. One is freed from self-limiting fears and phobias and develops a streamlined inner efficiency. She states, "In the fifth dimension you comprehend the third and fourth dimension perspectives without being limited by them or judging them. You understand why people think and act the way they do, even though it may not be efficient or in their best interests. The fifth is a powerful dimension for good, for creative manifestation and self-empowerment. It is the dimension where you truly create your own world and are not a victim anymore. From a fifth dimensional perspective, stressful times are seen simply as

<u>untransformed opportunities</u> for more love and empowerment."

Although Paddison[1] does not define the essence of consciousness for us, she does provide us with some important <u>human behavior correlates</u> associated with being in the state of consciousness designated as 3D, 4D or 5D. This is very useful in that it takes us beyond the channel capacity aspect of consciousness and greatly expands our perspective. She shows us that heart and love are necessary ingredients to be added to channel capacity to gain a fuller picture of consciousness. It is perhaps interesting to realize that if there was a truly evil person who wished to evolve to 5D consciousness, by focussing on the heart and expressing the various frequencies of love, the evil behavior patterns would dissolve and disappear as the individual transformed himself/herself to this higher level of consciousness. Although good and evil are powerful archetypal forces acting energetically at the lower dimensions of consciousness, they cease to have any power at the fifth dimension of consciousness.

We tend to think of logic and intuition as two very different qualities of human intelligence associated with deductive and inductive reasoning, respectively. We mostly associate logic with head processing whereas, from Paddison's comments above, intuition is more properly associated with heart processing. Certainly, from my own observation of IHM personnel, the more they practice the heart focus techniques, the more intuitive do they become. From my own personal experiences over the last four to five decades of my research, whether conventional or unconventional, my intuition has guided the research studies to the general territory where successful results might be found. Then, my cooperating logic and background knowledge begin to discriminate the various important details, eventually sorting them out into a heirarchical and orderly structure that makes sense to me and others of my profession. Sometimes a logical answer to a research question does not quiet the intuition signal at which point I know that it is necessary to keep probing—to reexamine my assumptions, to see what I might have missed, to create a new concept, etc., in order to provide a more complete answer. Only when the answer is complete to a satisfying level does the intuition signal decay to a quiet and comfortable level.

On reflection, the overall process is like sculpting in clay. The initial intuition shapes the broad outlines of the clay figure and then the science/logic craft whittles away at the object to provide the detailed features in an overall consistency of expression. In the completed work, the details modulate the initial intuitive signal and stand out in a satisfying and often dominant way— but the knowing eye can still discern the intuition—inspired beginnings. It is an interesting adventure to allow these two very different aspects of self to work patiently, trustingly and cooperatively in the creative process. The intuitive process is very non-linear and often leads one to make some outrageous suggestions, as viewed from the normal mindset, but patience and persistent directed-intention combined with technical knowledge and craft skills have often served to validate the initial idea. The heart/head combination (intuition/logic) make a formidable team when the leadership comes from the heart!

In closing this section, it is perhaps important to reflect on the different uses of the word <u>mind</u> in the realms of consciousness versus in the realms of energy. From the limited view that we have of consciousness, many people associate the word mind exclusively with some subtle but very important aspect of the brain. Others provide the statement "all of the brain is in the mind but not all of the mind is in the brain." This is probably also a consciousness-related viewpoint. In the earlier chapters of this book, I have used the word mind to identify a particular energy domain (10-dimensional) that is populated by both characteristic substances and radiations. Further, this mind substance and these mind radiations can be in <u>any</u> host substance, organic or inorganic, and in <u>any</u> body at the cellular, organ or body system level. Thus, they can be in the brain, or heart, or liver, etc. Once again, we appear to be limited by old language that leads to confusion when the same word is used to mean different things. This problem will continue until we invent a lexicon of new words to discriminate between these various possibilities. Until that day, we will need to exercise some patience with each other on this issue.

As we evolve to higher and higher states of consciousness it will be necessary for us to invent new words to describe the new phenomena we are experiencing and the new perspective of the world that is unfolding within us. This initial language cannot be too precise and must contain room for ambiguity, like fuzzy logic or metaphores, because we have little experience with the new territory and the listener is likely to be at a different level in the consciousness band than ourselves.

## Three Relationships of Humans

Our consciousness seems to be largely localized in three primary relational domains, (1) man in relationship to the cosmos, (2) man in relationship to his local self and (3) man in relationship to society[2]. Here, the word human (male or female) is meant by use of the word man.

**Man In Relationship To The Cosmos:** To put this in perspective, consider the relationship of our cells to our bodies. I tend to think that, at a certain stage of evolutionary development, those parts that went into the individual cell all had consciousness and they formed a grouping which became a single cell having a unique life function and a unique sense of oneness. Then these cells gathered into groups to form specialized functioning units like glands which, in turn, became strung together to form a stellar constellation of energy flow. This became a body, our body, and to the cell I suspect that we are "God".

In this regard, I tend to think that subtle structures at some critical level of organization form first in the human embryo and these form the energy field pattern or template that organizes physical cellular and organ development at a level sufficient for life functioning. Later, physical, emotional and mental self-management expand both the complexity and coherence of these energy field interactions so that the cells and organs can function at more efficient and effective levels.

Likewise, as we scale things up a level, man is a bit of consciousness located on the Earth biosphere and he/she is gradually becoming more organized and more coherent until, someday, the Earth will function as a harmonious cell in a galaxy gland located in a cosmological energy construct that can be called a body, if you like, and many are inclined to call that our "God". To be complete, this image should be drawn with counterparts in other dimensions than just the physical four-space with which we are familiar today. Finally, if scaled down deeply into the microcosm to the fundamental particle level or scaled up deeper into the macrocosm to structures beyond our present perceptions, we would find even more intricate rhythms in the fabric of Nature.

Looking at the whole overall pattern, the entire human species seems to be part of one vast organism, and we seem to be individuated and separated from each other at the physical level only because the physical sensory systems of our simulator work on the basis of contrast; i.e., on a difference or differential effect. Because of the "mirror principle", we can expect that the sensory systems of the etheric level will be based on an integral effect where we will seem to be part of a larger whole.

My current picture of the overarching cosmological process is similar to that expressed in the ancient teachings of eastern literature as "the out-breathing and the in-breathing of the All". We seem to be a part of a vast system which is only stable in a dynamic state of change; i.e., the process is a cyclical (or spiral) one which oscillates inexorably, via well-defined laws of Nature, from a state of maximum coherence to a state of minimum coherence and back again.

At certain periods, all essence and all substance at all dimensions of the cosmos are completely coherent, all wave functions are in total resonance and no differentiation exists so all is synchronously One[2]. As the process of change begins, a differentiation initiates and grows, eventually giving rise to substance populating different dimensions of the cosmos. The substance organizes into various stable forms with certain unique functions. Radiation from each dimension has the capacity of organizing substance in the next, less coherent, dimension so that life forms, societies and cultures can develop at different dimensions of the cosmos in a manner very analogous to what we know about the physical dimension. Within man, as this degree of incoherence grows, the dominantly functioning sensory system shifts gradually from dimension to dimension; i.e., from the spiritual to the mental, etc., down to the physical. Thus, the dimension of a human's perception, and thus their conscious action, also shifts as this evolutionary process inexorably unfolds.

The so-called "fall of man" should not be thought of as a moral judgement but rather as a process over which he/she had very little conscious control. We seem to be able to influence only the rate of change, not the direction of change. It is inexorable physics that directs man on the outward path away from the condition of maximum coherence and it is the same inexorable physics that impells him on the inbound path, once he has turned the corner, back towards the coherence state of oneness again.

It is my belief that we have turned that corner and are heading <u>home</u> again. We have come from advanced societies whose special technologies suited the great mental capacities of the inhabitants and we are heading back in that direction. We have come from societies where the inhabitants reliably sensed deeper dimensions of the universe than we presently do so that they readily manipulated space, time and matter, and we are heading back in that same direction. This seems to be the vector of transition for us and we are on the fringe of a mixed state wherein we regularly perceive the five physical senses realm but occasionally perceive aspects of another realm. The frequency of this <u>other</u> perception should increase with time and things should subtly change until it is the five physical senses realm that is only occasionally perceived.

At this point, etheric substance appears to be condensing more and more into host physical substance and the ambient deltron concentration is increasing as the grain size of the nodal networks increase concommitant with the increase in consciousness of some of the individuals on the planet. The veils between dimensions appear to be thinning so the incidence of "strange" phenomena should increase. All are indicators of the in-process cosmological change.

As we sense this new realm more and more, we have a type of precognitive awareness of it which allows it to play a growing role in our thoughts and actions. Thus, via the simulator mechanism, we program it into our future and, the more we do, the more adaptive to it do we become. Thus, the overarching cosmological flow process of change is linked intimately into the simulator process of change. Everything flows consistently. Ultimately, every member of the Family of God must return. When Spirit's original state of direct communication is reached, neither the simulator nor the seeming miracle, which are both learning aids, serve any further purpose.

**Man In Relationship To His Local Self:** This aspect was dealt with extensively in Chapter 5; however, some of it bears repeating for emphasis.

Just like the dual four-spaces, with one being the inverse of the other and the substance in one having a type of mirror relationship to that in the other, the human has an inner world and an outer world which vie for attention. Since the outer world appears to bear a direct relationship (a manifested reflection) to the superposed inner worlds of collective humanity, the outer world will only change in a significant way by major changes in the inner worlds of a large number of individuals. Our local outer world is the way it is because of a cooperative effect that sum the inner/outer projections of many individuals, local and non-local. Any individual, no matter how evolved, lives in this ambient outer environment and may influence it to some degree by the quality of their inner world state but probably not significantly (unless they build a group coherence with many others of similar consciousness).

Within the framework of the outer world "River of Life", any individual can, with directed-consciousness and intention, construct an inner world condition of the highest quality represented by their subtle level structures and by their spectrum of responses to the outer events encountered as they ride the river. This inner world state is built lifetime by lifetime for the entity while the outer world state is just the current "play" that the entity is acting in. The entity or being is growing inside the body simulator and is the <u>product of the process</u>. The outer world state is largely the vehicle for building the entity at the inner world level. The outer world condition is not insignificant, rather, it is important but not nearly so much (by orders of magnitude) as the inner world condition of any and all members of humanity. It is more important to pay attention to inner world self-development than press for immediate outer world changes and, by example, radiate our highest qualities to enrich those around us. Then, any outer world changes that are collectively initiated are stabilized by one's collective state of being. The entity enjoys the process most by becoming <u>one</u> with the river while building the individual consciousness to a level which can begin to alter the flow of the river.

When I first came to California in 1964, I learned the lesson of how long it can take to make the transition between a conscious awareness of the need to change something in self and the final fulfillment of that need in my automatic day-to-day behavior.

My wife lovingly alerted me to an unconscious tendency to be untidy in the bedroom of our new home — by leaving socks and underwear lying around (or even kicking them under the bed). Moi! Surely you are exagerrating, I protested. After about six to twelve months of these loving alerts, I began to stop completely ignoring them and began to try and justify my lack of consciousness about these things by referring to all the <u>important</u> things I was thinking about instead. But she wouldn't let me off the "hook" and patiently/lovingly kept trying to get me to change this habit. After about another year, I gave up trying to make excuses for myself and, because I loved her and it was important to <u>her</u>, I decided to seriously try and change this habit. Well, I tried and I failed and I tried and I failed and I tried again. It took so much of my consiousness just to remember about those "stupid" socks and underwear that I could have drafted a dozen scientific papers. However, after another three to five years I had completely broken the old habit and was tidy in the bedroom in a fully automatic fashion without the use of any obvious conscious effort. Of course, it only took me five to seven years overall to reach that achievement — some people are slow to change old habits!

**Man In Relationship To Society:** Aurobindo has said[3], To be wholly and integrally conscious of one's self and of all the truth of one's being is what is implied by the perfect emergence of the individual's consciousness — and it is towards that which evolution tends. All being is one, and to be fully conscious means to be integrated with the consciousness of all — with the universal self and force and action." Throughout history, it has been possible for <u>some</u> individuals to live this as a perennial philosophy which transcends temporal and cultural differences. However, this state of awareness has not been a reality for the preponderant <u>masses</u> of people. They have a very different self-image — and yet it is the <u>collective self-image</u> that drives the collective life simulator and <u>creates the new mass future</u> (or collective future).

As Elgin has pointed out[4], "a fundamental problem for democratic societies could arise when an image of man which is necessary for societal survival and development is not within the perceptual power of the population. In other words, one could perhaps describe an image of man which could make intelligible a way of life that would ensure our survival and our further evolutionary development, but which was not realizable because there was not a mass state of consciousness to translate the intellectual-linguistic constructs of the few into a living mindset for the many." And yet we are at a point in human history where the old image of man has created such an array of potentially terminal problems for our biological simulators that effective survival of this vehicle requires the deep acceptance of a new self-image. However, for an image to be feasible, it must be able to be internalized and this requires critical levels of perceptual sophistication in the masses. This need not be intellectual sophistication, intuitive sophistication would do just fine.

To achieve this goal, we will need to use all of our societal educational technologies, our biofeedback tools and whatever other mechanisms are at our disposal to allow people, through self-directed processes, to internalize such an evolutionary self-image and have it matched by a supportive state of consciousness, that is, it is necessary to proceed past the state of mere intellectual awareness to the stage of consistent, if not automatic, organismic response to this transcendental image of man.

Two examples of transformation at the physical level are worth considering in this regard. The first relates to two young men with identical manifested athletic prowess who wish to learn to run the "high hurdles". The one young man is impatient, he immediately sets up the high hurdles on the track and begins to run and jump them. He knocks each of them down in turn. He sets them all up again at the same full height and knocks them down again. He does this several times a day for a week and eventually gives up in disgust with the feeling that he is just not capable of running the high hurdles competitively. The other young man also initially sets up the hurdles at full height and also knocks them all down in his first attempt. However, he realizes that this experiment just shows that he has not reached the desired capability—yet. Next, he sets up the low hurdles and finds that he can jump over them at a running pace. He continues to practice at this level until he has developed a smooth rhythm at a swift pace. Then, he raises the bar a notch and continues practicing until he can hurdle this new level with a smooth rhythm and a swift pace. Then, he again raises the bar a notch and practices, and then another notch, etc., until the bar is eventually at the full height for high hurdles and he is able to swiftly jump these hurdles with an easy rhythm. The second young man succeeded in reaching his goal, whereas, the athletically equally capable first young man wasn't willing to accept the evidence <u>of where he was in the process</u> and thus to strive, with patience and persistence, via a series of small gains towards his desired goal. How often do we reflect on similar examples acted out in our own lives.

The second example deals with the building of a worthy protagonist. Let us suppose we realize that resistance and struggle are necessary for our growth as a wrestler or boxer (any choice will serve, even as a professor) but we do not have a worthy opponent to stretch us. We have only the raw material in the form of an athletically capable and interested but untutored individual. We decide to make him our protagonist and so begin the contest with only a small fraction of our ability brought into play. He struggles but finds that he is able to meet this level of force and eventually surmount it. Then, we slowly escalate the level of our functioning ability and we find that he can begin to match that too. We continue the escalation at a rate no greater than that which can be met and eventually surmounted by our adversary. In this manner, we are eventually led to bring our full manifested abilities into play. Our protagonist is now becoming quite confident and meets this level of force and skill, and then begins to surmount it — now it is our turn to stretch for we have truly built a worthy opponent! This type of procedure applies equally well to the building of a person, a company, a nation, or a world.

One of the prime lessons to be learned from these examples is that <u>real progress requires people evolvement</u> and it is wasteful effort to force it to proceed faster than people can change their deep-rooted habits, their mindsets or their developed capabilities. If one tries to push outer progress or outer change at a rate faster than they can alter their inner circuits to keep in confident tune with it; i.e., completely assimilate it, then either the people's potential will be degenerated or they will attempt to destroy the structure imposing such intolerable conditions on them.

All of the power and vitality of any organization or society ultimately rests with the people — they are the only lasting asset. The only real asset of our nation is the people with their skills, their ethics and their efforts; it is from the people that all greatness flows. <u>Build the people to manifest their potential fully and joyfully and they will create the solutions to all the needs of any society.</u>

One way of accelerating the desired transformation in individuals and societies is via human energy-field interactions. This can be illustrated by considering the mechanism of radiation influence that one finds in the guru/chela or teacher/student relationship. First, I wish to propose that every individual taps energy from the cosmos and transforms it into various wave components which may be utilized to build discrete patterns in his/her energy field that eventually become the materialized behavior patterns of that individual. Certain manifestations or materializations (at physical, mental or other levels) cannot be successfully formed if some of the key wave components are absent. The individual must therefore wait to materialize such a behavior pattern until either (a) he/she has developed sufficiently in consciousness to automatically generate them internally or (b) he/she receives them from the external radiation field of someone else.

It is also proposed that the radiation field of an individual contains all the wave components associated with all their manifested and materialized abilities. Thus, the guru radiates all the wave components consistent with his/her achievements. The aspirant tunes his/her attention to the guru and absorbs these wave components as they pass through their body on the energy stream. He/she is then able to manifest these abilities to some degree. However, his/her internal circuitry is adaptable and, as they manifest these new abilities, their circuitry also adapts and their consciousness changes so that they begin to become self-generators of the needed wave components. He/she has enhanced the integration of his/her extended energy structure and begins to be able to do new things, perceive new thoughts, etc., because he/she has grown in consciousness. It seems that the radiated wave component spectrum of an individual is intimately tied to the individual's <u>manifested</u> consciousness.

In this way, each of us may exercise some influence on the transformation of the masses — by our personal radiation fields. Especially those from the heart projecting the individual frequencies of love! This is also the pathway for healing the planet.

290

## Overcoming Powerful Social Conditioning Forms

As this book was going to press, a very important paper by Ingo Swann[6] appeared on the topic of PSI and exceptional experience. Since it deals with a most significant barrier to natural human unfoldment, it is vital that the reader recognize the adversary that stands in the way of humanity realizing its true potential. In what is to follow, I will quote a number of passages from this paper.

In Chapter 2, where the inner self-management/direct experience models were briefly discussed, it was stated that adepts of these three technologies developed "super physical" abilities. Now, we need to clarify why these are considered <u>non-normal</u> human abilities rather than just part of the spectrum of <u>normal</u> human abilities when humans get their "act" together and become more internally organized.

In a perhaps unintentional way, science has placed humanity in a deep potential well with respect to consciousness and it has been, up until now, impossible to tunnel through this barrier for most humans. Let me provide a series of paraphrases and quotes from Swann[6],

●  "In the supposed Modern Age of Scientific Progress, a status quo human condition of "normalcy" has been accepted and exceptional human experiences, especially those involving extra sensory perception, have been treated as <u>abnormal</u> and not a natural part of human expression."

●  "Exceptional human experience violates the presently prevailing superficial reality which tries in abundant ways to avoid facing such exceptional behavior facts in order to escape seriously altering its fundamental image of the human being and the human species."

●  "It's worth pointing out that the Modern Scientific Age was the first to condemn PSI and exceptional human experience on such a broad social scale, holding the basis for the condemnation to be self-evident fact. The assumption behind the condemnation of human supersenses and exceptional experiences was that the early influential leaders of modern science cemented it into its materialistic mold by establishing that humans possess only five physical senses. Because these five could not account for "psychic" supersenses or exceptional experiences, then the latter "must" arise from some <u>deranged aspect</u> of ourselves."

• "Modern Science has generated several incorrect models of the human species and its behavior. These incorrect models became socially accepted as correct ones, were broadly reinforced by educational standards based upon them and, in turn, were widely supported by media "analysis." Incorrect models, once assumed to be correct, have no need of statistical evidence that challenges their assumed correctness. Here then (in sum), correct evidence cannot be fitted into incorrect models, and efforts to do so only result in ghettoizing, if not bastardizing, the evidence. But incorrect social realities are nonetheless very powerful and, understandably, few can get up the steam to point out the incorrectness, such as authors Rivlin and Gravelle (see Reference 2 of Chapter 4) dared to do in their marginalized book about the 17 senses. The "Problem" of PSI and exceptional experiences is not that they exist, but that they can't be fitted into the passionately defended incorrect social models of the human species."

• "Significantly missing from the various popular books on "maps of the mind" are the maps that include mind-dynamic parameters for psychic abilities, supersenses and exceptional human experiences that clearly are associated with one of our most vaunted capabilities: our species-collective-creativity — that is variously limited by what we do not perceive because of our social conditioning, which is manufactured by ourselves. However, one cannot read such books without realizing something very important about our manufactured mind-maps — they are all social-order-making "software programs".

"I have now concluded that we don't have minds. What we have instead is something more akin to a hard disk in a computer awaiting a software program to be installed in it. The hard disk contains our indwelling genetic ability and experiential threshold pools, our social software programs (usually based on some incorrect model) are then installed via social software mind-map conditioning and the natural activity of the three pools is then configured and expressed in ways that accord or not with the incorrect model. In large part, our lines of reasoning are outputs from these installed social software programs (whatever their origin) and, when we encounter phenomena, events, happenings, circumstances or exceptional experiences that don't fit into the software, we tend to view all the latter as we do computer viruses. We hunt down the viruses in order to eradicate them so as to keep our preferred social software programming intact.

So far as I can tell, humans do not yet possess a socializing software program that accords with our species natural specifics that must exist in our hard-disk drives — and which account for the long-enduring historical presence of PSI and exceptional experience. But one thing about this social software programming seems patently clear. We are a socializing species that unequivocally depends on the benefits of social-group interacting and, without some kind of integrating social software program, we would not be able to do so. We need social software!"

● "All babies, at first, are "universal linguists" (they have access to the universal hard-disk language pool) and have, by the age of two or three, become Chinese, German, Swahili or English, etc., speakers. Clearly, then, universal linguistic abilities exist in our species ability pool — and infants depart from this universal linguistic potential in order to communicate in the special language of those around them. Infant humans also begin to adapt (begin to form software social programs of "begin the metamorphosis" as Life magazine puts it) into other environmental specializations, such as moral, ethical, political and religious specializations, so as to fit into them. They can "become" anything along these lines with the same equal ease that empowers them to specialize in a given language. So, down their lives a bit, they have become a human probably quite departed from the human universal ability pool because of specializing in what best fits them into family, peer pressure, and their social surrounds."

● "Geniuses somehow escape much of the social software programming that "mere mortals" labor within and so they can psych-out (or ken) meanings that others don't or can't because of adherence to the confusions inherent in their incorrect model of social software programming. Almost everyone still "kens" today and this results in their perception of meanings. Hence, observing, kenning and psyching-out all mean approximately the same thing. What parapsychologists call "PSI" is a kenning event, as are exceptional human experiences a kenning of something otherwise invisible. Babies ken until they've learned not to by their elders. Geniuses do too, having escaped the social programming not to."

● "We know very little about the extent of our species hard-disk abilities and experiential threshold pools because no systematic effort has been made to map or list them. Thus, piecemeal studying of the phenomena of PSI and exceptional experience may ultimately mean something, but it is not the correct task because they are only parts of the human's biopsychic-electromagnetic blueprint of our overall interacting genetic ability and experiential threshold pools. It is the full spectra-extents of all these pools that are the proper and real field of inquiry."

I have borrowed so extensively from Ingo Swann's paper[6], in order to strongly underscore the subtle constraining forces that our social programming imposes on us all as we seek to change in significant ways. Now, so as not to dwell on the bleak walls of our prison, let me return to the process path I have laid out in this book whereby we may, individually and collectively, tunnel our way out of that prison. A summary of that process path is given in Fig. 7.1 and I ask you to reflect on it awhile before moving on to the next, and last, section of this book.

A proposal for rectifying this bad social programming, which has good physics boundary conditions, would be to institute a specific federally funded program administered by open-minded psychologists and physical scientists. The program would study both the intelligence and the PSI spectra of our nation's children. Those falling in the 80, 90, 95 and 99 percentile would receive cash awards/parental income tax deductions/educational scholarships, etc., on an annual basis for such stellar achievements. Since we are a money-oriented society, such recognition by the nation at large would quickly generate respect for such human performance qualities in our collective gene pool and quickly change the present incorrect social software programming.

Fig. 7.1 Key Steps In The Path Of Human Transformation
Aspects of Stewardship

# Aspects of Stewardship

My Webster's Dictionary defines stewardship as "the individual's responsibility to manage his life and property with proper regard to the rights of others." Let us look more closely at this.

**Stewardship Of Our Own Bodies**: The first step would appear to be inner self-management at mental and emotional levels. In this category, Yoga, Qigong and HeartMath have already been discussed to a small degree. These practices build subtle and physical level circuits in our bodies so that the quality of consciousness associated with the quantity of in-dwelling spirit makes one aware, balanced, motivated and disciplined to pursue the self-building to higher levels of self-empowerment. For me, the strong focus on the heart, and on the transmitting of love from the area of the heart, has accelerated the building of these circuits. Childre[5] has indicated that such exercise opens, bit by bit, what he calls "heart crystals" in an ever-expanding heart crystal antenna system. It is his view that spirit enters the body largely through this system and that, as it develops, the individual's consciousness and self-empowerment strongly increase so that their intuitive intelligence, their influence on the properties of matter and their ability to transmit the various frequencies of love, all increase. The interesting thing about the HeartMath techniques is that they are very simple and were designed for the general man on the street so that the masses can be self-empowered just by continued practice.

About nine months ago (Spring 1994), I decided to do a simple subjective experiment on my own body to test my inner circuitry development in this area. For the previous year or so, I had been aware of two body problems that I did not like: (1) if I ate a little sweets or drank a small amount of alcohol in the evening, the next day I would find several red pimples on my face and I wondered if I was becoming pre-diabetic and (2) I found myself getting out of bed three to four times each night to relieve my bladder and I knew I had an enlarged prostate gland that seemed to be getting worse. I decided to try and correct these deficiencies by focussing through my heart and sending love to the appropriate body parts. I decided to start with the sweets/alcohol problem but I didn't quite know how to go about it; however, I decided that one or more of the pancreas, liver, kidneys, gall bladder, spleen, stomach and overall digestive tract were involved. Thus, I used the heart focus technique to first put myself into the entrainment mode of heart function (see Chapter 5) and then I sequentially sent/felt love for each of the members on the above list (I also silently and internally thought the words "love for this body's . . . " three or four times before I went on to the next member on the list). I did this every day (total elapsed time ~ 1/2 hour per day) for two weeks and was absolutely amazed to find that the condition seemed to be gone! I then turned to the prostate problem and the list was now urinary bladder, urethra, prostate, urinary valves, incidental urinary tubing and the overall body urine elimination system. I followed the same procedure as before with the intention this time of curing the bladder-induced bathroom trips at night and did the practice each day. By the end of three weeks, my bed-bathroom-bed circuitry was down to one or at most two times a night! It really worked and now, nine months later, I follow these intention focus routines about once a week for maintenance of the desired performance. By these words, I am not recommending that one should not see a doctor if one suspects some problems with the body; however, I am saying that there are things we can take care of ourselves, if the pathology hasn't gone too far and if we are sufficiently structured inside to effectively satisfy the requirements for some measure of success; i.e., achieve the entrainment mode of heart function, project a clear intention and be capable of transmitting love in some portion of its frequency band. I am also not saying that one personal experiment will produce a "forever" change in a particular body condition.

In Chapter 5, we saw that trained practitioners in HeartMath techniques were able to influence the structure of water and/or DNA in water sufficiently to change its ultraviolet band absorbance in a significant way. This is an example of the consciousness of the individual changing the properties of the materials around him/her. We can expect this type of thing to be commonplace as we continue to grow in consciousness — and we must be readily able to do that in order to be effective stewards of this planet. Fortunately our biological systems are very non-linear so that, even if your linear logical mind tells you that it is impossible for <u>you</u> to do such things, provided you practice, practice, practice, the day will come and suddenly you will do it — and you will realize that its really "no big deal".

At this point, it is also useful to reflect on the ~1 to 4.5 micron EM emission from Qigong masters mentioned in Chapter 2 and briefly discussed in Chapter 5. It is a clear indicator of cellular coherence development in the area of the second chakra via this particular type of practice, practice, practice. Since many individuals have become Qigong masters by following a straightforward discipline of inner self-management, there is reason to suspect that almost everyone is capable of doing it. I suspect that similar type experiments, carried out with HeartMath practitioners, would reveal coherent IR emissions from the heart when it is operating in either the entrainment mode or the internal coherence mode of functioning. In both of these cases the lasing action at the physical level requires external radiation pumping of the particular organelle responsible for the emissions. Here, the radiation is not coming from the physical space-time domain but from the higher dimensional domains and, in particular, from the etheric domain. Pumping of etheric domain cell structures from still higher levels is also possible and cooperative lasing action at the etheric level of these cells is also a likelihood. This type of process can occur at all higher levels as well; thus, the coherent radiance output from the heart or the second chakra region can be expected to be in a collection of bands — physical, etheric, emotional, mental, etc. It is quite possible that the existence of pacemaker cells in these two regions of the body is critical to this laser-like behavior. This is thought to be so because the pacemaker cells are able to alter their physiology more rapidly than other types of cells; i.e., they are more flexible.

The process path for this coherent IR emission is thought to be

| Subtle Photons | $\rightarrow$ | Particular Molecules on The Organelle Surface Molecules | $\rightarrow$ | Energy Transfer To Host Organelle | $\rightarrow$ | IR Emission From The Whole Organelle |

where the major organelles in the cell undergoing this process are thought to be the cell membrane and the nucleus membrane. The overall process is not too dissimilar from conventional photovoltaic conversion. Some other organelles of the cell are, to a much lesser degree, thought to be involved in this photon emission process. It is primarily the cooperative action mode of these cell membranes that yield emissions in this wavelength region of the IR. Although this type of subtle energy conversion process is expected to occur in all cell types of the body, it is the inherent flexibility of the pacemaker cells that allow the electric voltage gradient to act through the piezoelectric coefficients of the nucleus and cell membranes so as to produce significant mechanical movement and thus this high frequency IR emission. This same flexibility allows the group of cells to phase-shift and frequency-lock on the best emission frequency. Variations in the subtle photon flux leads to both a DC and AC components of the cell voltage. It is the cooperative action of such cells in the heart, under normal state circumstances, that provide the electrical power needed for the heart to function as a pump for the blood.

**Group Stewardship:** After all members of the group develop individual inner self-management to the degree that they can enter any one of the ordered heart function modes at will and can, through directed intention, influence the UV absorbance of water, they are ready to tackle the next level of internal development — sustained local group coherence. This requires that each member of the group be able to radiate the qualities of love (over a reasonably broad frequency band) to any and all members of the group at sufficient intensity that the density of local subtle energy fields allows strong member-to-member interactions. This produces, then, a collective group consciousness sufficient to potentially affect the local flow of the "River of Life". Once this attunement field has been created and each member is in the assigned inner state, as identified by ECG monitoring for example, attuning more closely to each other will lead to both frequency-locking and phase-locking of the heart rhythms for all members of the group. Now the group is ready to test the magnitude of its collective consciousness via its directed intention effect on the properties of matter around it. The simple test of UV absorbance change in either pure water or a water/DNA solution placed some distance from the group ( ~20 feet, for example) would serve as a measurement vehicle. With repeated practice, subtle level structures for the group as an entity are built and now the test solution can be placed further and further away ( ~1 mile or more).

When this subtle level group structure has been built to a robust level, the individual group members will be strongly linked even when not at the same physical location. Once again, this can be tested by dispersing the group members and prearranging a specific tune-in time (something like a telephone conference call) while setting the test vial of water or water/DNA solution at some specific location. A strong ability to alter the UV properties of the test water with this dispersed group configuration is a measure of the group's subtle level entrainment ability. A somewhat more difficult test probe should then be designed to further test the subtle level power of the group's focussed intentionality. One such test might be the following: take a particular poison that would be fatal to cells when dissolved in water and fed to the cells in vitro (cells growing in a dish). Perform such a test to gather the baseline data. Then, form the group in either the local or dispersed mode. Attune the group coherence and then focus its intentionality on neutralizing the effect of the poison on the cells. Then, redo the initial cell test with this group intentionality-treated poison. Now, the poison should have no influence on the in vitro cell growth. A heirarchy of graded test probes from changing water UV absorbance to healing humans, animals or plants to influencing weather to influencing the collective consciousness of a town, etc., could be readily designed and utilized to quantitatively measure the progress of this group's development. At some point in this process, the group is ready for serious stewardship and can begin the next phase in its growth.

**Stewardship Of The Earth**: Continued practice by the group builds richer and more robust subtle energy structures associated with their collective consciousness. Their radiated love both attracts additional inner self-managed members to bond with the group and increase its signal power and, as well, nurtures and heals the terrain of their focussed intention. As more such groups form and grow on the Earth, they constitute strong beacons of radiance, at both physical and subtle levels, that dissolve some of the planetary density around them. Thus, if we visualize the surface of the globe, we see separated patches of light forming and expanding from a number of isolated locations. With time, these patches of higher consciousness overlap each other until the entire surface of the Earth glows with this radiance. As more and more humans choose to become entrained into this collective group activity, the intensity of the surface radiance grows. As it does, this radiation is absorbed into the Earth, lightening the density and organizing the local nodal networks to become single crystalline as it penetrates deeper and deeper towards the core until all of the volume of the planet has been lifted in consciousness by the collective human consciousness of the inhabitants residing on the thin surface membrane. This healing at the consciousness level has now conditioned the planet to have a largely single crystal nodal network at subtle levels and the physical level. Now, those cosmological subtle level currents pulsing through the multidimensional universe can readily flow through the Earth, enervating its volume with frequencies heretofore absent. These new frequencies, in turn, activate new levels of awareness in humankind as they practice their stewardship role and this accelerates them into a new phase of their journey home.

The End.

# References

1. S. Paddison, "The Hidden Power Of The Heart", (Planetary Publications, Boulder Creek, CA 1992).
2. W.A. Tiller, <u>The Simulator And The Being</u>, Phoenix, $\underline{1}$ (1977), 2.
3. Sri Aurobindo, "The Adventure Of Consciousness" (Satprem, Pondicherry, India 1968).
4. D. Elgin, Private Communication, 1974.
5. Doc L. Childre, Private Communication, Summer 1994.
6. I. Swann, <u>An Autobiographical Essay Regarding PSI and Exceptional Human Experience</u>, Exceptional Human Experience, $\underline{12}$ (1994) 160.

# GLOSSARY

<u>Archetypal Code</u>: This is a specific procedure (a well-defined sequence of articulated instructions), much like a computer language set of instructions, for activating some cosmological software imprinted at the nodal network structure of 10-space (mind domain).

<u>Bénard Convection</u>: Fluid flow that arises due to a density inversion in the vertical direction of the fluid.

<u>Cognition</u>: The action or faculty of knowing. Our physical level of cognition involves the parameters of distance and time (the physical 4-space) to make sense of the phenomena in the direct space outside of ourselves. These parameters appear to be qualities associated with the intellectual brain's process-mechanism for this type of knowing. There are other types of knowing of which the most often mentioned is listed under the label "intuition". This book expands the parameters for cognition to higher dimensional spaces than the familiar four. In particular, it focusses especially on an 8-space consisting of two conjugate 4-spaces; one is the above-mentioned familiar 4-space while the other is its inverse. For observable phenomena, this automatically leads to wave-particle duality. For cognition, it leads to dual information maps which together form a whole. The familiar one is manifest in terms of shapes, textures, colors, etc., the other is manifest as a topography of wave crests and valleys in a coordinate frame (four orthogonal frequency directions) that is cognitively new to us. Unfortunately, at the present time, we can only visually represent this new information map on a piece of paper by using the familiar distance plots and change the labelling of the axes from $(x, y)$ to $(v_x, v_y)$.

<u>Consciousness</u>: Thought by most to be the totality of the impressions, thoughts and feelings of an individual. Here, it is all the output expressions from the manifested in-dwelling spirit of that individual.

<u>Constructive/Destructive Interference</u>: Wave emission from multiple sources separated in space-time, or scattered from multiple and similar objects separated in space-time, to produce a superposed wave envelope which has a greatly increased amplitude when all the wavelets are in phase with each other, and they add constructively, but a greatly decreased amplitude when they are out of phase with each other, and add destructively.

<u>Convolution/Deconvolution</u>: The condition of two or more things being rolled, interleaved or folded together or two mathematical functions, each describing

the action of a thing, being mixed in a particular way and then the unravelling, unmixing and separation of these individual qualities.

Coulomb Field: Named for Charles A. de Coulomb, it is the electrostatic field produced by the interaction between electric charges.

Electrostatic Potential ($\phi$): The scalar potential driving purely electrical phenomena via its mathematical relationship to electric charge density.

Ellipse Aspect Ratio: The ratio of the length to the width of an ellipse.

Ether: Sanskrit *akash*. Though not considered a factor in present scientific theory on the nature of the material universe, ether has for millenniums been so referred to by India's sages. Paramahansa Yogananda spoke of ether as the background on which God projects the cosmic motion picture of creation. Space gives dimension to objects; ether separates the images. This "background," a creative force that coordinates all spatial vibrations, is a necessary factor when considering the subtler forces – thought and life energy (*prana*) – and the nature of space and the origin of material forces and matter.

Frequency Space: (see k*-Space)

Gauge Theory: Represents a new synthesis of quantum mechanics and symmetry wherein gauge invariance is recognized as the physical principle governing the fundamental forces between all elementary particles. Such invariance must be satisfied for all observable quantities in order to ensure that any arbitrariness in A and $\phi$ do not affect the field strength.

Histological: Relating to the minute structure of organic tissue.

Hydrophobic Interaction: A repulsive interaction between water and another substance.

Hypnogogic State: One that induces sleep.

Intentionality: The Oxford dictionary gives "the quality or fact of being intentional; of or pertaining to purpose, pertaining to operation of the mind." As such, it represents the quality of one's conscious purpose, often thought of as self-directed mind. In this book, applied intentionality means placing a desire imprint from the level of spirit into the "simulator" at the mind level which then cascades through the various levels giving representative patterns at each level and materializes action at the physical distance-time level. This is, in turn, observed by the individual's physical cognition system.

Inverse Space: (see k*-Space)

Kenning: Mental cognition.

k-Space (reciprocal space): In solid state physics, the complex motions of atoms in a network are usually resolved into harmonic modes or waves with each being characterized by a wave vector, k, having the dimensions of inverse distance. Thus, it is common practice to describe and plot the energy of these waves in k-space or reciprocal space where the different components of the vector k are used as coordinate axes in such plots. As such, it is a mathematical convenience for computations concerning such waves, whether they be for electrons, atoms, defects, etc. In such plots, each value of k refers to a wave in physical space.

k*Space (frequency space, inverse space): In this space, waves or harmonic undulations of etheric (magnetic) substance are proposed to exist. The distribution of intensity in this space yields the topographic map for such magnetic substance. Although there may appear to be a close correspondence with the above item, k-space, there are profound differences. Here, an individual wave extends along $k_x^*$, $k_y^*$, etc., and has a k*-length analogous to a wavelength in direct space or physical space. A particular k*-value does not refer to a wave in physical space; however, an individual wave in the k*-space refers to a particle in direct space. The front cover of the book shows complementary information maps for an object perceived as a triangle (center) at the direct space level of physical reality (our conventional 4-space) and perceived as an intensity distribution of waves (center to edges) at the frequency space level of etheric reality. At present, quantum mechanics empirically maps these two conjugate information domains into a single 4-space description of nature that exhibits wave-particle duality.

Lattice: A periodic structure or variation of quality/non-quality such as atom/space in two or more dimensions. In a crystal lattice, the atom positions have a unique geometrical relationship.

Magnetic Vector Potential (A): In conventional electrodynamics, it is equation-connected to both the magnetic flux (or magnetic field, H) and the electric flux (or electric field, E) so it and the electrostatic potential define the two basic fields (E and H) involved in electromagnetism. Here, it is also used to connect the physical domain to the subtle domains.

*Science and Human Transformation:*

<u>Maxwell's Equations:</u>  Four coupled mathematical expressions created by James Clerk Maxwell in 1873 that beautifully synthesized the accepted electrical and magnetic phenomena of the 19th century.

<u>Mole Fraction</u>:  The ratio of the number of a given kind of molecules in a certain volume to the total number of molecules in the same volume.

<u>Nodal Network</u>:  A lattice of nodal points in which a key quality of the nodal species (vector direction, say) may be ordered or disordered at the various nodal site locations.  These nodal points are non-linear transducers of one type of energy into another.

<u>Non-Linear</u>:  Situation where the response is not simply proportional to the stimulus.

<u>Photoelectrochemical Devices</u>:  A class of device involving flows of chemical ions in response to an electric field that is modified by the flux of electromagnetic photons striking an active surface of the device.

<u>Polarization</u>:  The shifting away from neutral balance.  In dielectrics, it is associated with the displacement of positive and negative electric charges.  In light, it is associated with the average orientation of the electric vector for the photons.

<u>Proprioceptors</u>:  A unique set of structural elements in muscles.

<u>Quantum Perspective:</u>  A view of the very small at the sub-atomic/atomic particle size scale where energy flows in discrete packets and where most of seeming solid matter is empty space.

<u>Relativity Perspective</u>:  A view of relative motions of objects where the speed of the object is sufficiently high that space and time cannot be treated as independent variables but are intimately coupled.  Applies equally to things very large like planets and to things very small like electrons.

<u>Renormalization</u>:  In many mathematical particle theories, one sometimes gets a number turning out to be infinite which aught to be finite, like the model of the electron as a point charge.  By introducing a coupling constant or screening constant into the theory, an atmosphere of polarization collects around the bare particle so that the measurable entity is now the point particle plus atmosphere which now takes on finite values.  The theory has been mathematically renormalized.

<u>Scalar/Vector Property</u>: A quality which may vary in magnitude from point to point in space but which does not vary with orientational direction about such a point (scalar) versus one which also varies with direction (vector).

<u>Simulator</u>: A programmable device designed to simulate the particular set of motions or events that reproduce a particular experience or result.

<u>Stochastic Resonance</u>: Resonance produced by a sequence of random stimuli.

<u>Sub-Lattice/Reciprocal Lattice</u>: A secondary lattice within the space of the primary lattice. Every lattice has a special sub-lattice called the reciprocal lattice which has a unique mathematical relationship to the primary lattice. Only the hexagonal close-packed primary lattice has its reciprocal lattice at the same lattice points to become self-dual.

<u>Subtle Domains</u>: Potential cognitive domains of the universe beyond the domain of physical cognition by humans or present physical instruments. Some humans presently sense these domains, most do not. Here, they have been labelled etheric, astral or emotional, mind, spirit, divine.

<u>Subtle Energies</u>: All those energies existing in the universe beyond the four known to and accepted by present-day science. There may be more to be discovered at the physical level and there will certainly be many more to be discovered in the subtle domain levels beyond the physical band of consciousness.

<u>Subtle Radiations</u>: The analogues to physical level radiations, which are presently classified as "mediators" and will now be reclassified as P-mediators (see Table 2.3). We will use the terms E-mediators, A-mediators, M-mediators, etc., to denote the radiations of the etheric, astral (emotional), mental, etc., types. In the text, the photon has been used to designate the P-mediator for the electromagnetic interaction; for the counterpart E-mediator due to the magneto-electric interaction, we could provisionally use the term E-photon and, for the counterpart A-mediator, we could provisionally use the term A-photon.

<u>Subtle Substances</u>: The analogues to physical substance at the various subtle domain levels. Until better words are chosen, we shall use a simple extension of the physical level building blocks, leptons and quarks, redefining the general building blocks as (P-leptons/P-quarks), (E-leptons/E-quarks), (A-leptons/A-quarks), (M-leptons/M-quarks), etc., for the physical, etheric, astral (emotional) and mind domains, respectively. In this text, two subtle particle discriminations beyond the foregoing have already been made; i.e., the magnon

is the E-lepton counterpart to the electron, the most important P-lepton and the deltron is an A-substance counterpart of the P- and E-substances without finer discrimination at this point in time.

<u>Succussion</u>: The action of strongly shaking or jolting a fluid.

<u>Symmetry</u>: An operation that one can perform (at least conceptually) on a system that leaves the system invariant.

<u>Tensor</u>: A generalized vector with more than three components, each of which is a function of the coordinates of an arbitrary point in space of an appropriate number of dimensions.

<u>Thermistor</u>: An electrical device for measuring temperature via the accurate measurement of electrical resistance of a particular material (e.g., silicon).

<u>Titration</u>: The addition of a constituent in small steps to a suitable reagent of known properties, until a point is reached at which reaction occurs or ceases.

<u>Townsend Regime</u>: Named for the original investigator of this high voltage-very low current region of electrical discharges in gases that occurs just before the "glow" discharge region where ions and electrons recombine strongly emitting photons of visible light.

# Index

# Q

# R

# S

ABOUT THE AUTHOR

Dr. Tiller has been a professor in the department of Materials Science and Engineering at Stanford University from 1964 to the present, and chairman of that department from 1966 to 1971. As Professor Emeritus, he has been actively involved in research at Stanford since 1/1/92. He has been a consultant to government and industry in the fields of metallurgy and solid state physics, and an associate editor of two scientific journals. He has published more than 250 scientific papers, three technical books, and has five patents issued in his conventional science areas. Fields of specialization are crystal growth, surfaces and interfaces, physical metallurgy, semiconductor processing, thin film formation and computer simulation. He has also been an associate editor for the Journal of Holistic Medicine, and has published more than 70 additional papers and this book in the field of psychoenergetics.